Bus&Coach PRESERVATION HANDBOOK

CW00336975

Compiled by
**National Association
of Road Transport
Museums**

MIDLAND

159 COVENTRY
VIA MERIDEN

MIDLAND RED.D

BMO

SHA 431

Presbus PUBLISHING

Contents

First published 2010

ISBN 9780 9565 0611 5

© Presbus Publishing 2010

Visit the Presbus Publishing website at
www.presbuspublishing.com

Designed by Robert Wilcockson

Printed by Ian Allan Printing, Hersham, Surrey

Cover: **A member of the North East Bus Preservation Trust's varied vehicle collection is this splendid 1931 Duple-bodied Bedford WLB, new to Howards of West Byfleet, Surrey, but restored in the livery of Gypsy Queen, Langley Park, Co Durham.**
PHILIP LAMB

Title page: **Some restorations are long and painstaking, and it has taken many years to return BMMO LD8 class 4031 (SHA 431) to this condition. No 4031, an all-Leyland product dating from 1953, stands outside the latest of three large halls, the Power Hall, at The Transport Museum, Wythall.**
PHILIP LAMB

Useful addresses
NARTM, PO Box 5141, Burton-upon-Trent. DE15 0ZF
The Transport Trust, 202 Lambeth Road, London. SE1 7JW
British Bus Preservation Group, 7 Dukeries Lane, Oakwood, Derby DE21 2HA
The PSV Circle, 26 Ashville Grove, Halifax HX2 0PN

Information in this book is believed to be correct at the time of going to press

Note: Please be aware that vehicles on display can vary from time to time as not all museums display their entire 'fleets'. Visitors wishing to see a particular vehicle should make enquiries prior to their visit.

There are a modest number of foreign buses, trolleybuses and trams preserved in the UK. Alongside many native trolleybuses, a small number of foreign trolleys inhabit the East Anglia Transport Museum at Carlton Colville, near Lowestoft, where the overhead was extended and the road surface beneath laid to tarmac in 2008, allowing a full circle of the site. This trolley arrived that year. It is a Russian-built ZiU 682G1, which had seen service in Athens, and is an excellent example of a latter-day trolleybus, a species now long-extinct in Britain.
PHILIP LAMB

Welcome to our 2010 guide to museums and collections in the British Isles, in which you can find details of many of the thousands of buses and coaches built during the last century, and which are preserved today. This year we have a new title, a new publisher and a new format, and we hope that you will like the changes. There are more pages, more pictures, more information and extra features giving some background to the collections featured.

Developments

There are developments to report at many of the locations in the book, and some quite significant changes. The South Yorkshire Transport Museum, for the last couple of years in nearly new premises at Aldwarke, near Rotherham, has doubled in size by expanding into the adjoining industrial unit. It now features a collection of cars, with more room to display the buses to better effect and the best painted museum floor I have seen for many a long year! The collection includes some well restored local vehicles with a few more nearing completion in the excellent new workshops, as well as a splendid exhibition bus which is regularly taken out to schools and local events.

Bury Transport Museum, located next to the East Lancashire Railway near Manchester, is due to re-open this year after a major restoration project, thanks to assistance from the Heritage Lottery Fund. In contrast to South Yorkshire, the museum in Bury is housed in an old stone-built railway goods transfer shed that dates back to the 1840s. Prior to restoration, its timber roof trusses were in a dangerous condition, but have now been fully restored along with the rest of the building, which has changed out of all recognition with new doors, fresh limewash on the walls and new lighting. It will be well worth a visit once it opens its doors to the public.

A brand new transport museum is also in course of preparation at Jurby on the Isle of Man. The volunteers there are hard at work to make the buildings suitable for their new role, and plan to open their doors at Easter for the first time. They are busily collecting vehicles, and the associated items that are needed to tell the story of buses and coaches in their surroundings.

Some existing museums are also developing at present. These include the Lincolnshire Road Transport Museum, one of the longest established NARTM museums. It is run by the Lincolnshire Vintage Vehicle Society, which has just celebrated its 50th anniversary. The LVVS is constructing a new building that will effectively link the museum display hall with the workshops, giving significantly more covered accommodation for its vehicles. Castle Point Transport Museum on Canvey Island in Essex has built a new café in the past year and others, including Ipswich, Manchester, Carlton Colville have plans to improve visitor facilities either before the 2010 season or during the year.

What is NARTM?

NARTM stands for the National Association of Road Transport Museums, an organisation that continues to develop, welcoming several new members in the last year. After almost 30 years, we are in the process of making NARTM a company limited by guarantee and plan to achieve charitable status. NARTM holds two general meetings for members each year, usually at member's premises or nearby, and as a result we have recently visited Rotherham, Lincoln, London and Beamish. The committee meets more frequently and there is a fair traffic in e-mails between individual members!

Recent topics discussed have included Driver CPCs, our strengthening relationship with the Heritage Lottery Fund, improving links with government departments and agencies, encouraging volunteers, safety advice and risk assessments, vehicle testing standards, museum accreditation and an overhaul of the NARTM scoring system. The scoring system is a means of assessing vehicles against a set of standard criteria — their national and local importance, whether or not they were a technological advance, their relevance to any social or other change and their uniqueness.

This latter factor is checked using the NARTM database, which is updated every year and includes all the buses and coaches listed in this book. It also includes over 1,000 more vehicles, the owners of which have decided that they prefer their details not to be published at present. By checking a vehicle against others on the database, we can get a good idea if it is a unique survivor, or if there are other similar examples in existence. If there are, and they are already in good condition, then that vehicle would be given fewer points than if it was the only survivor of a once numerous type.

NARTM is also in the process of identifying the major stages in the development of the motorbus and motorcoach throughout the 20th century, and in due course will link that information with the scoring system, helping to ensure that key vehicles, important to our understanding of how buses have developed, are given a higher rating, ultimately helping them to survive in the long-term.

In the early years of the century, development was quite rapid as mechanical technology improved, but sadly very few vehicles have survived from that period. NARTM member Mike Sutcliffe has done a fantastic job in rebuilding several buses and even an original charabanc — without these we would have very few examples to represent over 20 years of significant developments.

Vehicle evolution

Other key stages in bus and coach development were the introduction of Leyland's Titan and Tiger quickly followed by AEC's equivalent, the Regent and the Regal in the late 1920s. these vehicles had lowered chassis frames and powerful, reliable engines. In the 1930s, metal-framed bus bodies and oil engines (diesel) were introduced, and then, in the 1950s, single-deck buses and coaches were fitted with engines under the floor, while double-deckers began to incorporate rear engines. More recently, the requirement to have accessible, low-floor buses has pushed almost all engines to the back of the vehicle. In addition, different types of fuels are undergoing trials.

These were all technical developments, but they often allowed social changes to take place. In many towns and cities, the new Regals and Tigers of the late-1920s allowed the rapid expansion of express bus services to places beyond the reach of electric trams. The development of many housing schemes and overspill estates took place as a result of the availability of high-capacity, reliable and economical double-deck buses in the 1930s and later.

Prior to that, the earliest motorbuses might not have been very fast, but they were quicker and cheaper to operate on rural routes and in the suburbs than the horsebuses they replaced. This often allowed the development of upper-class areas of population away from the polluted and crowded city centres. They also helped to connect villages with nearby towns or railway stations and played a vital role in improving communications. Rural buses often carried parcels, mail, spares for tractors and even livestock. Early charabancs allowed groups to make day trips out to the seaside or into the countryside — a great advance for people who would otherwise have been confined to a very dreary urban existence.

As coaches developed, they offered long-distance travel to compete with the more expensive (but faster) railways, and routes set up 80 or 90 years ago are still followed today by modern, air-conditioned coaches with Internet access and other mod cons. Coaches were also used for extended tours, again giving large numbers of people affordable access to more distant areas; this was linked to the introduction of paid holidays for many workers before and after World War 2.

Bus and coach travel reached peak volumes in most areas in the early-1950s. After that, the rise of the private car, the five-day week, television (as a stay at home leisure activity) and other factors have contributed to a steady decline in passenger numbers. In the same period, buses and coaches have continued to develop technically, with lower floors, more efficient engines, better brakes, automatic gearboxes and other devices to make them more comfortable and easier to drive. At last there are signs that the bus is making a comeback, with operators reporting increases in passenger numbers, but they are still far short of the peak volumes carried 50-odd years ago.

So a bus or coach isn't simply a piece of technology that improved over the years. In many ways they were social enablers, making things not otherwise possible happen, an aspect that many of the museums in this book are now focussing on. The vehicles do of course remain interesting in their own right, but museums are now looking beyond them too towards the extra things they allowed people to do. This makes our museums and collections much more attractive to a wider audience than in the past.

Visiting a collection

Increasingly visitors to museums featured in this book are family groups in addition to the die-hard enthusiasts who used to be the sole visitors. The enthusiast is still very welcome to visit of course, making a substantial contribution at open days and special events. It is, however, increasingly important to reach out to the family groups and the non-enthusiast market — one important tool in that process is, of course, the Internet. A good website, with the right search words, that is easy and quick to use, is invaluable in bringing our specialist collections to the notice of the general public. Key in 'museum' and a town or county name and you will quickly find one of the NARTM museums listed. Just the thing for a wet day when the kids want to go somewhere, but you don't fancy travelling too far or spending too much money! Better still look at the NARTM website at www.nartm.org.uk. You will also find much more related information and details of events and historic vehicle rallies in *Bus & Coach Preservation*, a monthly magazine available in most branches of W. H. Smiths, as well as other good bookstalls.

Our next aim is to get some of those family group members interested enough in our projects to join, and become supporters and even the volunteers of the future. At many of the projects you can visit, knowledgeable volunteer guides will show you around the exhibits, tailoring the visit to your group's needs and making for a jolly good day out. One day, you could become one of those volunteer guides, or perhaps get involved in the many and varied jobs behind the scenes — it can be good fun — honestly!

There is often much more to visiting a museum than simply looking at the exhibits and displays. Often the buses and coaches are used on heritage bus services allowing the public to get a much better idea of just what it was like to travel on vehicles from the past. Such services will sometimes operate 'off the road' and can involve trams at, amongst other places, the National Tramway Museum at Crich and trolleybuses as at The Black Country Living Museum, Dudley, where you can also enjoy a tram ride. Trolleybuses also operate at the Trolleybus Museum at Sandtoft, near Doncaster and at the East Anglia Transport Museum at Carlton Colville near Lowestoft, where also there are trams too. Other museums provide a useful transport facility on special days, linking event sites or providing a short trip to and from a car park or railway station.

Some groups, for example the Friends of King Alfred Buses (FoKAB), Aycliffe & District and the Ribble Vehicle Preservation Trust (RVPT) do not open their sites to the public as conventional museums, but take their buses and coaches out to the public. FoKAB takes over the town services in Winchester every New Year's Day, replacing modern buses with free travel on authentic buses that used to work in the city and the surrounding area. This has become one of the major events in the enthusiasts' calendar, but also attracts many members of the public. Aycliffe & District buses regularly attend events in the North-East, while the RVPT operates a number of ever-popular running days in the North-West using well-restored vehicles. These are just a few examples of opportunities to ride on old

buses. Almost every weekend someone somewhere is providing free rides — this book will help you to find out exactly when and where.

There are also a number of commercial operators using heritage buses and coaches in regular service, and you will find them listed in this book as well. Transport for London still operates the familiar red Routemaster buses on two routes in Central London, while other operators are to be found in more rural locations such as Somerset and Cumbria.

What next?

I will conclude this introduction with a realistic look to the future. We have already talked about the rarity of buses from the early years of the 20th century — they were quite lightly built and often only lasted a few years. In addition there was little spare time or money for people to even begin to think of saving old buses and coaches for the future. With the exception of London Transport, which had a duty to save examples of redundant types of bus, the preservation of such vehicles only started in a small way in the late-1950s, and then increasingly through the 1960s and 1970s and beyond, hence the majority of buses and coaches listed in this book date from the late 1940s through to the 1970s.

More recent buses are also being saved in quantity, with several 1980s minibuses in preservation as well as some of the first imported buses and coaches that replaced the well-established models once built in Britain. The majority of passenger vehicles saved for the future exist because an individual or group decided that they wanted to save one of a particular model. This is often a vehicle that people remember from their childhood, and many enthusiasts are only really keen on buses in use during that period of their lives. As those enthusiasts get older, eventually they may become unable to

look after their old buses and coaches and turn to younger colleagues for help and maybe to take on responsibility for the vehicles. That is quite an additional task for the younger generation, whose first interests will lie with the buses they in turn went to school on and will have less affection for the older machines. These people will then have two or more generations of vehicles to look after and in the longer term that could become unsustainable.

There are two ways around this issue — we must encourage more people to become involved with the preservation of older vehicles, the alternative being that some of the older examples will fall by the wayside and may even end up as scrap metal. That would be a great shame and the NARTM database and scoring system mentioned above are both useful tools to help identify vehicles that might be at risk and to confirm their importance in telling the story of bus and coach developments in the last 100 years. By using these tools, we will ideally be in a position to direct resources towards the long-term survival of the most important examples.

How can the reader help? Well, by visiting as many of the museums and collections described in this book as you can would be a good start! We hope you will enjoy your visits, and if so, why not ask about joining the volunteers who support the project? You won't need to be a time-served mechanic or a museum professional (but nice if you are!), just someone who can spare a few hours now and then to work alongside other like-minded people to help restore a vehicle, show people round the collection, sweep the floor or even brew up — all valuable work. Enjoy!

DENNIS TALBOT
NARTM chairman
Manchester
January 2010

For more information about NARTM please contact: NARTM, PO BOX 5141, Burton upon Trent, Staffordshire, DE15 0ZF or visit our website at www.nartm.org.uk.
E mail: email@nartm.org.uk.

More About NARTM

The National Association of Road Transport Museums has been in existence for almost 30 years and now has over 80 member organisations, with more joining each year. The buses and coaches that form part of the NARTM collections are generally regarded as forming the nucleus of the National Collection of Buses and Coaches. However, it must be stressed that many important examples are in private hands outside the scope of NARTM and its members.

Many of the people involved in running transport museums are busy people and have little spare time after making significant contributions to their own projects. This is why NARTM only holds two meetings each year at the various member museums. In between meetings, the quarterly NewsLink magazine keeps members in touch with each other. Indeed, one of the main functions of NARTM is to put people in contact with each other, and there are many instances of restoration projects progressing and spare parts being located through NARTM links.

NARTM's unique service to its members is also as an information exchange about running museums — after all as so many of our members are volunteers, their skills and experiences are often not within the heritage and leisure industry. It is often the case that a project in another area has already been faced with exactly the same issues as we have today, and by sharing ideas and pooling resources, progress can be made more quickly. A set of policies and documents to cover all aspects of museum and collections management is being assembled, to be made available to members.

Over the years NARTM has also taken a lead role in campaigning on new legislation to lessen its impact on the historic bus preservation movement. Vehicle licensing, driver licensing, tachographs and the retention of original registration numbers have all received attention, with some success in each case through our work in conjunction with other groups within the movement.

Recently a group of NARTM members have produced and subsequently updated a set of guidelines for the operation of free bus services. Such services have become popular at many events, as a means of bringing buses back to life for the general public and enthusiasts alike. The guidelines are now available to NARTM members and provide some background and assistance to those planning to operate such events.

NARTM is working closely with the Transport Trust to address the major issues currently facing the heritage transport movement — storage, documentation, human resources and skills, public access and the future of vehicles in preservation. A database of around 4,000 buses and coaches is now updated annually and lists all vehicles in NARTM and associated collections. This now forms a central part of a decision making process devised by NARTM to ensure that the most historically important vehicles have a secure long-term future.

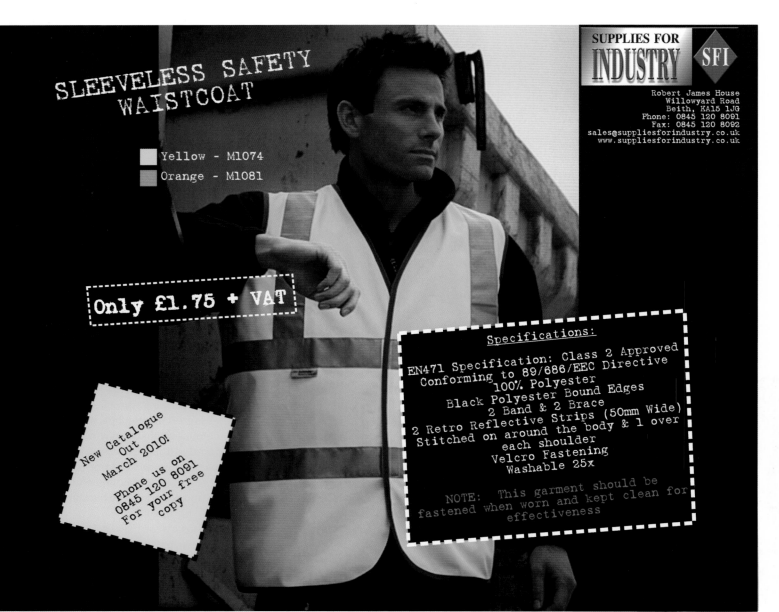

How to use this Book

This book lists both formal museums and the more informal types of collection, and gives detail of opening times, contact addresses and the facilities available, together with a list of the buses, trolleybuses and coaches on display. Many of the sites are open to the public on a regular basis. Admission fees vary and some are even free to visitors, although donations towards the up keep of the collection are always welcome. Please be aware that vehicles on display can vary from time to time. Not all museums are able to display their entire fleet and some practice the regular rotation of exhibits for added interest. In addition, some of the vehicles maybe in progress of restoration in a workshop off-site, and there is always possibility that a bus maybe on loan to another museum! Visitors wishing to see a particular vehicle should make enquires prior to the visit.

Some collections are not normally available for public access. However the owners usually welcome visitors and will arrange for viewing by prior application, in the addition, many such groups do have open or public days from time to time. Contact addresses are provided in the book, and those wishing to visit a particular site are asked to contact the address given. Please bear in mind that most are run by volunteers, so please enclose a stamped self-addressed envelope when writing and respect the privacy of individuals. This book does not grant or imply any permission whatsoever to enter premises to look at old buses except by the agreement of the group involved. Note that where buses are licensed for use on public passenger-carrying services, the use of individual vehicles will vary from time to time, as the demands of their preservation dictate.

Whilst some of the restored vehicles detailed here have been officially preserved by their former operators, the majority have been restored and conserved by volunteers, often working in difficult conditions with limited resources of time, money and materials. That there are so many busses and coaches fully restored is a testimony to the dedication of bus enthusiasts over the last 40 years or more, and it is intended that the vehicles will have a long and secure future.

The information used in this book is as provided by the organisations listed, for which the authors express their thanks. Any information on the further collections not included in the current edition will be most welcome. If you own vehicles, or are associated with such an organisation please contact NARTM at the address given on page 9.

Held annually over the Mayday Bank Holiday weekend, the three-day Llandudno Festival of Transport is a superb showcase for preserved vehicles of all kinds, with a sizeable contingent of vintage buses and coaches in attendance. Some of those present are used on the free bus service linking the seafront rally site with the town centre, where traditional fairground rides are set up in the streets. A regular performer on the service is Adrian Hunt's Bristol Tramways 1956 highbridge Bristol KSW6B C8322 (UHY 362). The bus is listed here as part of the West Midlands Bus Preservation Society collection, Adrian being a member of that group. PHILIP LAMB

Even though the road layout at the Pier Head at Liverpool has changed completely and the once busy bus station has gone forever, landmarks such as the Royal Liver Building remain, and still provide a realistic setting. Here the Merseyside Transport Trust's 1967 MCW-bodied Leyland Atlantean PDR1/1 L835 (FKF 835E) passes along the waterfront, watched over by one of the Liver Birds.
PHILIP LAMB

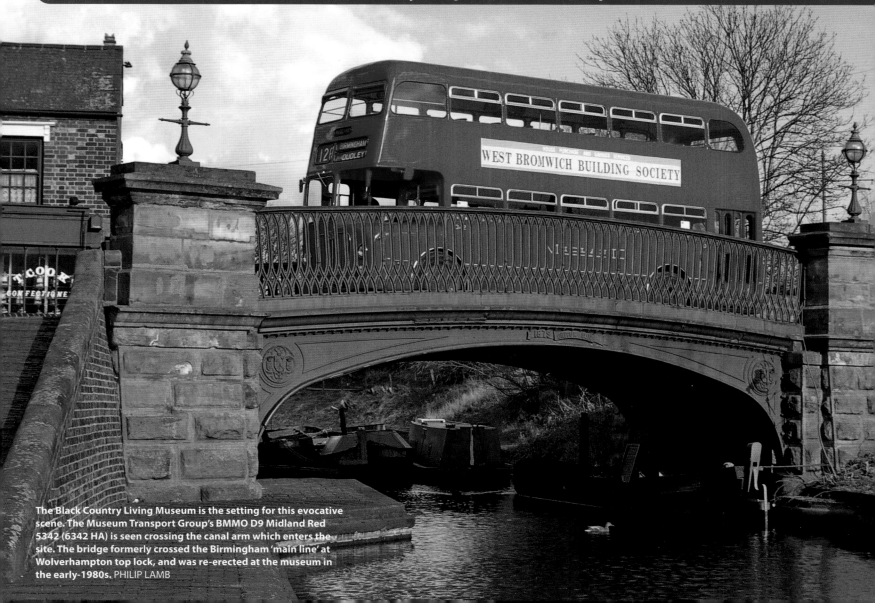

The Black Country Living Museum is the setting for this evocative scene. The Museum Transport Group's BMMO D9 Midland Red 5342 (6342 HA) is seen crossing the canal arm which enters the site. The bridge formerly crossed the Birmingham 'main line' at Wolverhampton top lock, and was re-erected at the museum in the early-1980s. PHILIP LAMB

Abbey Pumping Station Museum

Leicester

Contact address: Corporation Road, Leicester, LE4 5PX

Phone: 0116 299 5111

Fax: 0116 299 5125

Email: museums@leicester.gov.uk

Website address: www.leicester.gov.uk/museums

Brief description: The Museum is a Victorian pumping-station dating from 1892 with four beam-engines. The vehicle collection is on view during special open days. On these occasions, one of the beam- engines is steamed.

Events planned in 2010:

30 March 2010 — Bonnets & Biscuits 11.00–15.00

3 April 2010 — First Railway Day of 2010 11.00–16.30

18 April 2010 — April Steam and Food Fayre 13.00–17.00

1 May 2010 — May Day Magic & Railway Day 11.00–16.30

1 June 2010 — Scrapbook skills 11.00 – 15.00

5 June 2010 — Teddy Bears Picnic and Railway Day 11.00–16.30

26/27 June 2010 — Urban Steam Rally 13.00–17.00

3 July 2010 — Stars & Stripes Railway Day 11.00–16.30

7 August 2010 — Bring your Bike Railway Day 11.00–16.30

10 August 2010 — Magic tricks and Toys 11.00–15.00

4 September 2010 — Harvest Basket Train 11.00–16.30

12 September 2010 — Seaside Special Steam Day 12.00–17.00

2 October 2010 — Autumn Railway Day 11.00–16.30

19 October 2010 — Autumn Leaves 11.00–15.00

25 October 2010 — The Ghostly Engineer 19.00–21.30

5 December 2010 — Christmas Toys and Steam Day 13.00–17.00

16 January 2011 — Marvellous Meccano 13.00-17.00

6 February 2011 — Steam Toys in Action 13.00–17.00

Opening days/times: Museum open to the public from 11.00-16.30. Museum open from 1 February to 30 October 2010

Charges: Free except on event days

Registration	Date	Chassis make	Chassis model	Body make	Original operator	Fleet No	Status
Unregistered	1932	Horse Bus			Leicester City Transport		R
CBC 921	1939	AEC	Renown O664	Northern Counties	Leicester City Transport	329	R
TBC 164	1958	Leyland	Titan PD3/1	Willowbrook	Leicester City Transport	164	R
MTL 750	1958	Leyland	Tiger Cub PSUC1/2	Yeates	Delaine Coaches of Bourne	47	R
B401 NJF	1984	Ford	Transit 190D	Rootes	Midland Fox	M1	R

Directions by car: Follow signs for the National Space Centre, Abbey Pumping Station is located next to the attraction

Directions by public transport: Bus 54 and 70 (note 70 does not run on Sunday)

X6 Arriva leaves from St Margaret's bus station

10 and 40 clockwise and 11 and 41 anti clockwise (note 40 and 41 do not run on Sundays)

Facilities: A B (train ride on event days only) D E G H P R (on event days only) T

Abbey Pumping Station in Leicester plays host to a number of interesting buses including this 1939 AEC Renown with 64-seat Northern Counties bodywork, which served in the local City Transport fleet.
PHILIP LAMB

Note: Please be aware that vehicles on display can vary from time to time as not all museums display their entire 'fleet'. Visitors wishing to see a particular vehicle should make enquiries prior to their visit.

Registration	Date	Chassis make	Chassis model	Body make	Original operator	Fleet No	Status
RG 1173	1950	Albion	PMA28	Walker	Aberdeen Corporation	79	R
CWG 273	1951	Leyland	PS1	Alexander	W. Alexander & Sons	PA171	RP
WTS 937A	1961	Daimler	CVG6	Alexander (1960)	Aberdeen Corporation	160	RP
RRG 289	1965	Daimler	CVG6	Alexander	Aberdeen Corporation	289	A
CRG 325C	1966	Daimler	CVG6	Alexander	Aberdeen Corporation	325	R
EFP 521T	1967	Mercedes-Benz	0.317	Ludewig	Krefeld (Germany)	5561	RP
GRS 10E	1968	Leyland	Tiger Cub PSUC1/13	Alexander Y	Aberdeen Corporation	10	A
JRS 22F	1968	AEC	Swift MP2R	Alexander W	Aberdeen Corporation	22	RP
LRG 14G	1969	AEC	Reliance 6MU2RA	Alexander Y	Aberdeen Corporation	14	R
PRG 40J	1970	AEC	Reliance 6MU4RA	Alexander Y	Aberdeen Corporation	40	RP
PRG 124J	1971	Daimler	Fleetline CRG6LX	Alexander	Aberdeen Corporation	124	RP
SRS 56K	1972	AEC	Swift MP2R	Alexander Y	Aberdeen Corporation	56	R
HSO 61N	1975	Leyland	Leopard PSU4C/4R	Alexander Y	Grampian Regional Transport	61	R
ORS 209R	1977	Leyland	Atlantean AN68	Alexander	Grampian Regional Transport	209	R
XSS 345Y	1983	Leyland	Atlantean AN68/1R	Alexander	Grampian Regional Transport	345	RP
B121 MSO	1985	Leyland	Olympian ONLXB/1RV	Alexander RH	Grampian Regional Transport	121	A
C200 HGF	1985	Mercedes-Benz	L608D	Plaxton Mini Supreme	Richmond of Epsom		RP
E131 DRS	1988	Leyland	Olympian ONCL10/2RZ	Alexander RH	Grampian Regional Transport	131	R
K1 GRT	1992	Mercedes Benz-	0405G	Alexander	Grampian Regional Transport	1	R

Aberdeen & District Transport Preservation Trust

Alford

Organisation: Aberdeen & District Transport Preservation Trust

Address: c/o Grampian Transport Museum, Montgarrie Road, Alford, Aberdeenshire AB33 8AE

Contact address: c/o Gordon Mills, Ellengowan, Cults, Aberdeen AB15 9QJ

Phone: 01975 563679

Fax: 01224 869352

Email: gordon1.mills@btinternet.com

Website: http://gtm.org.uk/services/bus_collection.html

Brief description: Museum. Access by prior arrangement. A free bus service is laid on for GTM events to link the event car park.

Opening days/times: For 2010 Grampian Transport Museum season, a display will be open to the public on the first Wednesday of each month and by prior arrangement at other times.

Directions by car: The village of Alford lies 25 miles west of Aberdeen on the A944

Ample free car parking is available in the village car park just outside the museum

Directions by public transport: By Stagecoach bus from Aberdeen and Inverurie

Charges: Donations

Facilities: The collection has access for the disabled and the Grampian Transport Museum has a tea room and souvenir shop.

Owned today by First, this 1930 Walker-bodied Albion PMA28 is a resident at the Aberdeen Transport Museum. ABERDEEN TRANSPORT MUSEUM

Amberley Working Museum

Address: Amberley, Nr Arundel, West Sussex, BN18 9LT

Phone: 01798 831370

E-mail: office@amberleymuseum.co.uk

Website: www.amberleymuseum.co.uk

Brief description: A 36-acre industrial museum set in a beautiful location within the South Downs. Traditional resident craftspeople, working narrow-gauge railway and vintage bus service. Connected Earth Telecommunications display, electricity hall, nature trails, picnic areas, gift shop, restaurant and much more. Special events held throughout the main season — see website for details.

Events planned in 2010:

12 September — Bus Show

Opening days/times: 13 February–31 October (including Bank Holidays & West Sussex school holidays) 10.00–17.30 (last entry 16.30)

Directions by car: The Museum is situated in West Sussex on the B2139 adjacent to Amberley Railway Station, mid-way between Arundel and Storrington. Free coach and car parking is provided for Museum visitors.

Directions by public transport: Hourly rail service calls at Amberley station which is adjacent to the museum

Charges: £9.30 Adult, £8.30 concession (over 60 and students), £5.80 children (5-15yrs), under fives — FREE

Facilities: A B B(e) C D E F G H L P R T Dogs welcome on leads

Amberley is a haven for veterans like Southdown 517 (UF 1517), a 1927 Short-bodied Dennis 30cwt.
PHILIP LAMB

Note: Please be aware that vehicles on display can vary from time to time as not all museums display their entire 'fleet'. Visitors wishing to see a particular vehicle should make enquiries prior to their visit.

Registration	Date	Chassis make	Chassis model	Body make	Original operator	Fleet No	Status
IB 552	1914	Tilling-Stevens	TS3 Petrol-Electric	Newman	Worthing Motor Services	52	R
CD 5125	1920	Leyland	N	Short	Southdown Motor Services	125	R
CD 4867	1923	Tilling-Stevens	TS3A Petrol-Electric	(chassis only)	Southdown Motor Services	67	RP
BP 9822	1924	Shelvoke & Drewry	Freighter	Hickman (replica)	Tramocar of Worthing	1	R
MO 9324	1927	Tilling Stevens	B9A	Brush	Thames Valley Traction Co	152	R
UF 1517	1927	Dennis	30cwt	Short	Southdown Motor Services	517	R
BR 7132	1929	Leyland	Lion LT1	Leyland	Sunderland Corporation	2	R
UF 4813	1929	Leyland	Titan TD1	Brush	Southdown Motor Services	813	A
UF 6473	1930	Leyland	Titan TD1	Leyland	Southdown Motor Services	873	R
UF 6805	1930	Tilling-Stevens	B10A2	Short	Southdown Motor Services	1205	RP
UF 7428	1931	Leyland	Titan TD1	Short	Southdown Motor Services	928	R
ECD 524	1937	Leyland	Cub KPZ2	Park Royal	Southdown Motor Services	24	RP
EUF 184	1938	Leyland	Titan TD5	Leyland	Southdown Motor Services	0184	R
XMD 47A	1957	Leyland	Titan PD2/12	Metro-Cammell	Trent Motor Traction Co	1006	A

Registration	Date	Chassis make	Chassis model	Body make	Original operator	Fleet No	Status
	1925	AEC	S	Buckingham	Birmingham Corporation Tramways	215	A
OP 237	1926	(no chassis)		Short	Birmingham Corporation Tramways	208	A
EA 4181	1929	Dennis	E	Dixon	West Bromwich Corporation	32	R
HA 4963	1930	SOS	RR	(chassis only)	BMMO ('Midland Red')	963	A
JF 2378	1931	AEC	Regal 662	Burlingham	Provincial of Leicester	R1	R
OJ 9347	1933	Morris Commercial	Dictator	Metro-Cammell	Birmingham Corporation Tramways	47	RP
AOG 679	1935	Daimler	COG5		Birmingham Corporation Tramways	83	RP
EHA 775	1938	SOS	SON	(chassis only)	BMMO ('Midland Red')	2207	A
RC 7927	1940	BMMO	SON	Willowbrook	Trent Motor Traction Co	417	R
FON 630	1942	Leyland	Titan TD7	(chassis only)	Birmingham City Transport	1330	A
KHA 301	1948	BMMO	C1	Duple	BMMO ('Midland Red')	2382	R
KHY 383	1948	Bristol	L6B	Bristol Tramways & Carriage	Bristol Tramways	3301	R
GUJ 608	1950	Sentinel	STC4	Sentinel	Sentinel demonstrator		R
JOJ 222	1950	Leyland	Titan PD2/1	Park Royal	Birmingham City Transport	2222	A
JOJ 526	1950	Guy	Arab IV	Metro-Cammell	Birmingham City Transport	2526	A
JOJ 548	1950	Guy	Arab IV	Metro-Cammell	Birmingham City Transport	2548	RP
KHA 352	1950	BMMO	CL2	Plaxton	BMMO ('Midland Red')	3352	RP
SB 8155	1950	Guy	Wolf	Ormac	Alexander MacConnacher of Ballachulish		R
JOJ 847	1952	Daimler	CVG6	Crossley	Birmingham City Transport	2847	A
LOG 301	1952	Guy	Arab IV	Saunders Roe	Birmingham City Transport	3001	RP
LJW 336	1953	Guy	LUF	Saunders Roe	Guy Demonstrator		R
LOG 302	1954	Daimler	CLG5	Metro-Cammell	Birmingham City Transport	3002	R
MOF 90	1954	Guy	Arab IV	Metro-Cammell	Birmingham City Transport	3090	RP
TOB 377	1956	AEC	Reliance MU3RV	Burlingham	Flights of Birmingham		R
XDH 72	1956	Sunbeam	F4A	Willowbrook	Walsall Corporation	872	RP
773 FHA	1958	BMMO	D9	BMMO	BMMO ('Midland Red')	4773	A
1294 RE	1959	Guy	Arab LUF	Burlingham	Harper Bros of Heath Hayes	60	R
WLT 506	1960	AEC	Routemaster R2RH	Park Royal	London Transport	RM 506	R
3035 HA	1963	BMMO	D9	BMMO	BMMO ('Midland Red')	5035	RP
6479 HA	1963	BMMO	S17	Willowbrook	BMMO ('Midland Red')	5479	R
334 CRW	1963	Daimler	CVG6	Metro-Cammell	Coventry City Transport	334	RP
264 ERY	1963	Leyland	Titan PD3A/1	Park Royal	Leicester City Transport	264	R
6370 HA	1964	BMMO	D9	BMMO	BMMO ('Midland Red')	5370	R
KOX 663F	1967	AEC	Swift MP2R	MCW	Birmingham City Transport	3663	RP
LHA 870F	1967	BMMO	S21	BMMO	BMMO ('Midland Red')	5870	R
XNX 136H	1970	Leyland	Leopard PSU3A/4R	Alexander	Stratford-upon-Avon Blue Motors	36	R
XON 41J	1971	Daimler	Fleetline CRG6LX	Park Royal	West Midlands PTE	4041	R

Aston Manor Road Transport Museum

Birmingham

Contact address: 208 - 216 Witton Lane, Aston, Birmingham B6 6QE

Phone: 0121 322 2298

Fax: 0121 449 4606

E-mail: info@amrtm.org

Website: www.amrtm.org

Brief description: A display of commercial road transport vehicles, many with a West Midlands connection, housed in a former tram shed which retains some of its fittings from that era. Many of the buses are used on free bus services throughout the year. Smaller artefacts are also on display.

Events planned in 2010:

31 May — Two Museums Running Day

11 July — 23rd Museum Open Day and Outer Circle Running Day with vehicle gathering

11/12 September — Heritage Weekend Open Days

17 October — 60 years of new look Birmingham 'Standards'

28 November — 14th Annual Collectors' Fair

Opening days/times: Weekends throughout the year 11.00-17.00 (16.00 November-February). Bank Holiday Mondays, and Wednesdays during school holidays from Easter-October (16.00 closure)

Directions by car: Witton Lane is on the B4137 (follow signs to Aston Hall or Aston Villa F.C.) — we are a short distance from Villa Park.

Directions by public transport: National Express West Midlands 7 from Colmore Row in the City Centre, or the Outer Circle 11 to Witton Square

Charges: Adults £2, Children and concessions £1.50, Family ticket £6 (2 or 3 children). Events have a slightly higher charge.

Facilities: B(e) D G H P R S T

Registration	Date	Chassis make	Chassis model	Body make	Original operator	Fleet No	Status
JOV 714P	1976	Bristol	VRTSL6LX	MCW	West Midlands PTE	4714	R
NOE 602R	1977	Leyland	National 11351A/1R	Leyland National	Midland Red Omnibus Co	602	A
OOX 825R	1977	Leyland	National 11351A/1R	Leyland National	West Midlands PTE	6825	RP
SOA 658S	1977	Leyland	National 11351A/1R	Leyland National	Midland Red Omnibus Co	658	RP
BVP 784V	1979	Leyland	Leopard PSU3E/4R	Plaxton	Midland Red Omnibus Co	784	A
WDA 700T	1979	Leyland	Fleetline FE30AGR	MCW	West Midlands PTE	7000	A
A110 WVP	1984	MCW	Metrobus GR133/1	MCW	West Midlands PTE	8110	RP
F685 YOG	1988	MCW	Metrorider MF150/113	MCW	West Midlands Travel	685	RP
G292 EOG	1990	Leyland	Lynx LX2R11C15Z4R	Leyland Lynx	West Midlands Travel	1292	RP
G142 HNP	1990	Leyland	Lynx LX2R11C15Z4R	Leyland	Midland Red West	1142	A

The Aston Manor Road Transport Museum is home to Midland Red 3301 (KHA 301), a BMMO C1 coach with Duple centre-entrance body. It is seen here at the Golden Gates of Chatsworth House in Derbyshire on 25 June 2006. SIMON GILL

Black Country Living Museum Transport Group
Dudley

The Black Country Living museum has the longest overhead circuit in the country allowing trolleybuses like 1948 Roe-bodied Sunbeam W, Wolverhampton 433 (DUK 833) to be put through their paces. PHILIP LAMB

Registration	Date	Chassis make	Chassis model	Body make	Original operator	Fleet No	Status
UK 9978	1931	Guy	BTX	Guy	Wolverhampton Corporation	78	A
HA 8047	1933	SOS	REDD	Metro-Cammell	BMMO ('Midland Red')	1047	A
DKY 735	1946	Karrier	W	East Lancs	Bradford Corporation	735	RP
DUK 833	1946	Sunbeam	W	Roe	Wolverhampton Corporation	433	R
FEA 156	1949	Daimler	CVG5	Metro-Cammell	West Bromwich Corporation	156	RP
TDH 912	1955	Sunbeam	F4A	Willowbrook	Walsall Corporation	862	R
2206 OI	1958	Sunbeam	F4A	Harkness	Belfast Corporation	246	R
SCH 237	1960	Sunbeam	F4A	Roe	Derby Corporation	237	R
VRD 186	1961	Sunbeam	F4A	Burlingham	Reading Corporation	186	RP
6342 HA	1963	BMMO	D9	BMMO	BMMO ('Midland Red')	5342	R
GHA 327D	1965	Leyland	Leopard PSU4/4R	Plaxton	Midland Red Omnibus Co	5827	R
XDH 519G	1969	Daimler	Fleetline CRG6LX	Northern Counties	Walsall Corporation	119	RP

Contact address: Tipton Road, Dudley, West Midlands, DY1 4SQ

Phone: 0121 557 5308

Website: www.bcmtg.co.uk

Brief description: Tramway operation daily. Trolleybus operation on Sundays and Bank Holidays

Events planned in 2010:

Saturday 5-Sunday 21 June Trolleybus 2010 Rally

Opening days/times: Summer: daily 10.00-17.00. Winter: Wednesdays to Sundays 10.00-16.00. Some evening openings

Directions by car: M5 (jct 2) signposted on Motorway. Follow signs on A4123 to Black Country Living Museum

Directions by public transport: London Midland trains to Tipton station. National Express West Midlands 224, 263, 270, 311-313 to Museum

Facilities: A B B(e) C D E F G H L P R T

Registration	Date	Chassis make	Chassis model	Body make	Original operator	Fleet No	Status
Unregistered	1896	Horse bus			Edinburgh & District Tramways		R
XW 9892	1925	Tilling Stevens	TS7	Tilling	Thomas Tilling	0172	R
YT 3738	1927	Leyland	Lioness PLC1	Thurgood	King George V		R
JRN 29	1956	Leyland	Tiger Cub PSUC1/2	Burlingham	Ribble Motor Services	963	R
301 LJ	1962	Sunbeam	MF2B	Weymann	Bournemouth Corporation	301	R

Top: **Local operator Ribble is represented at the British Commercial Vehicle Museum in Leyland by this beautifully restored Leyland Tiger Cub fitted with classic Burlingham Seagull coachwork.** BCVM

Above: **Another vehicle on display at Leyland is this magnificent Thurgood-bodied Leyland Lioness built in 1927 as a shooting brake for King George V. It later saw service with Jersey Motor Transport, and was one of the earliest vehicles to enter preservation around 1960.** BCVM

Address: King Street, Leyland, Lancashire PR25 2LE

Phone: 01772 451011 (Opening Hours) 07928 641858 (Out of Hours)

E-mail: enquiries@bcvm.co.uk

Website: www.bcvm.co.uk

Brief description: A unique collection of over 60 vehicles covering nearly 120 years of commercial vehicle manufacture and use, including trucks, buses, fire engines, vans, steam traction engine, and the famous 'Popemobile'. The 'Engine Room' tells the story of the diesel engine. An extensive archive contains over 250,000 items of film, photographs and paper records.

Events planned in 2010:

18 April — Classic & Vintage Ford Day

9 May — Classic Motorscooter Event

16 May — The Spring Transport Show

6 June — Vintage and Classic Motorcycle Show

27 June — American Road Show

10/11 July — Leyland Transport Show (part of the Leyland Homecoming event)

25 July — Bus & Coach Show

15 August — Great British Lorries Day

19 September — Autumn Transport Show

24 October — Model Transport Exhibition

All events 10am to 4pm at Museum

Opening days/times: 13 February to 31 October 2010: Saturday and Sunday, and Bank Holiday Mondays

Also: **Thursday and Fridays** during Lancashire School Holidays

Museum open 10.00 to 17.00. Group Bookings welcome at other times/dates

Directions by car: From M6 (Junction 28) follow signs to British Commercial Vehicle Museum. From A6, A49, A59, M65 follow signs to Leyland, then follow signs for British Commercial Vehicle Museum.

British Commercial Vehicle Museum
Leyland

Directions by public transport: Travel on any bus for Leyland, alight in Hough Lane and follow signs for British Commercial Vehicle Museum (four minutes walk).

Travel on any train for Leyland, leave Station through Ticket Office, turn left (down hill) and follow signs for Town Centre, then follow signs for British Commercial Vehicle Museum (15 minutes walk).

Charges: Day Visitors: £5.50 Adult, £5 Seniors, £3 Children (4-15 years)

Discount for Groups: 12+ 10%, 24+ 20%

Facilities: A B(e) C D E F G H L P R S T

Castle Point Transport Museum

Canvey Island

Contact address: 105 Point Road, Canvey Island, Essex, SS8 7TD

Phone: 01268 684272

Website: www.castlepointtransportmuseum.co.uk

Brief description: This historic former Canvey & District bus depot, built in 1935, houses approximately 35 commercial vehicles spanning the years 1944 to 1988. Exhibits include buses, coaches, lorries, fire engines and military vehicles. They can be seen in varying stages from the fully restored to those awaiting restoration. The museum is run by volunteers.

Museum Open Day and Transport Show at Canvey Island on Sunday 10th October 2010.

10.00 - 16.30. Entries welcome from stallholders, bus, car, commercial vehicles, tractors and stationary engine owners.

Further details and entry forms from:
Castle Point Transport Museum,
105 Point Road, Canvey island, SS8 7TD
Events Office: 01268 684 272
(answerphone)
Paul Moss: 07809 550 395 /
07707 540 788
Email: paulmoss4@hotmail.com
www.castlepointtransportmuseum.co.uk

Event planned in 2010:

10 October — 31st Annual Show

Opening days/times: Open on1st /3rd Sundays, April to mid-October

Directions by car: A130 to Canvey Island; follow brown tourism signs on reaching the island

Directions by public transport: By rail to South Benfleet, then by bus to Leigh Beck, Canvey Island

Charges: Free admission. Donations welcome. A charge is made on the Transport Show day in October

Facilities: A B(e) D E G H P R S T

Other information: Hot drinks available

Registration	Date	Chassis make	Chassis model	Body make	Original operator	Fleet No	Status
FOP 429	1944	Daimler	CWA6	Duple	Birmingham Corporation Tramways	1429	R
JVW 430	1944	Bristol	K5G	ECW	Eastern National Omnibus Co	3885	RP
MPU 52	1947	Leyland	Titan PD1A	ECW	Eastern National Omnibus Co	3991	RP
CFV 851	1948	Bedford	OB	Duple	Seagull Coaches of Blackpool		R
LYR 997	1949	AEC	Regent III O961	Weymann	London Transport	RT2827	R
NEH 453	1949	Leyland	Titan OPD2/1	Northern Counties	Potteries Motor Traction Co	L453	R
ONO 49	1950	Bristol	L5G	ECW	Eastern National Omnibus Co	4029	R
PTW 110	1950	Bristol	L6B	ECW	Eastern National Omnibus Co	4107	RP
WNO 478	1953	Bristol	KSW5G	ECW	Westcliff-on-Sea Motor Services		R
XVX 19	1954	Bristol	Lodekka LD5G	ECW	Eastern National Omnibus Co	4208	R
859 ETW	1956	Bristol	LS5G	ECW	Eastern National Omnibus Co	417	R
381 BKM	1957	AEC	Reliance MU3RV	Harrington	Maidstone & District Motor Services	C381	RP
PHJ 954	1958	Leyland	Titan PD3/6	Massey	Southend Corporation	315	RP
236 LNO	1959	Bristol	Lodekka LDLX6G	ECW	Eastern National Omnibus Co	1541	R
217 MHK	1959	Bristol	MW6G	ECW	Eastern National Omnibus Co	480	R
VLT 44	1959	AEC	Routemaster R2RH	Park Royal	London Transport	RM44	R
SGD 407	1960	Leyland	Titan PD3/2	Alexander	Glasgow Corporation	L405	R
373 WPU	1961	Guy	Arab IV	Massey	Moore Bros of Kelvedon		R
28 TKR	1962	AEC	Reliance 2MU3RV	Harrington	Maidstone & District Motor Services	C28	R
138 CLT	1962	AEC	Routemaster R2RH	Park Royal	London Transport	RM1138	R
NTW 942C	1965	Bristol	Lodekka FLF6G	ECW	Eastern National Omnibus Co	2849	R
OWC 182D	1966	Bristol	MW6G	ECW	Tillings Transport	182	R
GJN 509D	1966	Leyland	Leopard PSU3/1R	Marshall	Southend Corporation	209	R
AVX 975G	1968	Bristol	Lodekka FLF6LX	ECW	Eastern National Omnibus Co	2614	R
CPU 979G	1968	Bristol	VRTSL/6LX	ECW	Eastern National Omnibus Co	3000	R
GNM 232N	1975	Bristol	LHS6L	Plaxton	Epsom Coaches		RP
YEV 308S	1978	Leyland	National 11351A/1R	Leyland National	Eastern National Omnibus Co	1850	R

Registration	Date	Chassis make	Chassis model	Body make	Original operator	Fleet No	Status
KID 154	1947	Leyland	Tiger PS1	Northern Ireland Road Transport Board	Northern Ireland Road Transport Board	A8520	A
FCI 323	1950	Bristol	LL5G	ECW	Crosville Motor Services	KG156	RP
ZJ 5904	1950	Leyland	Tiger OPS3/1	CIE	CIE	P164	R
IY 7383	1951	GNR	Gardner	Park Royal/GNR	Great Northern Railway (Ireland)	G389	R
IY 8044	1952	GNR	Gardner	Park Royal/GNR	Great Northern Railway (Ireland)	G396	A
ZO 6960	1953	Leyland	Titan OPD2/1	CIE	CIE	R541	RP
ZU 5000	1953	Leyland	Royal Tiger PSU1/9	Saunders Roe	Irish Army		RP
ZY 1715	1955	AEC	Regal IV 9622E	Park Royal/GNR	Great Northern Railway (Ireland)	345	R
ILI 98	1958	Bristol	SC4LK	ECW	Eastern National Omnibus Co	455	RP
71 AHI	1960	Leyland	Tiger Cub PSUC1/2	Metro-Cammell	Western Welsh Omnibus Co	1274	A
3945 UE	1960	Leyland	Tiger Cub PSUC1	Park Royal	Stratford-upon-Avon Blue Motors	45	A
AZD 203	1964	Leyland	Leopard L2	CIE	CIE	E140	R
BLH 123B	1964	Bedford	VAS2	Duple Midland	London County Council	3159	RP
EZH 155	1965	Leyland	Leopard PSU3/4R	CIE	CIE	C155	A
EZH 170	1966	Leyland	Leopard PSU3/4R	CIE	CIE	C170	R
UZH 258	1966	Leyland	Leopard PSU3/4R	CIE	CIE	C258	R
ZS 8621	1971	Daimler	Fleetline CRG6LX	Park Royal	West Midlands PTE	4130	A
78 D140	1978	Bedford	SB5	Marshall	Royal Navy		R
78 D824	1978	Bristol	RELL6G	Alexander (Belfast)	Ulsterbus	2193	R
85 D2412	1978	Bedford	SB5	Marshall	Royal Air Force		A
643 MIP	1980	Volvo	B58-61	Duple	North West Coachlines of Kirkham		A

Cavan & Leitrim Railway Bus Collection
Dromod

Contact address: Cavan & Leitrim Railway, Narrow Guage Station, Station Road, Dromod, Co Leitrim, Eire

Phone: 00353 71 9638599

E-mail: p.bedford@tcd.ie

Website: www.ucrrailways.com

Brief description: Half mile 3ft gauge steam railway with collection of railway vehicles (steam, diesel, carriages, wagons and railcars) together with a selection of vintage road vehicles, military equipment and vintage aircraft.

Opening days/times: April to September: Saturdays 10.00-17.00, Sundays 13.00-17.00, Mondays 10.00-17.00. Please telephone in advance if travelling long distance.

Rest of year: By request; please telephone, write or e-mail

Directions by car: Situated next to Irish Rail Station, Drumod

Directions by public transport: Train to Dromod Irish Rail station from Dublin Connolly (Dublin-Sligo line). Narrow guage station next to main line

Charges: Adult €8, Child €5, Family €17, OAP €5

Facilities: B(e) C D E G R (on request) S T

Registration	Date	Chassis make	Chassis model	Body make	Original operator	Fleet No	Status
Unregistered	1875	Horse Bus		LGOC	LGOC	HB2938	R
Unregistered	1890	Horse Bus			Andrews Star Omnibus Co		R
XO 1038	1923	AEC	405 (NS)	(chassis only)	London General Omnibus Co	NS174	RP
XO 7696	1923	AEC	405 (NS)	(chassis only)	London General Omnibus Co	NS524	A
XX 9591	1925	Dennis	4-ton	Dodson	Dominion Omnibus Co	D142	R
YH 1173	1927	AEC	405-410	(chassis only)		NS2405	
UU 6646	1929	AEC	Regal 662	LGOC	London General Omnibus Co	T31	R
GJ 2098	1930	AEC	Regent 661	Thomas Tilling	Thomas Tilling	ST922	R
GO 5170	1931	AEC	Renown 664	LGOC	London General Omnibus Co	LT1059	A

Cobham Bus Museum

Contact address: Redhill Road, Cobham, Surrey KT11 1EF

Phone: 01932 868665

E-mail: info@lbpt.org

Website address: www.lbpt.org

Brief description: This well-established museum contains the world's largest collection of ex-London Transport motor buses and two horse-buses, ranging from 1875 to 1979. Plans are afoot for the Museum to move to new purpose-built premises at Brooklands, subject to planning approval.

Events planned in 2010:

11 April — Spring Gathering at Wisley Airfield & Cobham Bus Museum.

Cobham Bus Museum is home to prototype Leyland-engined AEC Routemaster RML3 (SLT 53), seen here alongside production example RM2037 (ALM 37B) for comparison. PHILIP LAMB

In view of the proposed move to Brooklands, no other event days have been arranged for 2010. Please visit the website for further details

Opening days/times: Viewing possible on Wednesdays and at weekends but please telephone in advance to confirm

Directions by car: From M25 J10, take A3 north and turn left on to A245. Redhill Road is 1 mile on left

Directions by public transport: Network of special services on Spring Gathering Day. Infrequent bus service at other times to Brooklands Road, Byfleet then ½ mile walk

Charges: £10 on Spring Gathering Day

Facilities: B(e) D E P(Disabled only) R(limited) S T

Registration	Date	Chassis make	Chassis model	Body make	Original operator	Fleet No	Status
GN 8242	1931	AEC	Regal 662	Weymann	Queen Line Coaches of London	T357	A
AGX 520	1933	AEC	Regent I 661	Chalmers	London Transport	738J	R
AXM 693	1934	AEC	Regent 661	LPTB	London Transport	STL441	R
CGJ 188	1935	AEC	Q 0762	Birmingham RC&W	LPTB	Q83	R
CXX 171	1936	AEC	Regal O662	Weymann	LPTB	T448	RP
CGJ 174	1937	AEC	Q 0762	(chassis only)	LPTB	Q69	A
EGO 426	1937	AEC	Regent O661	LPTB	LPTB	STL2377	R
ELP 228	1938	AEC	Regal O662	LPTB	LPTB	T504	R
EYK 396	1938	AEC	Regent III	LPTB	LPTB	RT1	R
FJJ 764	1939	Leyland	Tiger FEC	(chassis only)	London Transport	TF67	A
HGC 130	1945	Guy	Arab II	Park Royal	LPTB	G351	R
JXC 288	1949	Leyland	Tiger PS1	Mann Egerton	London Transport	TD95	R
KGK 803	1949	Leyland	Titan 7RT	Park Royal	London Transport	RTL139	R
KGU 142	1949	AEC	Regent III 0961	(chassis only)	London Transport	RT2213	R
MYA 590	1949	Leyland	Comet CPO1	Harrington	Scarlet Pimpernel of Minehead		R
UMP 227	1949	AEC	Regal IV	Park Royal	AEC (prototype)		RP
LUC 210	1951	AEC	Regal IV 9821LT	Metro-Cammell	London Transport	RF10	RP
LUC 381	1951	AEC	Regal IV 9821E	ECW	London Transport	RFW6	RP
LYR 826	1952	AEC	Regent III 0961	Park Royal	London Transport	RT2775	RP
LYR 910	1952	AEC	Regent III 0961	Park Royal	London Transport	RT3491	R
MLL 740	1953	AEC	Regal IV 9822E	Park Royal	British European Airways		R
MXX 334	1953	Guy	Special NLLVP	ECW	London Transport	GS34	R
MXX 283	1953	AEC	Regal IV 9821LT	Metro-Cammell	London Transport	RF395	R
NLE 672	1953	AEC	Regal IV 9821LT	Metro-Cammell	London Transport	RF672	R
CDX 516	1954	AEC	Regent III 9613E	Park Royal	Ipswich Corporation	16	R
SLT 58	1958	Leyland	Routemaster	Weymann	London Transport	RML3	R
461 CLT	1962	AEC	Routemaster	Park Royal	London Transport	RMC1461	R
EGN 369J	1971	AEC	Swift 4MP2R	Park Royal	London Transport	SMS369	R
JPA 190K	1972	AEC	Reliance 6U2R	Park Royal	London Country Bus Services	RP90	R
OJD 172R	1976	Leyland	Fleetline FE30GR	(chassis only)	London Transport	DMS2172	R
WYW 6T	1979	MCW	Metrobus DR101/8	MCW	London Transport	M6	R

Registration	Date	Chassis make	Chassis model	Body make	Original operator	Fleet No	Status
SR 1266	1916	Maudslay	Subsidy A	(chassis only)			RP
EKV 966	1944	Daimler	CWA6	Roe	Coventry Corporation	366	A
JNB 416	1948	Maudslay	Marathon II	Trans-United	Hackett's of Manchester		R
KOM 150	1950	Daimler	CVD6	Wilsdon	Birmingham Post & Mail		R
SRB 424	1953	Daimler	CD650	Willowbrook	Tailby & George ('Blue Bus Services') Willington		R
PBC 734	1954	Karrier	Bantam Q25	Reading	Mablethorpe Homes of Leicester		R
333 CRW	1963	Daimler	CVG6	Metro-Cammell	Coventry Corporation	333	R
PDU 125M	1973	Daimler	Fleetline CRG6LX	East Lancs	Coventry Corporation	125	R
K232 DAC	1993	Peugeot	J5		Peugeot UK		A

Amongst the buses and coaches at Coventry Transport Museum is locally built 1948 Maudslay Marathon II JNB 416 fitted with a rare Trans-United 33-seat coach body. PHILIP LAMB

Coventry Transport Museum

Contact address: Coventry Transport Museum, Millinnium Place, Hales Street, Coventry, CV1 1JD

Phone: 024 7623 4270

Fax: 024 7623 4284

E-mail: enquiries@transport-museum.com

Website: www.transport-museum.com

Brief description: The museum has over 260 cars and commercial vehicles, over 120 motorcycles and around 300 bicycles. Various tableaux chart the development of the motor vehicle from the early years and Coventry's contribution to this can be in the many marques on display. Other exhibits include the Thrust 2 and Thrust SSC land speed record cars, several thousand die-cast models and a walk-through audio visual display of the Coventry Blitz experience.

Opening days/times: Open all year 10.00-17.00 (last admission 16.30) except 24/25/26 December and 1 January

Directions by car: Coventry's Ring Road circles the city centre and is encountered whichever direction you come from. Once on it follow the brown Transport Museum signs and turn off at junction 1. Nearest car park (pay and display) is signposted and is in Tower Street at the back of the Museum.

Directions by public transport: The museum is opposite Pool Meadow bus/coach station. Use National Express West Midlands bus 17 or 27 from Coventry railway station to Broadgate (5min walk downhill to Museum from Broadgate).

Facilities: A B(e) C D E F G H L R S T

Other information: The vehicles are frequently stored off site while new developments are built. Please phone to check which vehicles are on display.

Admission: Free

Note: Please be aware that vehicles on display can vary from time to time as not all museums display their entire 'fleet'. Visitors wishing to see a particular vehicle should make enquiries prior to their visit.

Dover Transport Museum
Whitfield

Address: Willingdon Road, Port Zone, Old Park, Whitfield, Dover CT16 2HQ.

Phone: 01304 822409 (museum)

E-mail: jhnlines@aol.com

Website: www.dovertransportmuseum.org.uk

Brief description: The Museum houses various vehicles from double deck buses through to motorcycles. There are a number of street displays, shop fronts, a garage and police display.

Dover Transport Museum
White Cliffs Bus Rally
13th June 2010
www.dovertransportmuseum.org.uk

Registration	Date	Chassis make	Chassis model	Body make	Original operator	Fleet No	Status
CC 9305	1930	Dennis	G	Roberts	Llandudno UDC	4	R
MFN 888	1957	Guy	Arab IV	Park Royal	East Kent Road Car Co		R
569 KKK	1960	AEC	Reliance 2MU3RA	Duple	Ayers Coaches of Dover		R
GJG 751D	1966	AEC	Regent V 2D3RA	Park Royal	East Kent Road Car Co		R
GJG 757D	1966	AEC	Regent V 2D3RA	Park Royal	East Kent Road Car Co		A
FKM 706L	1972	Leyland	Atlantean PDR1A/1	MCW	Maidstone & District Motor Services	5706	A
NPD 145L	1973	Leyland	National 1151/1R/0402	Leyland National	London Country Bus Services	LNC45	A
WKO 137S	1978	Bristol	VRT/SL3/6LXB	ECW	Maidstone & District Motor Services	5137	R
BJG 674V	1979	Bristol	VRT/SL3/6LXB	ECW	East Kent Road Car Co	7674	A
B147 EDP	1984	MCW	Metrobus DR102/44	MCW	Reading Corporation		A

Events planned in 2010:

13 June — Bus Rally

18 July — Classic Car Rally

15 August — Cars, buses and trains

All events in conjuction with East Kent Light Railway — buses operate between the Museum and Railway on event days

Opening days/times: October to Easter: Sundays only 10.30-17.00

Easter to end of September: Wednesdays, Thursdays and Fridays 13.30-1700; Sundays and Bank Holidays 10.30-17.00

School parties and groups at other times by arrangement

Directions by car: The Museum is located just off the A2 at the Whitfield Roundabout. Follow brown tourism signs to the Museum. Satellite navigation CT16 2HQ

Directions by public transport: Stagecoach 61 from Priory Street in Dover town centre to Honeywood Road, Whitfield. Every ten minutes Monday to Saturday. Stagecoach 60a every two hours on a Sunday. Bus times can be obtained at www.stagecoachbus.com.

Charges: Adults £4, Senior Citizens £3, Children £2, Family £9

Facilities: D P R T

Ayres Coaches of Dover once operated this splendid Duple Britannia-bodied AEC Reliance, now on display in that town's transport museum. PHILIP LAMB

A highlight of the Carlton Colville year is its 'Twilight Trolleys' event held over the second weekend in September. Here at the combined tram and trolleybus terminus, an all-London turnout sees LCC HR2 tramcar 1858 competing for passengers with London Transport trolleybuses Nos 1201 (EXV 201) and 1521 (FXH 521), members of the K2 and L3 classes respectively.
PHILIP LAMB

Registration	Date	Chassis make	Chassis model	Body make	Original operator	Fleet No	Status
EX 1128	1924	Guy	BB	United	Great Yarmouth Corporation	30	A
AH 79505	1926	Garrett	O type	Strachan & Brown	NESA (Copenhagen)	5	RP
WX 3567	1930	Gilford	168SD	Fielding & Bottomley	Oade of Heckmondwike		RP
ALJ 986	1935	Sunbeam	MS2	Park Royal	Bournemouth Corporation	202	R
CUL 260	1936	AEC	664T	Metro-Cammell	London Transport	260	R
EXV 201	1938	Leyland	LPTB70	Leyland	London Transport	1201	R
FXH 521	1940	Metro Cammell		Metro-Cammell	London Transport	1521	R
GBJ 192	1947	AEC	Regent II O661	ECW	Lowestoft Corporation	21	R
Unregistered	1948	Berna		Hess	Biel (Switzerland)	39	R
KAH 408	1948	Bristol	L4G	ECW	Eastern Counties Omnibus Co	LL 108	A
BDY 809	1948	Sunbeam	W	Weymann	Hastings Tramways Co	34	RP
NBB 628	1950	BUT	9641T	Metro-Cammell	Newcastle Corporation	628	RP
EX 6566	1950	Leyland	Titan PD2/1	Leyland	Great Yarmouth Corporation	66	R
KXW 234	1950	AEC	Regent III O961 RT	Weymann	London Transport	RT3125	R
ERV 938	1951	BUT	9611T	Burlingham	Portsmouth Corporation	313	R
SG 2030	1952	Henschel	üHIII/s	Uerdingen	Solingen (Germany)	1	R
DRC 224	1953	Sunbeam	F4	Willowbrook	Derby Corporation	224	R
LCD 52	1953	BUT	9611T	Weymann	Brighton Corporation	52	R
ONE 744	1956	BUT	9612T	Burlingham	Manchester Corporation	1344	R
YTE 826	1956	BUT	9612T	Bond	Ashton-under-Lyne Corporation	87	R
YLJ 286	1959	Sunbeam	MF2B	Weymann	Bournemouth Corporation	286	R
557 BNG	1962	Bristol	Lodekka FL6G	ECW	Eastern Counties Omnibus Co	LFL57	R
918 NRT	1963	AEC	Regent V MD3RV	Massey	Lowestoft Corporation	8	A
AEX 85B	1964	AEC	Reliance 2MU3RA	Pennine	Great Yarmouth Corporation	85	RP
YRT 898H	1969	AEC	Swift 2MP2R	ECW	Lowestoft Corporation	4	R
OCK 985K	1972	Bristol	VRTSL2/6LX	ECW	Ribble Motor Services	1985	R
D103 DAJ	1986	Mercedes-Benz	L608D	Reeve Burgess	Hartlepool Transport	13	R
Unregistered	1989	ZiU	682G1	ZiU	ILPAP (Athens)	5088	R
K62 KEX	1995	Dennis	Dart 9SDL	East Lancs	Great Yarmouth Transport	62	A

East Anglia Transport Museum
Carlton Colville

Contact address: Chapel Road, Carlton Colville, Lowestoft, Suffolk NR33 8BL

Phone: 01502 518459

Fax: 01502 584658

E-mail: eastangliatransportmuseum@live.co.uk

Website: www.eatm.org.uk

Brief description: The Museum is the only place in Britain that offers tram, train and trolleybus rides to visitors. Vehicles on display include buses, trams, trolleybuses, cars and commercials. Vehicles operate along a period streetscene. Various exhibition rooms tell the story of transport.

Events planned in 2010:

24/25 April — Classic and Vintage Weekend. Classic and vintage cars and motorcycles displayed

11 July — Bus and Coach Event. Buses and coaches displayed and in service.

11/12 September — Trolleybus Weekend. After-dark rides on Saturday evening with all available vehicles in service during the weekend

Opening days/times: Opening days: Sundays, Thursdays and Bank Holiday Mondays 1 April to 3 October; Saturdays 5 June to 2 October; Whitsun holiday daily 1 June to 5 June; Tuesdays and Wednesdays 20 July to 1 September during school summer holidays

Opening hours: Sundays and Bank Holiday Mondays 11.00-17.00. All other days 14.00-17.00. Last admission one hour before closing

Directions by car: Close to the A146 Lowestoft to Norwich road and A12 Lowestoft to Ipswich road. Museum signed with brown tourist signs

Directions by public transport: Buses from Lowestoft, Norwich and Gorleston stop close to the Museum

Charges: Adults £6.50, Senior Citizens £5.50, Children £4.50

Facilities: B(e) D E F G H P R S T

Grampian Transport Museum

Alford

Contact address: Alford, Aberdeenshire AB33 8AE

Phone: 01975 562292

Fax: 01975 562180

E-mail: info@gtm.org.uk

Website: www.gtm.org.uk

Brief description: Dramatic displays, working exhibits and video presentations trace the history of travel and transport in the region. New exhibition for 2010 looks at long distance coach travel with a 1801 Mail Coach and 1840 stage coach and their private equivalents. Also a look at 'Cars for the Future'.

Events planned in 2010: Full outdoor events programme on the 15 acre site and road circuit. Please see website for listing.

Registration	Date	Chassis make	Chassis model	Body make	Original operator	Fleet No	Status
JFM 238D	1966	Bristol	Lodekka FS6G	ECW	Crosville Motor Services	DFG238	R
NRG 154M	1974	Leyland	Atlantean AN68/1R	Alexander	Grampian Regional Transport	154	R

Opening days/times: April to October inclusive, 10:00–17:00

Directions by car: On A944 west from Aberdeen (27 miles)

Directions by public transport: Stagecoach bus services from Aberdeen and Inverurie

Charges: Adults £6, Senior Citizens £5, Children £3, Family £15

Facilities: A B(e) C D E F G H L M P R S T

Other information: New 'Collections Centre' shared with a large bus collection is open first Wednesday each month.

The Cruden Bay Tramway operated two single-deck cars, which were stored in a small shed beside the laundry at the Cruden Bay Hotel. In 1988, both tram bodies were rescued from their respective fates as a summerhouse and a shed, and were combined to form one good body for preservation. The resulting tram now resides at the Grampian Transport Museum. GRAMPIAN TRANSPORT MUSEUM

Imperial War Museum

London

Contract address: Lambeth Road, London, SE1 6HZ

Phone: 020 7416 5320

Email: mail@iwm.org.uk

Website: www.iwm.org.uk

Brief description: Revel in the history of the nation, through the world wars and much more besides. Regular exhibitions and displays of considerable educated value. The single bus in the collection fills a significant gap in transport history and is on display in the museum atrium.

Opening days/times: Daily 10.00-18.00 (closed 24/25/26 December)

Directions by car: South of Waterloo Station, close to

Registration	Date	Chassis make	Chassis model	Body make	Original operator	Fleet No	Status
LN 4743	1911	LGOC	B	LGOC	London General Omnibus Co	B43	R

Elephant & Castle. Parking difficult but coach park at Vauxhall Bridge. Disabled parking by prior arrangement only — telephone 020 7416 5397

Directions by public transport: Underground to Lambeth North, Waterloo or Elephant & Castle

Bus 1, 3, 12, 53, 59, 68, 155, 159, 171, 172, 176, 188, 344, 453 , 468 and C10, with 45, 63, 100 nearby

Charges: Free entry to main displays

Facilities: A C D G H R T

One of the more unusual war memorials at the Imperial War Museum is this London General B43 (LN 4743), known as 'Ole Bill'. Along with other similar buses, 'Ole Bill' was used during World War 1 to transport troops on the Western Front. JOHN G. LIDSTONE

Seen at Felixstone Ferry is the Ipswich Transport Museum's Eastern Counties Bristol K6B no LK374 (KNG 374). Built in 1949, LK374 is fitted with an ECW 55-seat lowbridge body. NIGEL APPLEFORD

Registration	Date	Chassis make	Chassis model	Body make	Original operator	Fleet No	Status
DX 3988	1923	Railless		Short	Ipswich Corporation	2	R
DX 5610	1926	Ransomes Sims & Jefferies	D	Ransomes Sims & Jefferies	Ipswich Corporation	9	A
DX 5617	1926	Ransomes Sims & Jefferies	D	(chassis only)	Ipswich Corporation	16	R
DX 5629	1926	Garrett	O type	Strachan & Brown	Ipswich Corporation	26	A
DX 6591	1927	Tilling Stevens	B9B	Eastern Counties	Eastern Counties Road Car Co	78	A
VF 2788	1928	ADC	425A	Eastern Counties	United Automobile Services	J379	A
DX 7812	1929	Tilling Stevens	B10A2	(chassis only)	Eastern Counties Road Car Co	116	R
VF 8157	1930	Chevrolet	LQ	Bush & Twiddy	Final of Hockwold	4	R
WV 1209	1932	Bedford	WLB	Waveney	Alexander of Devizes		A
PV 817	1933	Ransomes Sims & Jefferies		Ransomes Sims & Jefferies	Ipswich Corporation	46	A
CVF 874	1939	Bristol	L5G	ECW	Eastern Counties Omnibus Co	LL574	A
CAH 923	1940	Dennis	Ace	ECW	Eastern Counties Omnibus Co	D23	A
PV 8270	1948	Karrier	W	Park Royal	Ipswich Corporation	105	RP
KAH 407	1949	Bristol	L4G	ECW	Eastern Counties Omnibus Co	LL407	R
KNG 374	1949	Bristol	K6B	ECW	Eastern Counties Omnibus Co	LK374	R

Events planned in 2010:

5 April — The Easter Bus Event, 11.00-16.00

2 May — The 40th Ipswich to Felixstowe Historic Vehicle Run

16 May — 'ADX 1 Day' 50 Years of Ipswich Motorbuses, 11.00-16.00

6 June — Family Fun Day, 11.00-16.00

26 June — Ipswich Transport & Model Festival, 10.00-16.00

18 July — Ipswich Engineering Day, 11.00-16.00

1 August — Middy Joint admission day, 10.00-16.00

30 August — Ride a Fire Engine day, 11.00-16.00

3 October — Come and Ride on our Buses 2010, 11.00-16.00

16 October — Wheels by Lamplight, 19.00-21.00. We cannot admit children to this event

4 December — Christmas Cracker 11.00-16.00

Opening days/times: Sundays 28 March to 28 November (except 4 May). Good Friday 2nd April. Easter Monday 5 April. Bank Holiday Mondays 3 May, 31 May and 30 August. School Holidays 6-16 April, 1-4 June, 26 July to 31 August, 25-29 October. Group visits or special opening available at other times.

Directions by car: Leave A14 at Junction 57 (signed Ransomes EuroPark). Follow direction for Town centre and follow Brown Signs with car symbol

Directions by public transport: Ipswich Buses 2 (Monday to Friday only) and First Eastern Counties 62 and 62A. Bus services frequently change — please check with TRAVELINE.

Charges: Adult £4.50, Concession £4, Children £2.50, Families (2+3) £13

Different prices apply on summer special event days — please see website for details

Facilities: A B(e) D E G H P R T

Other information: Access to extensive archives available by appointment

Another Ipswich resident is Eastern Counties LFS125 (GNG 125C). A Bristol FS6G, LFS125 is seen at Martlesham Heath when newly restored in 2009.
NIGEL APPLEFORD

Note: Please be aware that vehicles on display can vary from time to time as not all museums display their entire 'fleet'. Visitors wishing to see a particular vehicle should make enquiries prior to their visit.

Registration	Date	Chassis make	Chassis model	Body make	Original operator	Fleet No	Status
PV 9371	1949	Bedford	OB	Duple	Mulleys Motorways of Ixworth	26	R
ADX 1	1950	AEC	Regent III 9612E	Park Royal	Ipswich Corporation	1	R
ADX 196	1950	Sunbeam	F4	Park Royal	Ipswich Corporation	126	R
MAH 744	1951	Bristol	LSX4G	ECW	Eastern Counties Omnibus Co	LL744	R
BPV 9	1953	AEC	Regal IV 9822E	Park Royal	Ipswich Corporation	9	A
ADX 63B	1964	AEC	Regent V 2D2RA	Massey	Ipswich Corporation	63	R
APW 829B	1964	Bristol	MW6G	ECW	Eastern Counties Omnibus Co	LS829	R
GNG 125C	1965	Bristol	Lodekka FS5G	ECW	Eastern Counties Omnibus Co	LFS125	R
DPV 68D	1966	AEC	Regent V 2D2RA	Neepsend	Ipswich Corporation	68	A
JRT 82K	1971	AEC	Swift 2MP2R	Willowbrook	Ipswich Corporation	82	R
MRT 6P	1976	Leyland	Atlantean AN68/1R	Roe	Ipswich Corporation	6	R
XNG 770S	1978	Leyland	National 11351/1R	Leyland National	Eastern Counties Omnibus Co	LN770	A

Registration	Date	Chassis make	Chassis model	Body make	Original operator	Fleet No	Status
DL 5084	1927	Daimler	CK	Dodson	Dodson Bros ('Vectis')	11	A
NG 1109	1931	Reo	Pullman	Taylor	Reynolds of Overstrand		RP
CDL 792	1938	Bedford	WTB	Duple	Shotters of Brightstone		R
DDL 50	1940	Bristol	K5G	ECW	Southern Vectis Omnibus Co	703	R
26-81-HB	1940	Bristol	K5G	ECW	Hants & Dorset Motor Services	1086	RP
EDL 657	1947	Bristol	K5G	ECW	Southern Vectis Omnibus Co	721	RP
FDL 676	1949	Bedford	OB	Duple	Southern Vectis Omnibus Co	216	R
GDL 764	1950	Leyland	Titan PD2/1A	Leyland	Seaview Services		R
ODL 400	1957	Bedford	SBG	Duple	Moss Motor Tours of Sandown		R
PDL 515	1958	Bristol	MW6G	ECW	Southern Vectis Omnibus Co	315	RP
PDL 519	1958	Bristol	Lodekka LD6G	ECW	Southern Vectis Omnibus Co	559	R
VJW 882	1958	Commer	Avenger IV	Duple	Don Everall of Wolverhampton		R
SDL 268	1959	Bristol	Lodekka LD6G	ECW	Southern Vectis Omnibus Co	563	R
ADL 459B	1964	Bedford	SB3	Duple	Pauls Tours of Ryde	9	RP
CDL 479C	1965	Bristol	Lodekka FLF6G	ECW	Southern Vectis Omnibus Co	611	R
FDL 927D	1966	Bristol	MW6G	ECW	Southern Vectis Omnibus Co	806	R
KDL 885F	1968	Bristol	RESH6G	Duple	Southern Vectis Omnibus Co	301	R
NDL 490G	1969	Bristol	VRTSL/6LX	ECW	Southern Vectis Omnibus Co	622	A
SDL 638J	1971	Bristol	VRTSL/6LX	ECW	Southern Vectis Omnibus Co	628	R
TDL 564K	1971	Bristol	RELL6G	ECW	Southern Vectis Omnibus Co	864	R
RDL 309X	1982	Leyland	Leopard PSU3G/4R	ECW	Southern Vectis Omnibus Co	309	A
A700 DDL	1984	Leyland	Olympian ONLXB/1R	ECW	Southern Vectis Omnibus Co	700	A

Isle of Wight Bus Museum Trust

Contact address: Seaclose Quay, Newport, Isle of Wight, PO30 2EF

Phone: 01983 533352

E-mail: info@iowbusmuseum.org.uk

Website: www.iowbusmuseum.org.uk

Brief description: The collection ranges from a former Ryde Pier electric tram rebuilt in 1911 and a 1927 Daimler CK to a 1984 Olympian. Many of the vehicles are of Southern Vectis origin.

Events planned in 2010:

9 May — Running Day for IOW vehicles

17 October — Running Day

Opening days/times: Opening days vary through the year with daily opening in summer holiday season. Please check website or telephone 01983 533352 to confirm opening days before your visit. Times on all opening days 10.30-16.00

Directions by car: Bus Museum is adjacent to Boat Museum, with both signed from Fairlee Road through Seaclose Park to Quay past Travel Inn

Directions by public transport: Bus to Newport bus station. 12 minutes walk to north of town, passing Church, then via Quay Street and Quay

Charges: £4 Adult, £3.50 Senior Citizen, £2.50 Child, £10 Family

Facilities: B(e) D G S

Other information: Car parking nearby. Refreshments and toilets at adjacent Boat Museum. Some vehicles are stored away from the museum. Please enquire for details

In times past, coach tours on the Isle of Wight were big business. Apart from company operator Southern Vectis, numerous independents plied for trade. Moss Motor Tours of Sandown was one of the best-known island coach operators, and is represented here by ODL 400, a 1957 Duple Vega-bodied Bedford SBG. Alongside is VJW 882, a Duple Corinthian-bodied Commer Avenger IV, fitted with a TS3 engine, new to Don Everall of Wolverhampton in 1958. DAVID JUKES

29

Keighley Bus Museum

Address: Riverside Technology Park, Dalton Lane, Keighley.

Phone: 01282 413179

E-mail: Shmdboard@aol.com

Website: www.kbmt.org.uk

Brief description: Includes over 60 buses, trolleybuses and ancillary vehicles from operators across the North of England including the West Yorkshire Core Collection representing the former municipal fleets of Bradford, Halifax, Huddersfield & Leeds. Class 6 buses (single deck, double deck & open top) are available for private hire at competitive rates.

Events planned in 2010:

2-5 April — 'Day out with Thomas'

25 April — 'Go Local Sunday' Town Tour

3 May — 'A Grand Day Out' at Bradford Industrial Museum

29-31 May — 'Day out with Thomas'

KEIGHLEY BUS MUSEUM

Hire a Heritage Bus for your Wedding, Private Party or Evening Excursion. For quotations tel. 01282 413179 or e-mail shmdboard@aol.com

See our website for details of Special Events. www.kbmt.org.uk

Registration	Date	Chassis make	Chassis model	Body make	Original operator	Fleet No	Status
WT 7101	1924	Straker Clough		Brush	Keighley Corporation Tramways	5	R
KW 2260	1927	Leyland	Lion PLSC3	Leyland	Bradford Corporation	325	A
KY 9106	1931	AEC	Regent I O661	Weymann	Bradford Corporation	046	A
TF 6860	1931	Leyland	Lion LT3	Leyland	Rawtenstall Corporation	61	RP
ANW 682	1934	AEC	Regent 661	Roe	Leeds City Transport	139	R
FWX 914	1948	Sunbeam	F4	East Lancs	Mexborough & Swinton Traction Co		R
MNW 86	1948	Leyland	Tiger PS1	Roe	Leeds City Transport	28	R
JWU 886	1951	Bristol	LL5G	ECW	West Yorkshire Road Car Co	SGL16	R
LYR 533	1951	AEC	Regent III O961	Park Royal	London Transport	RT3314	R
MTE 635	1951	AEC	Regent III 6812A	Weymann	Morecambe & Heysham Corporation	73	RP
UUA 214	1955	Leyland	Titan PD2/11	Roe	Leeds City Transport	214	A
GJX 331	1956	Daimler	CVG6	Roe	Halifax Corporation	119	R
VTU 76	1956	Daimler	CVG6	Northern Counties	SHMD Board	76	R
XLG 477	1956	Atkinson	Alpha PL745H	Northern Counties	SHMD Board	77	A
7514 UA	1959	Daimler	CVG6-30	Roe	Leeds City Transport	514	RP
WLT 736	1961	AEC	Routemaster	Park Royal	London Transport	RM736	R
PJX 232	1962	Leyland	Leopard L1	Weymann	Halifax Joint Omnibus Committee	232	R
WBR 246	1963	Atkinson	Alpha PM746HL	Marshall	Sunderland Corporation	46	RP
6204 KW	1964	AEC	Regent V 2D3RA	Metro-Cammell	Bradford Corporation	204	A
6203 KW	1964	AEC	Regent V 2D3RA	Metro-Cammell	Bradford Corporation	203	A
6220 KW	1964	AEC	Regent V 2D3RA	Metro-Cammell	Bradford Corporation	220	R
CUB 331C	1965	Leyland	Atlantean PRD1/1	Weymann	Leeds City Transport	331	RP
ENW 980D	1966	AEC	Regent V 2D2RA	Roe	Leeds City Transport	980	RP
HNW 131D	1966	Daimler	Fleetline CRG6LX	Roe	Leeds City Transport	131	R
NWU 265D	1966	Bristol	Lodekka FS6B	ECW	York-West Yorkshire	YDX221	R
KVH 473E	1967	Daimler	Fleetline CRG6LX	Roe	Huddersfield Corporation	473	R
TWW 766F	1967	Bristol	RELH6G	ECW	West Yorkshire Road Car Co	CRG6	R
YLG 717F	1967	Bristol	RESL6G	Northern Counties	SHMD Board	117	A
LAK 309G	1969	Leyland	Titan PD3A/12	Alexander	Bradford Corporation	309	R
LAK 313G	1969	Leyland	Titan PD3A/12	Alexander	Bradford Corporation	313	RP
TKU 467K	1971	Leyland	Atlantean PDR2/1	Alexander	Bradford Corporation	467	A
WFM 801K	1972	Leyland	National 1151/2R/0403	Leyland National	Crosville Motor Services	SNL801	R
XAK 355L	1972	Daimler	Fleetline CRL6	Alexander	Bradford Corporation	355	RP
GWY 690N	1975	Leyland	Leopard PSU4B/4R	Plaxton	West Yorkshire PTE	64	RP
XBU 17S	1978	Leyland	Fleetline FE30AGR	Northern Counties	Greater Manchester PTE	8017	RP
DNW 840T	1978	Leyland	National 10351B/1R	Leyland National	West Yorkshire Road Car	1002	RP
JUM 505V	1980	MCW	Metrobus DR101/7	MCW	West Yorkshire PTE	7505	RP

Registration	Date	Chassis make	Chassis model	Body make	Original operator	Fleet No	Status
NKU 245X	1981	Leyland	National NL116AL11/1R	Leyland National	Yorkshire Traction	245	R
A577 NWX	1984	Leyland	Olympian ONLXB/1R	ECW	West Riding Automobile Co	577	RP
C147 KBT	1985	Leyland	Olympian ONLXB/1R	Optare	West Yorkshire PTE	5147	RP
D275 OOJ	1987	Freight Rover	Sherpa	Carlyle	Carlyle (demonstrator)		R

A recent restoration at Keighley Bus Museum is Yorkshire Traction 245 (NKU 245X), a Leyland National 2. When new, no 245 was allocated to Huddersfield and used on Metro Services. PHILIP LAMB

Registration	Date	Chassis make	Chassis model	Body make	Original operator	Fleet No	Status
KW 474	1927	Leyland	Lion PLSC1	Leyland	Blythe & Berwick of Bradford		R
TE 8318	1929	Chevrolet	LQ	Spicer	Jardine of Morcambe		R
VL 1263	1929	Leyland	Lion LT1	Applewhite	Lincoln Corporation	5	R
WH 1553	1929	Leyland	Titan TD1	Leyland	Bolton Corporation	54	R
KW 7604	1930	Leyland	Badger TA4	Plaxton	Bradford Education Committee	023	R
TF 818	1930	Leyland	Lion LT1	Roe	Lancashire United Transport	202	R
FW 5698	1935	Leyland	Tiger TS7	Burlingham	Lincolnshire Road Car Co	1411	R
RC 2721	1935	SOS	DON	Brush	Trent Motor Traction Co	321	R
FHN 833	1940	Bristol	L5G	ECW	United Automobile Services	BG147	RP
BFE 419	1941	Leyland	Titan TD7	Roe	Lincoln Corporation	64	R
VV 8934	1945	Daimler	CWD6	Duple	Northampton Corporation	129	RP
AHE 163	1946	Leyland	Titan PD1	Roe	Yorkshire Traction	726	RP

19/20 June — Away days at the Royal Armouries

4 July — Keighley Festival of Transport

17/18 July — Leeds Waterfront Festival

Sundays 1-22 Aug also 5/12 Sept — Open Top Scenic Service 22

28-30 August — 'Day out with Thomas'

11 September — Heritage Day in Bradford

12 September — Heritage Tours in Bradford and Keighley

Opening days/times: Riverside Depot (behind Dalton Mills) is normally open to visitors throughout the year on Tuesdays 19.00-21.00 and Saturdays 10.00 to 16.00 when our volunteers are working. Please always telephone 01282 413179 in advance of your visit to make sure someone is available to welcome you.

Directions by car: From M62 (Jct 24) follow A629 to Keighley Railway Station, right turn into Dalton Lane, forward ½ mile, right turn into Riverside, forward through Factory Gates at end.

Directions by public transport: Northern trains (Airedale Line) from Leeds Station or Bradford Forster Square Station to Keighley. Turn right out of Station and right again into Dalton Lane (eight minutes walk to Riverside), or take Transdev Keighley and District 708 or 711 from Keighley bus station or railway station.

Charges: None

Facilities: B(e)

Lincolnshire Road Transport Museum
North Hykeham

Contact address: Whisby Road, North Hykeham, Lincoln LN6 3QT

Phone: 01522 500566

E-mail: info@lvvs.org.uk

Website: www.lvvs.org.uk

Three LVVS vehicles line up in the wintry weather during January 2010. From left to right they are: Lincolnshire 2318 (LFW 326) a 1955 Bristol LD6B, Doncaster 122 (KDT 393) a 1951 Roe-bodied AEC Regent III and Lincolnshire 2115 (DBE 187), a 1946 highbridge Bristol K6A. *LVVS*

www.nextstopproductions.co.uk

Cheques or Postal Orders made payable to 'Next Stop Productions'

12 Marshall Street, Heanor, Derbyshire DE75 7AT   **01773 716102**

NOW ACCEPTING TELEPHONE ORDERS

DVD TITLES

AEC Society Rally 2008	£10.00
Amersham Running Day 2009	£10.00
Aston Manor Spring Running Day 2007	£7.00
Aston Manor Running Day 2 2007	£7.00
Atlantean Roundup	£7.00
Atlantean 50 running day 2008	£10.00
Burton Rally 2008	£5.00
Bristol RE Roundup a collection of RE's at rallies	£5.00
Bristol Lodekka Roundup a collection of Lodekkas at Rallies	£5.00
Bristol VR Roundup a collection of VR's at rallies	£5.00
Coach Roundup a collection of coaches at rallies & service	£5.00
Chatsworth Running Day and Rally 2007	£7.00
Chatsworth Running Day and Rally 2008	£10.00
Chatsworth Running Day Rally 2009 HD WIDE SCREEN	£10.00
Cobham Rally 2007	£7.00
Chester Buses Running Day 2008	£7.00
Chesterfield Running Day 2009 HD WIDE SCREEN	£7.00
Chasewater Bus Running Day 2009 HD WIDE SCREEN	£7.00
Collecting the Fares - Birmingham 2007	£7.00
Collecting the Fares - Bus Wars Nottingham	£10.00
Collecting the Fares - Cambridge 2006	£7.00
Collecting the Fares - Chesterfield Special 2007(Running Day)	£7.00
Collecting the Fares - Derby 2001	£7.00
Collecting the Fares - Derby 2007	£7.00
Collecting the Fares - Derby 2008	£7.00
Collecting the Fares - Edinburgh 2007	£7.00
Collecting the Fares - Leeds 2003	£5.00
Collecting the Fares - Lincoln Bus Station Revisited 2006	£7.00
Collecting the Fares - London 2001	£7.00
Collecting the Fares - London 2007	£7.00
Collecting the Fares - Malta 2007	£7.00
Collecting the Fares - Nottingham 2006	£7.00
Collecting the Fares - Nottingham's Buses 2007	£7.00
Collecting the Fares - Nottingham 2008	£7.00
Collecting the Fares - Nottingham 2009 HD WIDE SCREEN	£7.00
Collecting the Fares - Oxford 2004	£5.00
Collecting the Fares - Reading 2007	£7.00
Collecting the Fares - Round Up	£5.00
Collecting the Fares-Scarborough 2008	£7.00
Collecting the Fares - Sheffield 2001	£5.00
Collecting the Fares - Sheffield 2007	£7.00
Collecting the Fares - Taunton Xmas Park & Ride 2007	£5.00
Collecting the Fares - Walsall 2006	£5.00
Collecting the Fares: York 2008	£5.00
Crosville Rally 2006	£7.00
Delaine Leyland Day 2007	£7.00
Duxford EFE Showbus 2006	£7.00
Duxford EFE Showbus 2007	£7.00
Events in Brief 2 (Rally Roundup 1992)	£7.00
Events in brief 3 Ribble 2009 & Liverpool Running Day 2008	£5.00
Friends of King Alfred 2008 Running Day	£10.00
Gateshead Metro-Centre Rally 2007	£7.00
Gateshead Metro-Centre Rally 2008	£10.00
Gloucestershire Warwickshire running Day HD WIDE	£7.00
Half Cab Roundup	£7.00
Halfcab Roundup 2 The Cine years	£10.00
Hemel Hempstead Running Day 2009 HD WIDE SCREEN	£10.00
Hulleys of Baslow a Brief History	£7.00
Leatherhead Running Day 2009	£10.00
Leeds Bus Rally Running Day 2009 HD WIDE SCREEN	£10.00
Leyland National Roundup	£5.00
Leyland Gathering, Crich 2008	£10.00
Lincolnshire Road Transport Museum Running Day 2007	£7.00
Lincolnshire Road Transport Museum Running Day 2008	£7.00
Lincolnshire Road Transport Museum Easter Running 2009	£5.00
Llandudno Rally 2006	£7.00
London Bus Day 2008 (GMPTE)	£7.00
Lynx & Metrobus Running Day 2009	£7.00
Lorry Roundup a collection of classic lorries from rallies	£5.00
MCW Roundup a collection of MCW buses at rallies	£5.00
North Weald Rally 2008	£10.00
Nottingham Bus Remembered	£7.00
Nottingham Heritage Vehicles Rally 2007	£7.00
Nottingham Heritage Vehicles Rally 2008	£10.00
Nottingham Heritage Vehicles Rally 2009 HD WIDE	£10.00
Nottingham & District Omnibus 2008 (Routemasters)	£7.00
Potteries Vehicle Gathering 2008 (the Buses)	£10.00
Potteries Vehicle Gathering the Buses HD WIDE SCREEN	£10.00
Potteries Connection Running Day HD WIDE SCREEN	£7.00
Peterborough Bus Rally Running Day 2009 HD WIDE	£10.00
Ribble Rally and Road Run 2007	£7.00
Routemaster Roundup	£7.00
Routemasters, RTs and RFs Running Day 2007	£7.00
Routemaster Owners Club Milton Keynes Gath 2008	£10.00
RT Roundup a collection of RT's at rallies	£5.00
Sandtoft 2008	£5.00
Seaburn Rally and Running Day 2006	£7.00
Seaburn Rally and Running Day 2007	£7.00
Seaburn Rally and Running Day 2008	£10.00
Sheffield Gathering 2006	£7.00
Sheffield Gathering 2007	£7.00
Sheffield Gathering 2009 Buses & Commercials HD Wide	£10.00
Slough Rally and Running Day 2007	£7.00
South Notts 80 years (Documentary)	£7.00
South Cheshire Bus Running Day 2009	£7.00
St Albans Running Day 2007	£7.00
Stevensons Running Day 2007	£7.00
Teesside Running Day 2008	£7.00
Trolleybus Roundup Derby, Reading, Nottm and others	£7.50
West Midlands Bus Archive 60's, 70's and 80's	£10.00
Whitley Bay Rally and Running Day 2006	£7.00
Whitley Bay Rally and Running Day 2007	£7.00
Routemaster Owners Club York Running Day 2007	£7.00
Routemaster Owners Club York Running Day 2008	£7.00
VMCV-Swiss trolleybuses 1990	£7.00
Worthing Running Day 2009 HD WIDE SCREEN	£10.00

This fine pair of Roe-bodied AEC Regent IIIs, formerly owned by the late Tony Peart, can now be seen at the Lincolnshire Road Transport Museum. KDT 393 is a Doncaster Corporation vehicle, whilst JDN 668 was No 64 in the York Pullman fleet. SIMON GILL

Brief description: The museum houses a collection of over 65 vintage cars, buses and commercial vehicles spanning over 80 years of road transport history. There are also many interesting displays of transport history including a traditional garage workshop.

Events planned in 2010:

4 April — Open Day at Museum (includes bus running day)

6 June — Castle Rally (cars / motorcycles / small commercials) at Lincoln Castle

7 November — Open Day at Museum (includes bus running day)

Opening days/times:

May to October : Monday-Friday 12.00-16.00 pm and Sundays 10.00-16.00

November to April : Sundays 13.00-16.00

Usually open Bank Holiday Mondays from Easter to August, but please phone or check website to confirm

Additional hours at special events

Directions by car: Off B1190 Doddington Road. Leave A46 (Lincoln bypass) at B1190 Doddington Roundabout and follow brown tourist signs

Special arrangements apply on Museum Open Days when Park & Ride bus service is provided locally.

Directions by public transport: Stagecoach in Lincolnshire 44 to Doddington Road, 'Swanholme Tavern' and five minutes walk; or train to Hykeham Station and 5-10 minutes walk

Charges: Admission £3 adults, accompanied children free. (Different charges may apply for special events)

Facilities: B(e) D H P T

Other information: Group and School visits welcome by prior arrangement outside normal opening hours

Registration	Date	Chassis make	Chassis model	Body make	Original operator	Fleet No	Status
DBE 187	1946	Bristol	K6A	ECW	Lincolnshire Road Car Co	2115	R
GUF 727	1947	Leyland	Tiger PS1/1	ECW	Southdown Motor Services	677	R
DFE 383	1948	Guy	Arab III	Guy	Lincoln Corporation	23	R
HPW 133	1949	Bristol	K5G	ECW	Eastern Counties Omnibus Co	LKH133	R
OHK 432	1949	Daimler	CVD6	Roberts	Colchester Corporation	4	R
ONO 59	1949	Bristol	K5G	ECW	Eastern National Omnibus Co	4038	R
FFU 860	1950	AEC	Regal III 9621E	Willowbrook	Enterprise of Scunthorpe	60	R
KDT 393	1951	AEC	Regent III 9613A	Roe	Doncaster Corporation	122	R
FDO 573	1953	AEC	Regent III 9613E	Willowbrook	J. W. Camplin & Sons ('Holme Delight') of Donington		A
JDN 668	1954	AEC	Regent III 6812A	Roe	York Pullman Bus Co	64	R
OLD 714	1954	AEC	Regent III O961	Weymann	London Transport	RT4494	RP
LFW 326	1955	Bristol	Lodekka LD6B	ECW	Lincolnshire Road Car Co	2318	R
OVL 465	1960	Bristol	MW5G	ECW	Lincolnshire Road Car Co	2245	R
RFE 416	1961	Leyland	Titan PD2/41	Roe	Lincoln Corporation	89	R
952 JUB	1964	AEC	Regent V 2D2RA	Roe	Leeds City Transport	952	RP
CVL 850D	1966	Bristol	RELH6G	ECW	Lincolnshire Road Car Co	1431	RP
EVL 549E	1967	Leyland	Panther PSUR1/1R	Roe	Lincoln Corporation	41	RP
UVL 873M	1973	Bristol	RELL6L	Alexander	Lincoln Corporation	73	RP
NFW 36V	1980	Bristol	VRTLL3/6LXB	East Lancs	Lincoln City Transport	36	R
PFE 542V	1980	Bristol	VRTSL3/6LXB	ECW	Lincolnshire Road Car Co	1958	R

Registration	Date	Chassis make	Chassis model	Body make	Original operator	Fleet No	Status
Unregistered	1829	Horse bus		LGOC	George Shillibeer		R
Unregistered	1875	Horse bus		Thomas Tilling	Thomas Tilling		R
LA 9928	1911	LGOC	B	LGOC	London General Omnibus Co	B340	R
EXV 253	1939	Leyland	LPTB70	Leyland	London Transport	1253	R
FJJ 774	1939	Leyland	FEC	LPTB	London Transport	TF77	R
737 DYE	1963	AEC	Routemaster 2R2RH	Park Royal	London Transport	RM1737	R
EGP 1J	1970	Daimler	Fleetline CRG6LXB	Park Royal	London Transport	DMS1	R

Recent new displays at the London Transport Museum's Covent Garden home now feature this line-up of three generations of London's buses. Centre stage is AEC Routemaster RM737 (737DYE), whilst to the left we can see Daimler Fleetline DMS1 (EGP 1J). The pair are joined by 1939 Leyland FEC TF77 (FJJ 774), one of a number built for Green Line services. DAVID JUKES

London Transport Museum

Covent Garden

Contact address: 39 Wellington Street, London, WC2E 7BB

Phone: 020 7565 7299

E-mail: enquiries@ltmuseum.co.uk

Website: www.ltmuseum.co.uk

Brief description: Lively new galleries tell the story of London's transport system and how it shaped the lives of people living and working in London, including current and future transport developments. The Design for Travel gallery showcases original artworks and advertising posters.

Events planned in 2010:

Please check website for information regarding, talks, Friday Lates and new exhibitions.

13/14 March — Museum Depot, Acton Open Weekend: London's transport in miniature.

16/17 October — Museum Depot, Acton Open Weekend: Family Open Weekend.

Opening days/times: Saturday to Thursday: 10.00-18.00 (last admission 17.15)

Friday 11.00-18.00 (last admission 17.15)

Directions by public transport: Underground: Covent Garden, Charing Cross, Holborn and Leicester Square stations.

Nearest main line station: Charing Cross

Bus: to Strand or Aldwych

Charges: Adults £10; Senior citizens £8; Students £6

Accompanied children under 16 FREE

These prices include a voluntary Gift Aid donation

Facilities A B(e) D E F G L R S T

Manchester Museum of Transport

Cheetham

Address: Boyle Street, Cheetham, Manchester M8 8UW

Phone: 0161 205 2122

Fax: 0161 202 1110

E-mail: email@gmts.co.uk

Website: www.gmts.co.uk

Brief description: The Museum houses over 70 buses and coaches from the Greater Manchester area, from an 1870s horse bus to a 1990 Metrolink tram. Travel back to a time of twopenny singles and coach trips to Blackpool. Extensive displays of photographs, uniforms and models complement the vehicles.

Events planned in 2010:

27/28 March — Spring Transport Festival

18 April — London Bus Day

16 May — Rear-Engined Buses at 50: Rear-Engined Bus Gathering

26 June — Busmen's Holiday

24/25 July — Festival of Model Tramways (Please note revised admission prices will apply for this event: Adult £7, Over 65s £6, Under 16s free)

5 September — Trans Lancs Rally at Heaton Park (Museum closed)

17 October — Remembering the Number 9: Number 9 Bus Gathering

4/5 December — The Christmas Cracker

Opening days/times: Wednesdays, Saturdays, Sundays and Bank Holidays 10.00-16.30 all year round. Open every day from 26 July to 3 September (inclusive). Please check for Christmas and New Year opening days.

Directions by car: From M60/M62 Junction 18, follow brown tourist signs for Castlefield along A665 to Cheetham. From City follow the A665; Museum is signposted from Manchester Fort.

*Limited parking on special event days so we suggest parking at the MEN Arena or other central car park before using our free heritage buses from Victoria Station to the Museum.

Directions by public transport: Bus 135 from City centre to Queen's Road and follow signs

Registration	Date	Chassis make	Chassis model	Body make	Original operator	Fleet No	Status
Unregistered	1876	Horse bus		Manchester Carriage Co	Manchester Carriage Co	2	R
CK 3825	1927	Leyland	Lion PLSC1	Leyland	Ribble Motor Services	295	R
VM 4439	1928	Leyland	Tiger TS1	Metro-Cammell/ Crossley	Manchester Corporation	138	A
VY 957	1929	Leyland	Lion PLSC1	Ribble	York Corporation	2	R
VR 5742	1930	Leyland	Tiger TS2	Manchester Corporation Car Works	Manchester Corporation	28	R
ANB 851	1934	Crossley	Mancunian	Crossley/MCT	Manchester Corporation	436	A
AXJ 857	1934	Leyland	Titan TD3	(chassis only)	Manchester Corporation	526	R
JA 7585	1935	Leyland	Tiger TS7	English Electric	Stockport Corporation	185	A
AJA 152	1939	Bristol	K5G	Willowbrook	North Western Road Car Co	432	R
BBA 560	1939	AEC	Regent 0661	Park Royal	Salford Corporation	235	R
JP 4712	1940	Leyland	Titan TD7	Leyland	Wigan Corporation	70	RP
FTB 11	1941	Leyland	Titan TD7	Northern Coachbuilders	Leigh Corporation	84	A
BJA 425	1946	Bristol	L5G	Willowbrook	North Western Road Car Co	270	R
HTB 656	1946	Leyland	Tiger PS1	Roe	Ramsbottom UDC	17	R
HTF 586	1947	Bedford	OB	Scottish Motor Traction	Warburton Bros of Bury		R
CDB 224	1948	Leyland	Titan PD2/1	Leyland	North Western Road Car Co	224	R
CWH 717	1948	Leyland	Titan PD2/4	Leyland	Bolton Corporation	367	R
DBU 246	1948	Leyland	Titan PD1/3	Roe	Oldham Corporation	246	RP
JND 791	1948	Crossley	DD42/8S	Crossley	Manchester Corporation	2150	R
JNA 467	1949	Leyland	Titan PD1/3	Metro-Cammell	Manchester Corporation	3166	RP
LMA 284	1949	Foden	PVSC6	Lawton	Coppenhall of Comberbach		R
BEN 177	1950	AEC	Regent III 9613A	Weymann	Bury Corporation	177	R
CWG 206	1950	Leyland	Tiger PS1	Alexander	W. Alexander & Sons	PA164	R
FBU 827	1950	Crossley	DD42/8	Crossley	Oldham Corporation	368	RP
LTC 774	1950	Crossley	Empire TDD42/2	Crossley	Ashton-under-Lyne Corporation	80	RP
EDB 562	1951	Leyland	Titan PD2/1	Leyland	Stockport Corporation	308	A
EDB 575	1951	Crossley	DD42/7	Crossley	Stockport Corporation	321	R
JND 646	1951	Leyland	Titan PD2/3	Metro-Cammell	Manchester Corporation	3245	R
JVU 755	1951	Crossley	Dominion TDD64/1	Crossley	Manchester Corporation	1250	R
NNB 125	1953	Leyland	Royal Tiger PSU1/13	Northern Counties	Manchester Corporation	25	R
UMA 370	1955	Atkinson	PD746	Northern Counties	SHMD Board	70	R
JBN 153	1956	Leyland	Titan PD2/13	Metro Cammell	Bolton Corporation	77	R
NDK 980	1956	AEC	Regent V D2RA6G	Weymann	Rochdale Corporation	280	R
PND 460	1956	Leyland	Titan PD2/12	Metro-Cammell	Manchester Corporation	3460	R

MUSEUM OF **TRANSPORT** Greater Manchester

Discover Greater Manchester's transport history

Bolton | Bury | Manchester
Oldham | Rochdale | Salford
Stockport | Tameside | Trafford | Wigan

From an 1890s Victorian horse bus to the prototype Metrolink tram

Open every Wednesday, Saturday and Sunday
from 10am to 4.30pm

Boyle Street, Cheetham, Manchester
M8 8UW | Tel: 0161 205 2122

Admission charges apply

gmts.co.uk

Greater Manchester Transport Society
Registered Charity number 509772

Seen at Manchester Victoria is the first of many Northern Counties-bodied Daimler Fleetlines, which together with a sizeable number of Leyland Atlanteans built over more than a decade, became known as Manchester 'Standards'. No 7001 (VNB 101L) carries SELNEC Central livery as delivered in 1972. PHILIP LAMB

Below: **Although predominantly a Leyland fleet, Manchester operated other makes too. No 4632 (4632 VM) is a 1963 Daimler CVG6K with 65-seat Metro-Cammell bodywork.** PHILIP LAMB

Left: **Also seen at Victoria is Ramsbottom 11 (TTD 386H), the last Leyland Titan built for the home market. No 11 is a PD3/14 and carries an East Lancs 73-seat forward-entrance body.** NIGEL APPLEFORD

Registration	Date	Chassis make	Chassis model	Body make	Original operator	Fleet No	Status
DJP 754	1957	Leyland	Titan PD2/30	Northern Counties	Wigan Corporation	115	R
NBU 494	1957	Leyland	Titan PD2/20	Roe	Oldham Corporation	394	R
SDK 442	1958	Leyland	Worldmaster RT3/2	Plaxton	Ellen Smith of Rochdale		RP
122 JTD	1958	Guy	Arab IV	Northern Counties	Lancashire United Transport	27	R
TNA 496	1958	Leyland	Titan PD2/40	Burlingham	Manchester Corporation	3496	R
TNA 520	1958	Leyland	Titan PD2/34	Burlingham	Manchester Corporation	3520	R
YDK 590	1960	AEC	Reliance 2MU3RA	Harrington	Yelloway Motor Services of Rochdale		R
UNB 629	1960	Leyland	Atlantean PDR1/1	Metro-Cammell	Manchester Corporation	3629	R
HEK 705	1961	Leyland	Titan PD3A/2	Massey	Wigan Corporation	57	A
3655 NE	1962	Leyland	Tiger Cub PSUC1/12	Park Royal	Manchester City Transport	55	A
TRJ 112	1962	Daimler	CVG6	Metro-Cammell	Salford City Transport	112	R
414 CLT	1963	AEC	Routemaster 2R2RH	Park Royal	London Transport	RM1414	R
REN 116	1963	Leyland	Atlantean PDR1/1	Metro-Cammell	Bury Corporation	116	A
4632 VM	1963	Daimler	CVG6K	Metro-Cammell	Manchester Corporation	4632	R
8860 VR	1964	AEC	Regent V 2D3RA	East Lancs Neepsend	A. Mayne & Son of Manchester		R
BND 874C	1965	Leyland	Panther Cub	Park Royal	Manchester Corporation	74	R
DDB 174C	1965	Daimler	Fleetline CRG6LX	Alexander	North Western Road Car Co	174	R
DBA 214C	1965	Leyland	Atlantean PDR1/1	Metro-Cammell	Salford City Transport	214	R
PTE 944C	1965	Leyland	Titan PD2/37	Roe	Ashton-under-Lyne Corporation	44	R
PTC 114C	1965	AEC	Renown 3B3RA	East Lancs	Leigh Corporation	15	R
FRJ 254D	1966	Leyland	Titan PD2/40	Metro-Cammell	Salford City Transport	254	R
HVM 901F	1968	Leyland	Atlantean PDR1/1	Park Royal	Manchester City Transport	1001	R
KDB 408F	1968	Leyland	Leopard PSU4/1R	East Lancs	Stockport Corporation	408	RP

Amongst the numbers of Wigan buses in preservation is this 1961 Massey-bodied Leyland PD3A/2.
NIGEL APPLEFORD

Registration	Date	Chassis make	Chassis model	Body make	Original operator	Fleet No	Status
KJA 871F	1968	Leyland	Titan PD3/14	East Lancs	Stockport Corporation	71	R
MJA 897G	1969	Leyland	Titan PD3/14	East Lancs	Stockport Corporation	97	R
MJA 891G	1969	Leyland	Titan PD3/14	East Lancs	Stockport Corporation	91	R
TTD 386H	1969	Leyland	Titan PD3/14	East Lancs	Ramsbottom UDC	11	R
SRJ 328H	1970	Leyland	Atlantean PDR2/1	MCW	SELNEC PTE	1205	RP
TXJ 507K	1972	Leyland	National 1151/2R/0202	Leyland National	SELNEC PTE	EX30	R
VNB 101L	1972	Leyland	Atlantean AN68/1R	Park Royal	SELNEC PTE	7001	R
XVU 352M	1974	Seddon	Pennine IV-236	Pennine	Greater Manchester PTE	1722	R
GNC 276N	1975	Seddon-Lucas		Pennine	Greater Manchester PTE	EX62	R
HVU 244N	1975	AEC	Reliance 6U3ZR	Plaxton	Yelloway Motor Services of Rochdale		R
ORJ 83W	1981	MCW	Metrobus DR102/21	MCW	Greater Manchester PTE	5083	A
A706 LNC	1984	Leyland	Atlantean AN68D/1R	Northern Counties	Greater Manchester PTE	8706	A
B65 PJA	1984	Leyland	Olympian ONLXB/1R	NCME	Greater Manchester PTE	3065	A
C208 FVU	1986	MCW	Metrobus DR132/8	Northern Counties	Greater Manchester PTE	5208	RP
D63 NOF	1986	Freight Rover	400 Special	Carlyle	Manchester Minibuses (Bee Line Buzz Co)		A
D676 NNE	1987	MCW	Metrorider MF151/3	MCW	Greater Manchester Buses	1676	R
M939 XKA	1994	Mercedes-Benz	609D	Devon Conversions	Greater Manchester Accessible Transport		R

Midland Road Transport Group
Butterley

Contact address: 37 Park Road, Mansfield Woodhouse, Mansfield NG19 8EG

Phone: 01623 629136

E-mail: midland.railway@btconnect.com

Website: www.mrtg.org.uk

Brief description: A purpose-built museum building housing a collection of buses and lorries fully or partially restored. Situated at the Swanwick Junction site of the Midland Railway Centre. All vehicles are privately-owned by individual preservationists who provided finance to build the museum, which was completed in 2004.

Registration	Date	Chassis make	Chassis model	Body make	Original operator	Fleet No	Status
ESV 811	1947	AEC	Regal III O963	Weymann	Carris of Lisbon	141	RP
HVO 937	1947	AEC	Regent II O661	Weymann	Mansfield District	126	R
KRR 255	1949	AEC	Regal III 9621E	Weymann	Mansfield District	9	R
BNU 679G	1969	Bristol	VRTSL/6LX	ECW	Midland General Omnibus Co	315	RP
PNU 114K	1971	Leyland	Atlantean PDR1A/1	Northern Counties	Chesterfield Corporation	114	RP
RCH 629L	1972	Bristol	VRTSL/6LX	ECW	Trent Motor Traction Co	629	R
NNU 123M	1973	Daimler	Fleetline CRL6-30	Roe	Chesterfield Corporation	123	R
NNU 124M	1973	Daimler	Fleetline CRL6-30	Roe	Chesterfield Corporation	124	R
SHN 80L	1973	Bristol	RELH6G	ECW	United Automobile Services	6080	R
UOA 322L	1973	Leyland	National 1151/1R/0401	Leyland National	Eastern National Omnibus Co	1702	A
LRA 801P	1975	Bristol	VRT/SL3/501	ECW	Midland General Omnibus Co	801	R
PRA 109R	1976	Leyland	Leopard PSU3C/4R	Alexander	Trent Motor Traction Co	109	R
UHG 353Y	1982	Leyland	Atlantean AN68A/1R	East Lancs	Blackpool Corporation	353	R
D278 FAS	1987	Leyland	Tiger TRCTL11/2RH	Alexander	Western Scottish	438	R
J216 AET	1992	Mercedes-Benz	811D	Alexander	Chesterfield Transport	16	R

Events planned in 2010:

11 July — Annual Road Transport Rally

Opening days/times: The Centre is open daily except for 25/26 December. Please telephone before visiting for opening times to avoid disappointment

Directions by car: From M1 Junction 28 take A38 towards Derby, then B6179 to Ripley. Follow brown tourist signs to Midland Railway Centre

Directions by public transport: Trent / Barton 9.1 or 9.2 from Derby, Heanor or Alfreton to Butterley station

Facilities: R S T

Seen arriving at the Sheffield Transport Rally at Meadowhall on 9 September 2007 is PRA 109R, a Leyland Leopard PSU3C/4R with Alexander T-type body. New to Trent Motor Traction in 1976, it later passed to Chesterfield Transport and is seen in its livery carrying fleet number 306 in the associated Whites of Calver fleet. SIMON GILL

Registration	Date	Chassis make	Chassis model	Body make	Original operator	Fleet No	Status
BK 2986	1919	Thornycroft	J	Dodson	Portsmouth Corporation	10	R
RV 3411	1933	Leyland	Titan TD2	English Electric/ Portsmouth Corporation	Portsmouth Corporation	17	R
RV 6368	1935	Leyland	Titan TD4	English Electric	Portsmouth Corporation	8	R
EY 5218	1935	Thornycroft	Lightning GC/SC6		Jones of Menai Bridge		R

Contract address: Leisure Park, Churchill Way, Basingstoke, Hants, RG22 6PG

Phone: 01256 477766 / 0845 603 5635

Website: www.milestones-museum.com

Brief description: Step indoors into a huge award winning living history museum. Explore a network of full size streets from late Victorian times to 1945. See period shops, vintage vehicles, a village green and even a working pub, and factory buildings depicting Thornycroft and Taskers works.

Opening days/times: Tuesday-Friday and Bank Holiday Mondays 10.00-17.00, Saturday and Sunday 11.00-17.00. Last admission 16.00. Closed Mondays, 25/26 December and New Year Day

Directions by car: From M3 junction 6, take the Ringway Road (west) and follow the brown tourist signs for Leisure Park and Milestones. At Thornycroft Rounabout, take first exit into Churchill Way West, signed Milestones. At West Ham Roundabout, follow brown tourist sign for Milestones.

Milestones Hampshire's Living History Museum
Basingstoke

Charges: Adults £7.50 Concessions £6.75 Children £4.50 Family £22 Under 5 free. Reduced prices available for pre-booked groups of 15 or more. Schools programmes available. (Prices valid at time of publication)

Facilities: A D F P R T G S

Glasgow

Contact address: Kelvin Hall, 1 Bunhouse Road, Glasgow G3 8DP

Phone: 0141 287 2720
(school booking on 0141 565 4112/3)

Fax: 0141 287 2692

Website: www.glasgowmuseums.com

Brief description: The museum displays many items of transport history dating from the mid 19th century onwards. The museum will close in early Spring to enable relocation to a new Museum of Transport on the Clyde. The Riverside Museum will be a landmark museum that will create a more accessible and environmentally stable home for Glasgow's significant Transport and Technology collections, and will open in 2011. In the interim, some exhibits will be moved to the Glasgow Museums Resource Centre and will be accessible by arrangement. Please see website for details.

Opening days/times: Monday to Thursday and Saturday 10.00-17.00; Friday and Sunday 11.00-17.00 (closed from early Spring to 2011)

Directions by car: From M8 junctions 17 or 19

Directions by public transport: Buses 9, 16, 18, or 62 from city centre (Dumbarton Road) to Kelvin Hall

Underground to Kelvin Hall

Nearest mainline railway station is Partick

Charges: Free

Facilities: D F G H R T

Other information: Guided tours, exhibitions and events also held

Three buses are housed at the Museum of Transport Glasgow including Croft-bodied Albion Venturer CX37S, Glasgow B92 (EGA 79). PHILIP LAMB

Note: Please be aware that vehicles on display can vary from time to time as not all museums display their entire 'fleet'. Visitors wishing to see a particular vehicle should make enquiries prior to their visit.

Registration	Date	Chassis make	Chassis model	Body make	Original operator	Fleet No	Status
EGA 79	1949	Albion	Venturer CX37S	Croft	Glasgow Corporation	B92	R
FYS 988	1958	BUT	RETB1	Burlingham	Glasgow Corporation	TBS13	R
FYS 998	1958	Leyland	Atlantean PDR1/1	Alexander	Glasgow Corporation	LA1	R

Registration	Date	Chassis make	Chassis model	Body make	Original operator	Fleet No	Status
WT 7108	1924	Straker Clough	T29	Brush	Keighley Corporation Tramways	12	A
UP 551	1928	BMMO SOS	QL	Brush (Replica)	Northern General Transport Co	338	RP
VK 5401	1931	Dodge	UF30A	Robson of Consett	Batey of Rookhope		RP
LTN 501	1948	Sunbeam	S7	Northern Coachbuilders	Newcastle Corporation	501	R
J 2503	1988	Renault		Osborne	Beamish of the North of England Open Air Museum		R

Contact address: Beamish, Co Durham DH9 0RG

Phone: 0191 370 4000

Fax: 0191 370 4001

E-mail: museum@beamish.org.uk

Website: www.beamish.org.uk

Brief description: Beamish is an open-air museum which vividly recreates life in the North of England in the early 1800s and early 1900s. Buildings from throughout the region have been brought to Beamish, rebuilt and furnished as they once were. Costumed staff welcome visitors and demonstrate the past way of life in The Town, Colliery Village, Home Farm, Railway Station, Pockerley Manor and 1825 Railway. A one-mile length circular period tramway carries visitors around the Museum and a replica 1913 Daimler bus operates between The Town and Colliery Village.

Opening days/times: Please see website for details

Directions by car: Follow A1(M) to junction 63 (Chester-le-Street exit). Take A693 towards Stanley and follow Beamish Museum signs.

Directions by public transport: 709 from Newcastle, 720 from Durham, and 775/778 from Sunderland all serve Beamish

Charges: Please see website for details

Facilities: B E F G H M P R T

Other information: Free leaflet available in advance for visitors with disabilities and mobility limitations. Some vehicles not on display — please telephone for information.

The North of England Open Air Museum plays host to this beautiful Sunbeam S7 trolleybus with Northern Coachbuilders 70-seat bodywork, new to Newcastle in 1948. PHILIP LAMB

Registration	Date	Chassis make	Chassis model	Body make	Original operator	Fleet No	Status
AFY 971	1934	Leyland	Titan TD3	English Electric	Southport Corporation	43	A
ATD 683	1935	Leyland	Lion LT7	Massey	Widnes Corporation	39	A
RV 6360	1935	Leyland	Titan TD4	English Electric	Portsmouth Corporation	117	R
EWM 358	1945	Daimler	CWA6	Duple	Southport Corporation	62	A
ANQ 778	1946	AEC	Regent III 0961	Commonwealth Engineering	Dept of Road Transport & Tramways of Sydney	1984	A
DED 797	1946	Leyland	Titan PD1	Alexander	Warrington Corporation	16	A
FFY 404	1947	Leyland	Titan PD2/3	Leyland	Southport Corporation	87	R
KTD 768	1948	Leyland	Titan PD2/1	Lydney	Leigh Corporation	16	R
NTF 466	1952	Daimler	CVG5	Northern Counties	Lancaster City Transport	466	R
MXX 421	1953	AEC	Regal IV 9821LT RF	Metro-Cammell	London Transport	RF444	R
RFM 641	1953	Guy	Arab IV	Massey	Chester Corporation	1	R
CDJ 878	1954	Leyland	Titan PD2/9	Davies	St Helens Corporation	E78	A

Address: 51 Hall Street, St Helens, WA10 1DU

Phone: 01744 451681

E-mail: information@hallstreetdepot.info

Website: www.nwmort.co.uk

Brief description: Houses a collection of approximately 80 historic vehicles predominantly from the North West area, around 60 of which are on display at any one time. Also on display are several fire engines and classic cars from the 1960s and 1970s.

Events planned in 2010:

12/13 June — Summer Sizzler Transport Festival

19 September — Crosville Running Day

18/19 December — Christmas Santa Specials

Opening days/times: Saturday and Sunday 12.00-16.00

Directions by car: In St Helens Town Centre adjacent to St Helens Central railway station

Directions by public transport: One minutes walk from St Helens Central railway station

Charges: £3.50 adult, £2 child/concessions, £10 family

Facilities: B D G H S T

A number of Chester buses can be found at the North West Museum of Road Transport, including No 35 (FFM 135C), a 1965 Massey-bodied Guy Arab V.
PHILIP LAMB

Registration	Date	Chassis make	Chassis model	Body make	Original operator	Fleet No	Status
XTC 684	1955	Leyland	LFDD	Metro-Cammell	Leyland Demonstrator		A
434 BTE	1957	Crossley	Regent V D3RV	East Lancs	Darwen Corporation	17	R
GDJ 435	1957	AEC	Regent V MD3RV	Weymann	St Helens Corporation	H135	RP
KRN 422	1957	Leyland	Titan PD2/10	Crossley	Preston Corporation	31	R
FHF 456	1959	Leyland	Atlantean PDR1/1	Metro-Cammell	Wallasey Corporation	6	A
KDJ 999	1959	AEC	Regent V 2D3RA	East Lancs	St Helens Corporation	K199	A
LDJ 985	1960	Leyland	Titan PD2A/27	Weymann	St Helens Corporation	K175	RP
562 RTF	1961	Leyland	Titan PD2/40	East Lancs	Widnes Corporation	31	R
574 TD	1962	Guy	Arab IV	Northern Counties	Lancashire United Transport	110	R
TRJ 109	1962	AEC	Reliance 2MU3RV	Weymann	Salford City Transport	109	RP
201 YTE	1963	Leyland	Titan PD2/37	East Lancs	Lancaster City Transport	201	R
TDJ 612	1963	AEC	Reliance 2MU3RA	Marshall	St Helens Corporation	212	R
1975 TJ	1963	AEC	Renown 3B3RA	East Lancs	Leigh Corporation	28	RP
AJA 139B	1964	Bedford	VAL 14	Strachan	North Western Road Car Co	139	RP
4227 FM	1964	Bristol	Lodekka FS6G	ECW	Crosville Motor Services	DFG157	R
JTD 300B	1964	Guy	Arab V	Northern Counties	Lancashire United Transport	166	A
HTF 644B	1964	Leyland	Titan PD2/40	East Lancs	Widnes Corporation	38	R
FFM 135C	1965	Guy	Arab V	Massey	Chester Corporation	35	R
BCK 367C	1965	Leyland	Titan PD3/6	Leyland/Preston Corporation	Preston Corporation	61	A
BED 731C	1965	Leyland	Titan PD2/40 Special	East Lancs	Warrington Corporation	50	R
BED 732C	1965	Leyland	Titan PD2/40 Special	East Lancs	Warrington Corporation	51	RP
UTC 768D	1966	Leyland	Leopard L2	Plaxton	Lancashire United Transport	216	R
MDJ 555E	1967	Leyland	Titan PD2A/27	East Lancs	St Helens Corporation	55	A
OBU 163F	1967	Leyland	Atlantean PDR1/1	Roe	Oldham Corporation	163	R
SMK 701F	1967	AEC	Routemaster	Park Royal	London Transport	RML2701	R
HCK 204G	1968	Leyland	Panther PSUR1A/1R	MCW	Preston Corporation	204	RP
KJA 299G	1968	Bristol	RESL6G	Marshall	North Western Road Car Co	299	R
DFM 347H	1969	Guy	Arab V	Northern Counties	Chester Corporation	47	R
JFM 650J	1970	Daimler	Fleetline CRG6LX	Northern Counties	Chester Corporation	50	RP
NWA 257K	1972	Daimler	Fleetline CRG6LXB	Alexander	Sheffield Corporation	257	A
OFM 957K	1972	Daimler	Fleetline CRG6LX-30	Northern Counties	Chester Corporation	57	R
DKC 301L	1972	Leyland	Atlantean AN68/1R	Alexander	Merseyside PTE	1301	A
PDJ 269L	1972	AEC	Swift 3MP2R	Marshall	St Helens Corporation	269	A
RTC 645L	1972	Leyland	National 1151/1R/0101	Leyland National	Widnes Corporation	1	R
YFM 280L	1973	Bristol	RELL6G	ECW	Crosville Motor Services	ERG280	R
HEN 868N	1975	Leyland	Leopard PSU4C/2R	Northern Counties	Chester Corporation	68	A
LED 71P	1976	Bristol	RESL6G	East Lancs	Warrington Corporation	71	R

Registration	Date	Chassis make	Chassis model	Body make	Original operator	Fleet No	Status
LED 73P	1976	Bristol	RESL6G	East Lancs	Warrington Corporation	73	R
FWA 475V	1980	Leyland	National NL106L11/1R	Leyland National	South Yorkshire PTE	1075	R
GEK 14V	1980	Leyland	Atlantean AN68A/1R	East Lancs	Warrington Corporation	14	A
RMA 435V	1980	Bristol	VRTSL3/501	ECW	Crosville Motor Services	DVL435	R
XLV 140W	1980	Leyland	National II NL116AL11/1R	Leyland National	Merseyside PTE	6140	R
BMA 521W	1981	Bristol	VRTSL3/6LXB	ECW	Crosville Motor Services	DVG521	R
YMA 99W	1981	Dennis	Dominator DD121B	Northern Counties	Chester City Transport	99	RP
A323 GLV	1983	Leyland	Atlantean AN68D/1R	Alexander	Merseyside PTE	1003	R
A910 SYE	1983	Leyland	Titan TNLXB2RR	Leyland	London Transport	T 910	R
C214 CBU	1986	Leyland	Olympian ONLXB/1R	Northern Counties	Greater Manchester PTE	3214	RP
D275 JVR	1987	Leyland	Olympian ONLXB/1R	Northern Counties	Greater Manchester Buses	3275	RP
F98 STB	1989	Dennis	Dominator DDA1017	East Lancs	Warrington Borough Transport	98	R
H35 HBG	1991	Leyland	Lynx LX2R11C15Z4R	Leyland	Halton Corporation	35	R

Above: **Seen in Llandudno is the NWMRT's 1968 Marshall-bodied Bristol RESL6G, North Western 299 (KJA 299G).** PHILIP LAMB

Right: **St Helens 54 (MDJ 554E), an East Lancs-bodied Leyland PD2A/27, is one of a number of former St Helens vehicles still garaged at the former undertaking's Hall Street premises, now the North West Museum of Road Transport.** PHILIP LAMB

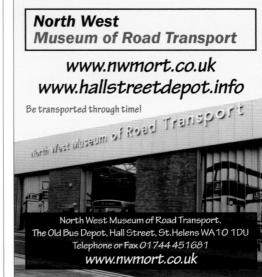

Nottingham Transport Heritage Centre

Ruddington

Address: Mere Way, Ruddington, Nottingham, NG11 6NX

Phone: 0115 940 5705

Website: http://www.nthc.co.uk

Brief description: The centre offers exhibits covering road and rail transport, and provides the opportunity to experience travel of a bygone age.

Events planned in 2010: Please see enthusiast press for details.

Opening days/times: Easter to mid October: Sundays and Bank Holiday Mondays 10.45-17.00

Directions by car: Three miles south of Nottingham just off A52 ring road and main A60 road via small roundabout at Ruddington

Directions by public transport: Buses from Nottingham pass near museum

Charges: Adults £8, Senior Citizens £6.50, Children £3.50

Facilities: B B(e) D E G H P R S T

Registration	Date	Chassis make	Chassis model	Body make	Original operator	Fleet No	Status
VO 8846	1932	Leyland	Lion LT5	Willowbrook	South Notts Bus Co of Gotham	17	A
DJF 349	1947	Leyland	Titan PD1	Leyland	Leicester City Transport	248	RP
JVO 230	1948	Leyland	Titan PD1A	Duple	Barton Transport of Chilwell	507	R
MAL 310	1951	Leyland	Royal Tiger PSU1/11	Duple	South Notts Bus Co of Gotham	42	A
OTV 161	1953	AEC	Regent III 9613E	Park Royal	Nottingham City Transport	161	R
866 HAL	1960	AEC	Reliance 2MU3RV	Plaxton	Barton Transport of Chilwell	866	RP
CUV 218C	1965	AEC	Routemaster R2RH/1	Park Royal	London Transport	RCL2218	R
KVO 429P	1975	Leyland	National 11351/2R	Leyland National	Trent Motor Traction Co	429	A
ORC 545P	1976	Leyland	Atlantean AN68/1R	ECW	Northern General Transport Co	3299	R
ARC 666T	1979	Leyland	Atlantean AN68A/1R	Northern Counties	Nottingham City Transport	666	R

Amongst the residents at the Nottingham Heritage Centre is this former Northern General ECW-bodied Leyland Atlantean AN68/1R, now converted to open top. PHILIP LAMB

Note: Please be aware that vehicles on display can vary from time to time as not all museums display their entire 'fleet'. Visitors wishing to see a particular vehicle should make enquiries prior to their visit.

Registration	Date	Chassis make	Chassis model	Body make	Original operator	Fleet No	Status
BM 2856	1913	Commer	WP3	Commer	Lord Lonsdale		R
DU 4838	1915	Daimler	Y	City of Oxford Electric Tramways	City of Oxford Electric Tramways	39	A
Unregistered	1916	Daimler	Y	(chassis only)			RP
Unregistered	1916	Daimler	Y	(chassis only)			A
Unregistered	1917	Daimler	Y		City of Oxford Electric Tramways		A
YL 740	1925	Morris Commercial	1 ton				R
JO 5032	1932	AEC	Regal 642	(chassis only)	City of Oxford Motor Services	GC41	R
JO 5403	1932	AEC	Regent 661	Brush	City of Oxford Motor Services	GA16	R
DBW 613	1948	Bedford	OB	Duple	Oliver of Long Handborough		A

The Oxford Bus Museum, situated in Long Hanborough, a village out to the west of the city, has a comprehensive collection of former City of Oxford Motor Services vehicles including this 1960 Park Royal-bodied 44-seat AEC Reliance saloon. PHILIP LAMB

Oxford Bus Museum

Long Hanborough

Contact address: Station Yard, Main Road, Long Hanborough, Witney, Oxfordshire OX29 8LA

Phone: 01993 883617 (opening hours) 01296 337622 (at other times)

Website: www.oxfordbusmuseum.org.uk

Brief description: About 40 vehicles are on display, some fully restored and roadworthy. Those under restoration can be viewed from the workshop gallery. There are regular free bus rides during the summer months.

Events planned in 2010

14 March — Mothers' Day

4 April — Easter Chick Hunt

8/9 May — Model and Collectors' Exhibition

30 May — Teddy Bear Day

20 June — Fathers' Day

17 October — Bus and Classic Vehicle Rally

21 September — British Transport Films Evening

11/12 December — Santa Days

Opening days/times: Sundays, Wednesdays and Bank Holidays (except Christmas) 10.30-16.30, plus Saturdays April-October

Directions by car: The Museum can be found on the A4095, which links Bicester and Witney. From the M40, leave at junction 9 and follow the signs to Blenheim Palace until the roundabout on the outskirts of the village of Bladon. Drive through Bladon and as the edge of Long Hanborough is reached, the Museum is signposted on the left. If approaching by way of the A40 or the A34, leave these roads on the northern outskirts of Oxford and again follow the signs for Blenheim Palace until the same roundabout.

Directions by public transport: By bus there are services operated by Stagecoach to Long Hanborough on Wednesday and Saturday, but not on Sunday. Service 242 from Woodstock to Witney passes the Museum entrance, while service 11 from Oxford to Witney serves the centre of Long Hanborough, about 20-minutes walk away.

Charges: Adult £4 Child £2 Concessions £3 Family (2+2) £9

Facilities: A B D F G H L P R S T

Other information: Free bus rides on the first Sunday of the month from March to October, and on the days of events listed (except the films evening).

PLACES TO STAY

Riding Guest House
Oxford OX1 4TA, 01865 248364

Artemis House
Oxford OX1 4SP, 01865 244357

Newton House
Oxford OX1 4PL, 01865 240561

Becket House
Oxford OX1 1PP, 01865 724675

Wholly representative of the City of Oxford fleet in its heyday is No 928 (TWL 928), a 1953 Park Royal-bodied AEC Regent III. Being of highbridge layout, this bus was primarily used on city services.
PHILIP LAMB

Registration	Date	Chassis make	Chassis model	Body make	Original operator	Fleet No	Status
JVF 528	1949	Bedford	OB	Duple	Bensley of Martham		R
NJO 703	1949	AEC	Regal III 9621A	Willowbrook	City of Oxford Motor Services	703	R
OFC 393	1949	AEC	Regent III 9612A	Weymann	City of Oxford Motor Services	H892	A
OFC 205	1950	AEC	Regal III 6821A	Duple	South Midland Motor Services	66	A
PWL 413	1950	AEC	Regent III 9613A	Weymann	City of Oxford Motor Services	L166	R
SFC 610	1952	AEC	Regal IV 9821S	Willowbrook	City of Oxford Motor Services	610	R
TWL 928	1953	AEC	Regent III 9613S	Park Royal	City of Oxford Motor Services	H928	R
956 AJO	1957	AEC	Regent V MD3RV	Park Royal	City of Oxford Motor Services	H956	R
756 KFC	1960	AEC	Reliance 2MU3RV	Park Royal	City of Oxford Motor Services	756	R
304 KFC	1961	Dennis	Loline II	East Lancs	City of Oxford Motor Services	304	R
305 KFC	1961	Dennis	Loline II	East Lancs	City of Oxford Motor Services	305	R
14 LFC	1961	Morris	FF	Wadham	Morris Motors		R
850 ABK	1962	AEC	Reliance 2MU3RA	Duple	Don Motor Coach Co of Southsea		RP
FWL 371E	1967	AEC	Renown 3B3RA	Northern Counties	City of Oxford Motor Services	371	R
NAC 416F	1967	Leyland	Atlantean PDR1A/1	Northern Counties	Stratford-upon-Avon Blue Motors	10	A
UFC 430K	1971	Daimler	Fleetline CRL6	Northern Counties	City of Oxford Motor Services	430	A
EUD 256K	1972	AEC	Reliance 6MU4R	Plaxton	Chiltern Queens of Woodcote		R
VER 262L	1972	AEC	Reliance 6U3ZR	Alexander	Premier Travel of Cambridge	262	RP
HUD 476S	1977	Bristol	VRTSL3/6LXB	ECW	City of Oxford Motor Services	476	R
BBW 21V	1980	Leyland	Leopard PSU3E/4R	Duple	City of Oxford Motor Services	21	R
JUD 597W	1980	Ford	R1014	Plaxton	House of Watlington		A
BBW 214Y	1982	Leyland	Olympian ONLXB/1R	ECW	City of Oxford Motor Services	214	A
B106 XJO	1985	Ford	Transit 160D	Carlyle	South Midland	SM6	R
C724 JJO	1986	Ford	Transit	Carlyle	City of Oxford Motor Services	724	R
D122 PTT	1987	Ford	Transit 190D	Mellor	Thames Transit	122	R
L247 FDV	1994	Fiat	49-10	Mellor	Bay Line of Exeter	2110	R

Registration	Date	Chassis make	Chassis model	Body make	Original operator	Fleet No	Status
CD 7045	1922	Leyland	G7	Short	Southdown Motor Services	135	R
GE 2446	1928	Leyland	Titan TD1	Leyland	Glasgow Corporation	111	R
RU 8678	1929	Leyland	Lion PLSC3	Leyland	Hants & Dorset Motor Services	268	RP
SO 3740	1929	Leyland	Tiger TS2	Alexander	Scottish General (Northern) Omnibus Co	P63	R
VD 3433	1934	Leyland	Lion LT5A	Alexander	Central SMT Co		R
WG 1620	1934	Gilford	Hera L176S	no body	Alexander	Y49	R
AAA 756	1935	Albion	Victor PK114	Abbott	King Alfred Motor Services		R
WG 3260	1935	Leyland	Lion LT5A	Alexander	W. Alexander & Sons	P705	A
WS 4522	1935	Leyland	Tiger TS7	Cowieson	Scottish Motor Traction Co		RP
CS 3364	1936	Leyland	Cheetah LZ2	Alexander	Western SMT Co		A
ATF 477	1937	Leyland	Tiger TS7T	Fowler	Singleton of Leyland		A
AUX 296	1939	Sentinel-HSG		Cowieson	Sentinel of Shrewsbury (demonstrator)		RP
WG 8107	1939	Leyland	Tiger TS8	Alexander	W. Alexander & Sons	P528	RP
WG 8790	1939	Leyland	Tiger TS8	Alexander	W. Alexander & Sons	P573	RP
HF 9126	1940	Leyland	Titan TD7	Metro-Cammell	Wallasey Corporation	74	A
WG 9180	1940	Leyland	Titan TD7	Leyland	W. Alexander & Sons	R266	R
DSG 169	1942	Leyland	Titan TD5	Alexander	Scottish Motor Traction Co	J66	R
CDR 679	1943	Guy	Arab II	Duple	Plymouth Corporation	249	R
JWS 594	1943	Guy	Arab II	Duple/Nudd	London Transport	G 77	R
BRS 37	1945	Daimler	CWD6	Duple	Aberdeen Corporation	155	R
ACB 904	1947	Guy	Arab II	Northern Coachbuilders	Blackburn Corporation	76	RP
AWG 623	1947	AEC	Regal I 0662	Alexander	W Alexander & Sons	A36	R
AWG 639	1947	AEC	Regal I 0662	Alexander	W Alexander & Sons	A52	R
GSU 378	1947	Albion	Venturer CX19	Comeng	DRTT of Sydney	1877	R
XG 9304	1947	Leyland	Titan PD1A	Northern Counties	Middlesbrough Corporation	52	A
AWG 393	1948	Guy	Arab III	Cravens	W. Alexander & Sons	RO607	R
BMS 405	1948	Daimler	CVD6	Burlingham	W. Alexander & Sons	D10	A
BWG 39	1948	Bedford	OB	Scottish Motor Traction	W. Alexander & Sons	W218	RP
CU 4740	1948	Leyland	Tiger PS1	Burlingham	Hall of South Shields		A
ESG 652	1948	Guy	Arab III	Metro-Cammell	Edinburgh Corporation	739	R
FSC 182	1949	Daimler	CVG6	Metro-Cammell	Edinburgh Corporation	135	R
CWG 283	1950	Leyland	Tiger PS1	Alexander	W Alexander & Sons	PA181	R
DCS 616	1950	Daimler	CVD6	Massey	Hunter (A1) of Dreghorn	16A	R
EVA 324	1950	Guy	Arab III	Guy	Central SMT Co	K24	R
GVD 47	1950	Guy	Arab III	Duple	Hutchinson's Coaches of Overtown		R
SJ 1340	1950	Bedford	OB	Duple	Gordon of Lamlash		RP
SS 7486	1950	Bedford	OB	Duple	Stark's Motor Services of Dunbar		A

Scottish Vintage Bus Museum

Lathalmond

Contact address: M90 Commerce Park, Lathalmond, By Dunfermline, Fife KY12 0SJ

Website: www.busweb.co.uk/svbm

Brief description: Acknowledged as the main focal point of bus restoration and operation in Scotland. It houses around 170 vehicles on a 49-acre site, mostly of Scottish origin and in varying levels of condition, from dilapidated to fully restored.

Events planned in 2010:

4 April-3 October — Guide Sunday

16 May — Annual Running Day

14/15 August — Annual Open Weekend

Free Vintage Bus Service available at all Events

Opening days/times: Guide Sunday 12.30-17.00. Events 10.00–17.00

Directions by car: From M90 Jct 4, take westbound B914, then B915 for approximately one mile

Directions by public transport: Not served by public transport

Charges: Guide Sunday Adult £4 Child/Concession £2. Events vary

Facilities: B D E G P S T

Standing outside one of the impressive buildings at Lathalmond is Glasgow 111 (GE 2446), a Leyland Titan TD1 with Leyland open-staircase bodywork, new in 1928. SIMON GILL

Registration	Date	Chassis make	Chassis model	Body make	Original operator	Fleet No	Status
SS 7501	1950	Bedford	OB	Duple	Fairbairn of Haddington		R
AYJ 379	1951	Daimler	CVD6	Croft	Dundee Corporation	127	R
DGS 536	1951	Leyland	Tiger PS1/1	McLennan	A. & C. McLennan of Spittalfield		R
DGS 625	1951	Leyland	Tiger PS1/1	McLennan	A. & C. McLennan of Spittalfield		R
DMS 820	1951	Leyland	Tiger OPS2/1	Alexander	W. Alexander & Sons	PB7	A
DMS 823	1951	Leyland	Tiger OPS2/1	Alexander	W. Alexander & Sons	PB10	RP
DWG 526	1951	Leyland	Royal Tiger PSU1/15	Leyland	W. Alexander & Sons	PC30	A
BMS 222	1952	Leyland	Royal Tiger PSU1/15	Alexander	W. Alexander & Sons	PC1	R
JVB 908	1952	Leyland	Royal Tiger PSU1/13	Mann Egerton	Homeland of Croydon		RP
CYJ 252	1953	AEC	Regent III 9613E	Alexander	Dundee Corporation	137	R
FGS 59D	1953	Bedford	SB	Mulliner	Royal Navy		RP
LFS 480	1954	Leyland	Titan PD2/20	Metro-Cammell	Edinburgh Corporation	480	R
ETS 964	1955	Daimler	CVG6	Metro-Cammell	Dundee Corporation	184	RP
FWG 846	1955	Bristol	LS6G	ECW	W. Alexander & Sons	E11	RP
HRG 209	1955	AEC	Regent V D2RV6G	Crossley	Aberdeen Corporation	209	A
TYD 888	1955	AEC	Reliance MU3RV	Duple	Wakes of Sparkford		R
UFF 178	1955	AEC	Regent V D2RV6G	Crossley	Aberdeen Corporation	207	A
OFS 777	1957	Leyland	Titan PD2/20	Metro-Cammell	Edinburgh Corporation	777	R
OFS 798	1957	Leyland	Titan PD2/20	Metro-Cammell	Edinburgh Corporation	798	RP
OWS 620	1957	Bristol	Lodekka LD6G	ECW	Scottish Omnibuses	AA620	RP
FAS 982	1959	Albion	Victor FT39KAN	Reading	Jersey Motor Transport Co	5	R
SWS 671	1959	AEC	Reliance 2MU3RV	Alexander	Scottish Omnibuses	B671	R
SWS 715	1959	AEC	Reliance 2MU3RV	Park Royal	Scottish Omnibuses	B715	A
EDS 50A	1960	AEC	Routemaster R2RH	Park Royal	London Transport	RM 560	R
EDS 320A	1960	AEC	Routemaster R2RH	Park Royal	London Transport	RM 606	RP
NMS 366	1960	AEC	Reliance 2MU3RV	Alexander	W. Alexander & Sons	AC155	RP
RAG 578	1960	Daimler	CVG6LX	Northern Counties	T. Hunter (A1) of Kilmarnock		R
VSC 86	1960	Leyland	Tiger Cub PSUC1/3	Weymann	Edinburgh Corporation	86	R
WAJ 112	1960	Albion	Nimbus NS3N	Plaxton	Watson of Huntingdon		A
XSL 945A	1960	Bristol	MW6G	Alexander	Western SMT Co	T1590	A
XSN 25A	1960	Bristol	MW6G	Alexander	Western SMT Co	T1591	A
ABV 33A	1961	Leyland	Titan PD2/12	Metro-Cammell	Trent Motor Traction Co	1012	RP
RAG 411	1961	Bristol	Lodekka LD6G	ECW	Western SMT Co	1645	R
RCS 382	1961	Leyland	Titan PD3A/3	Alexander	Western SMT Co	1684	R
RMS 714	1961	Leyland	Tiger Cub PSUC1/2	Alexander	W. Alexander & Sons (Fife) Ltd	FPD225	R
YSG 101	1961	Leyland	Leopard PSU3/2R	Alexander	Edinburgh Corporation	101	R
YYJ 914	1961	Leyland	Tiger Cub PSUC1/2	Alexander	Stark's Motor Services of Dunbar	H8	A
LDS 201A	1962	AEC	Routemaster R2RH	Park Royal	London Transport	RM1607	R

Above: **Awaiting departure for Dunfermline bus station on 19 August 2006 is W. Alexander & Sons (Fife) FRD199 (BXA 464B) a Bristol FS6G/ECW new in 1964.** SIMON GILL

Left: **A recent arrival at Lathalmond following a change of owner during 2009 is Highland AL41 (BCS 256C), an Albion Lowlander LR7 with Northern Counties lowheight bodywork. AL41 was new to Western SMT in 1965 carrying fleet number 1923. It is shown here at the Cobham event at Longcross on 1 April 2007.** SIMON GILL

Below: **One of the newest buses at Lathalmond is Lothian Regional Transport 777 (C777 SFS), a long-wheelbase Leyland Olympian with dual-door ECW body new in 1985. It is shown at the museum on 17 August 2008.** SIMON GILL

Registration	Date	Chassis make	Chassis model	Body make	Original operator	Fleet No	Status
NSJ 502	1962	AEC	Reliance 2MU3RV	Alexander	W. Alexander & Sons (Northern)	NAC205	R
7424 SP	1962	AEC	Reliance 2MU3RV	Alexander	W. Alexander & Sons (Fife) Ltd	FAC4	R
UCS 659	1963	Albion	Lowlander LR3	Northern Counties	Western SMT Co	N1795	R
AFS 91B	1964	AEC	Reliance 4MU3RA	Alexander	Eastern Scottish	B91	R
ARG 17B	1964	AEC	Reliance 2MU3RA	Alexander	W. Alexander & Sons (Northern) Ltd	NAC246	RP
ASC 665B	1964	Leyland	Titan PD3/6	Alexander	Edinburgh Corporation	665	R
AWA 124B	1964	Bedford	SB13	Duple	J. O. Andrew of Sheffield		R
BXA 464B	1964	Bristol	Lodekka FS6G	ECW	W. Alexander & Sons (Fife) Ltd	FRD199	R
CSG 29C	1965	Bristol	Lodekka FLF6G	ECW	Eastern Scottish		R
CSG 43C	1965	Bristol	Lodekka FLF6G	ECW	Scottish Omnibuses	AA43	RP
DMS 325C	1965	Leyland	Leopard PSU3/3R	Alexander	W Alexander & Sons (Midland) Ltd	MPE40	RP
DMS 359C	1965	Leyland	Leopard PSU3/3R	Alexander	W Alexander & Sons (Midland) Ltd	MPE73	R
ESF 801C	1965	Leyland	Atlantean PDR1/1	Alexander	Edinburgh Corporation	801	R
EWS 130D	1966	AEC	Reliance 2U3RA	Alexander	Eastern Scottish	ZB130	A
EWS 168D	1966	Bristol	RELH6G	Alexander	Scottish Omnibuses (Eastern Scottish)	XA168	RP

Above: **Working on the internal bus service at Lathalmond on 17 August 2008 is SO 3740. A Leyland Tiger TS2 chassis new in 1929, the bus passed from the Scottish General (Northern) Omnibus Company to W. Alexander & Sons in 1930. Numbered P63 in 1932, it was rebodied by Alexander in 1934 as shown here.** SIMON GILL

Below: **Alexander T-bodied Seddon Pennine VII poses in Lathalmond's Leyland Way. This former Western Scottish coach is used for longer trips away by the Scottish Vintage Bus Museum.** PHILIP LAMB

Far right top: **Former Hutchinson's Coaches of Overtown GVD 47, a 1950 Guy Arab III with stylish Duple highbridge bodywork's, seen in the livery of McGill's Bus Service of Barrhead which acquired the vehicle in 1952. It is seen here working on the free internal service within the museum grounds on 19 August 2006.** SIMON GILL

Far right bottom: **Parked at the Scottish Vintage Bus museum awaiting its next trip is Western SMT KN1795 (UCS 659), a 1963 Albion Lowlander LR3 with Alexander lowheight body showing the distinctive Albion badge on the front grille.** SIMON GILL

Registration	Date	Chassis make	Chassis model	Body make	Original operator	Fleet No	Status
EWS 812D	1966	Leyland	Atlantean PDR1/1	Alexander	Edinburgh City Transport	812	R
FFV 447D	1966	AEC	Reliance 2U3RA	Plaxton	J. Abbott & Sons of Blackpool		R
GRS 343E	1967	Albion	Viking VK43AL	Alexander	W. Alexander & Sons (Northern) Ltd	NNV43	R
HDV 639E	1967	Bristol	MW6G	ECW	Western National Omnibus Co	1434	R
HGM 335E	1967	Bristol	Lodekka FLF6G	ECW	Central SMT Co	BL335	R
HGM 346E	1967	Bristol	Lodekka FLF6G	ECW	Central SMT Co	BL346	R
JSC 869E	1967	Leyland	Atlantean PDR1/1	Alexander	Edinburgh City Transport	869	RP
JSC 900E	1967	Leyland	Atlantean PDR2/1	Alexander	Edinburgh Corporation	900	R
LUS 524E	1967	AEC	Reliance 2U3RA	Willowbrook	David MacBrayne of Glasgow	150	R
KGM 664F	1968	Leyland	Leopard PSU3/1R	Alexander	Central SMT Co	T64	A
LFS 294F	1968	Bristol	VRTLL/6LX	ECW	Eastern Scottish	AA294	RP
LFS 288F	1968	Bristol	VRTLL/6LX	ECW	Scottish Omnibuses	AA288	R
NTY 416F	1968	AEC	Reliance 6MU3R	Plaxton	J. Rowell of Prudhoe		RP
NAG 120G	1969	Bristol	REMH6G	Alexander	Western SMT Co	T2214	RP
XFM 42G	1969	Guy	Arab V	Northern Counties	Chester Corporation	42	R
SSF 237H	1970	Bedford	VAL70	Duple	Edinburgh Corporation	237	A
TMS 585H	1970	Leyland	Leopard PSU3/1R	Alexander	Road Transport Industry Training Board	84	A
TGM 214J	1971	Daimler	Fleetline CRG6LX	ECW	Central SMT Co	D14	R
XWS 165K	1971	Bedford	J2SZ2	Plaxton	Glass of Haddington		R
BFS 1L	1972	Leyland	Atlantean AN68/1R	Alexander	Edinburgh City Transport	1	R
BWG 833L	1972	Leyland	Leopard PSU3/3R	Alexander	W. Alexander & Sons (Midland) Ltd	MPE133	A
YSD 350L	1972	Leyland	Leopard PSU3/3R	Alexander	Western SMT Co	L2390	R
BFS 463L	1973	Bedford	YRQ	Alexander	Scottish Omnibuses (Eastern Scottish)	C463	A
BWS 105L	1973	Seddon	Pennine IV-236	Seddon	Edinburgh Corporation	105	R
SCS 333M	1974	Leyland	Leopard PSU3/3R	Alexander	Western SMT Co	L2464	R
SCS 366M	1974	Leyland	Leopard PSU3/3R	Alexander	Western SMT Co	L2497	R
XXA 859M	1974	Leyland	Leopard PSU3/3R	Alexander	Alexander (Fife)	FPE59	R
LSX 16P	1975	Volvo Ailsa	B57	Alexander	Alexander (Fife)	FRA16	A
MSF 750P	1976	Seddon	Pennine VII	Alexander	Scottish Omnibuses (Eastern Scottish)	XS750	R
NCS 16P	1976	Leyland	Fleetline FE30AGR	Alexander	Hill (A1) of Stevenston		RP
SMS 120P	1977	Daimler	Fleetline CRG6LXB	Alexander	W. Alexander & Sons (Midland)	MRF120	RP
OSJ 629R	1977	Leyland	Leopard PSU3C/3R	Alexander	Western SMT Co	L2629	RP
RRS 46R	1977	Leyland	Leopard PSU3E/4R	Duple	W. Alexander & Sons (Northern)	NPE46	R

Registration	Date	Chassis make	Chassis model	Body make	Original operator	Fleet No	Status
XMS 252R	1977	Leyland	Leopard PSU3C/4R	Alexander	W. Alexander & Sons (Midland)	MPE252	A
NDL 656R	1978	Bristol	VRTSL3/6LXB	ECW	Southern Vectis Omnibus Co	656	RP
GLS 265S	1978	Leyland	Leopard PSU3E/4R	Alexander	Alexander (Midland)	MPE265	R
CSG 792S	1978	Seddon	Pennine VII	Plaxton	Scottish Omnibuses (Eastern Scottish)	S792	A
CSG 773S	1978	Volvo Ailsa	B55-10	Alexander	Scottish Omnibuses (Eastern Scottish)	VV773	R
JSF 928T	1978	Seddon	Pennine VII	Alexander	Scottish Omnibuses	S928	RP
JTU 588T	1978	Leyland	National 10351B/1R	Leyland National	Crosville Motor Services	SNG588	RP
SAS 859T	1978	Leyland	Fleetline FE30AGR	ECW	Highland Omnibuses	D17	RP
JSX 595T	1979	Leyland	Atlantean AN68A/1R	Alexander	Lothian RegionTransport	595	R
LIL 9929	1979	Bedford	VAS	Plaxton	Blood Transfusion Service		RP
RLS 469T	1979	Ford	R1014	Alexander	W. Alexander & Sons (Midland)	MT69	RP
WTS 266T	1979	Volvo Ailsa	B55-10	Alexander	Tayside Regional Council	266	R
DSD 936V	1979	Seddon	Pennine VII	Alexander	Western SMT Co	S2936	R
SSX 602V	1980	Seddon	Pennine VII	Alexander	Scottish Omnibuses (Eastern Scottish)	S602	R
ESF 647W	1980	Guy	Victory Mk2	Alexander	China Motor Bus	LV36	R
LMS 374W	1980	Leyland	Leopard PSU3F/4R	Alexander	W. Alexander & Sons (Midland)	MPE374	RP
RHS 400W	1980	Wales & Edwards		JSP	South of Scotland Electricity		R
FES 831W	1981	Volvo	B58-61	Duple	Stagecoach of Perth		RP
YFS 310W	1981	Leyland	National 2 NL116L11/1R	Leyland National	Scottish Omnibuses	N310	A
HSC 173X	1981	Leyland	Cub CU435	Duple	Lothian Region Transport	173	RP
RRM 386X	1981	Leyland	National NL116AL11/1R	Leyland National	Cumberland Motor Services	386	R
GSC 667X	1982	Leyland	Olympian ONTL11/1R	Alexander	Lothian Region Transport	667	R
KSX 102X	1982	Leyland	National 2 NL116AL11/2R	Leyland National	Lothian Region Transport	102	R
ULS 716X	1982	Leyland	Leopard PSU3G/4R	Alexander	W. Alexander & Sons (Midland)	MPE416	RP
ULS 717X	1982	Leyland	Leopard PSU3G/4R	Alexander	W. Alexander & Sons (Midland)	MPE417	RP
NFS 176Y	1982	Leyland	Leopard PSU3G/4R	Alexander	W. Alexander & Sons (Fife)	FPE176	RP
A108 CFS	1983	Leyland	National NL116L11/2R	Leyland National	Lothian Region Transport	108	R
B349 LSO	1985	Leyland	Olympian ON5LXCT/1R	Alexander	W. Alexander & Sons (Midland)	NLO49	A
C777 SFS	1985	Leyland	Olympian ONTL11/2R	ECW	Lothian Region Transport	777	R

South Yorkshire Transport Museum

Aldwarke

Address: Unit 9, Waddington Way, Aldwarke, Rotherham S65 3SH.

Contact address: 206, London Road, Sheffield S2 4LW.

Phone: 0114 255 3010

E-mail: info@sytm.co.uk

Website: www.sytm.co.uk

Brief description: The Museum has doubled in size and now houses 50 vehicles including a Sheffield tram body, buses and coaches from the 1940s through to the 1980s, commercials, cars and bicycles. Displays compliment the full sized vehicles. The Museum also has a comprehensively stocked shop and good-sized cafe.

Events planned in 2010:

14 March, 11 April, 9 May, 13 June, 11 July, 8 August, 10 October, 14 November, 12 December — Museum Event Days. On these dates there will be a vintage shuttle bus running between the Museum and Rotherham Transport Interchange

19 September — Museum Event Day to coincide with the Sheffield Transport Rally

Opening days/times: Saturdays 11.00-16.00 for casual visitors. The best time to visit is on an Event Day.

Directions by car: From the North: Leave the M1 at Junction 35. Take the A629 towards Rotherham. At the third roundabout take the A630 towards Doncaster. At the third roundabout turn left on to the A6123 (Aldwarke Lane). Turn left just before the car wash on to Waddington Way and the Museum is about ½ mile on the left.

From the South: Leave the M1 at Junction 33. Follow the A630 towards Rotherham and then the A630 towards Doncaster and then as above.

Directions by public transport: Nearest bus service is the X78 to Mushroom Roundabout (the junction of the A630 and A6123) which is about a mile away.

Charges: Event Days: Adults £3.50, Concessions £2, Family (2 Adults and up to 3 Children) £8.

Other dates: Donation accepted

Facilities: A B(e) C D F G P R S T

Registration	Date	Chassis make	Chassis model	Body make	Original operator	Fleet No	Status
GWJ 724	1941	AEC	Regent O661	Sheffield Transport Department	Sheffield Corporation	G54	A
JWB 416	1947	Leyland	Tiger PS1	Weymann	Sheffield Corporation	216	A
HD 7905	1948	Leyland	Tiger PS1	Brush	Yorkshire Woollen District Transport Co	622	R
KWE 255	1948	AEC	Regent III 9612E	Weymann	Sheffield Corporation	G55	R
MHY 765	1950	Leyland	Comet ECPO/1R	Duple	Orient Coaches of Bristol	-	RP
OWE 116	1952	AEC	Regent III 9613A	Roe	Sheffield Joint Omnibus Committee	116	RP
KET 220	1954	Daimler	CVG6	Weymann	Rotherham Corporation	220	R
RWB 87	1954	Leyland	Titan PD2/12	Weymann	Sheffield Corporation	687	R
WRA 12	1955	AEC	Monocoach MC3RV	Park Royal	Booth & Fisher of Halfway	-	R
VDV 760	1958	Bristol	Lodekka LD6G	ECW	Western National Omnibus Co	1943	R
TDK 322	1959	AEC	Regent V D2RA	Weymann	Rochdale Corporation	322	R
TET 135	1959	Daimler	CVG6-30	Roe	Rotherham Corporation	135	RP
6330 WJ	1960	AEC	Regent V 2D3RA	Roe	Sheffield Joint Omnibus Committee	1330	A
1322 WA	1961	AEC	Reliance 2MU3RA	Plaxton	Sheffield United Tours	322	RP
449 CLT	1963	AEC	Routemaster	Park Royal	London Transport	RM1449	RP
388 KDT	1963	Leyland	Titan PD2/40	Roe	Doncaster Corporation	188	R
824 KDV	1963	Bristol	Lodekka FLF6G	ECW	Western National Omnibus Co	2019	R
KWE 374D	1966	AEC	Reliance	Plaxton	Sheffield United Tours	374	R
LJF 30F	1967	Leyland	Titan PD3A/12	MCW	Leicester City Transport	30	RP
BWB 148H	1969	Leyland	Atlantean PDR2/1	Park Royal	Sheffield Corporation	748	R
DWB 54H	1970	AEC	Swift 5P2R	Park Royal	Sheffield Transport	54	RP
UWA 296L	1973	Leyland	Atlantean AN68/1R	Alexander	Sheffield Transport	296	RP
CWG 756V	1979	Leyland	Atlantean AN68A/1R	Roe	South Yorkshire PTE	1756	R
C53 HDT	1985	Dennis	Domino SDA	Optare	South Yorkshire PTE	53	A

Other information: A vintage shuttle bus runs between the Museum and Rotherham Transport Interchange on Event Days. See the Museum's website or telephone 0114 255 3010 for bus times.

Buses available for hire.

Weddings provide a good source of income where museums have suitably taxed, insured and MoT'd vehicles. Leyland Titan PD2/40, Doncaster 188 (388 KDT) was new in 1963, but fitted with a Roe body of 1955 vintage, salvaged from a withdrawn trolleybus. PHILIP LAMB

Many museums in this book have other form of transport history on display. Here at the South Yorkshire Transport Museum, a Hudswell Clarke industrial saddle tank keeps company with Leyland Atlantean AN68A/1R, South Yorkshire 1756 (CWG 756V). This Roe-bodied bus has been restored in Mainline livery, as carried in its latter years in service in South Yorkshire. PHILIP LAMB

Registration	Date	Chassis make	Chassis model	Body make	Original operator	Fleet No	Status
DNF 204	1937	Crossley	Mancunian	Metro-Cammell/ Crossley	Manchester Corporation	129	RP
DBN 978	1949	Crossley	SD42/7	Crossley	Bolton Corporation	8	R
JND 728	1950	Daimler	CVG6	Metro Cammell	Manchester Corporation	4127	RP
FRJ 511	1951	Daimler	CVG6	Metro Cammell	Salford City Transport	511	R
422 CAX	1961	AEC	Regent V MD3RV	Massey	Bedwas & Machen UDC	5	R
7209 PW	1962	Bedford	J2SZ2	Plaxton	H. & I. Jarvis of Downham Market	4	R
105 UTU	1962	Leyland	Titan PD2/37	Northern Counties	SHMD Board	5	RP
WRJ 179	1963	Leyland	Titan PD2/40	Metro Cammell	Salford City Transport	179	R
BWO 585B	1964	AEC	Regent V 2MD3RA	Massey	Bedwas & Machen UDC	8	A
NMA 328D	1966	Daimler	Fleetline CRG6LX	Northern Counties	SHMD Board	28	RP

A small, but interesting collection of vehicles at Tameside includes this 1949 all-Crossley saloon, once No 8 in the Bolton fleet. PHILIP LAMB

Tameside Transport Collection
Mossley

Contact address: Roaches Ind Estate, Manchester Road, Mossley, Greater Manchester

Brief description: A working museum comprising a small but varied collection of vehicles ranging from 1929 to the 1960s. There is also a display of transport-related items.

Opening days/times: Last weekend of each month (except December) 10.00-15.00

Charges: No charge but donations welcome

Directions by car: From Ashton-under-Lyne take A635 (Huddersfield) through Mossley. Museum is 1 mile on right-hand side, adjacent to Claybank Terrace.

Directions by public transport: Bus 350 Ashton-Oldham — alight at the Royal George and walk towards Mossley

Bus 354 Ashton-Uppenmill — alight before Royal George

By rail to Mossley Station (approx 1 mile walk towards Greenfield)

Facilities: D R T

Other information: Car parking is limited

The Transport Museum
Wythall

Contract address: Chapel Lane, Wythall, Worcestershire B47 6JX

Phone: 01564 826471

E-mail: enquiries@wythall.org.uk

Website: www.wythall.org.uk

Brief description: Three halls accommodate around 100 buses and battery-electric vehicles from the Midlands and beyond. The Power Hall shows the development of the operating and manufacturing sides of the bus industry. Industry leader Midland 'Red' built its own buses for half a century. Miniature steam railway operates on major days.

Many prewar buses in preservation have spent many more years in museums then they ever did in revenue-earning service. One such bus is Birmingham 1107 (CVP207), a 1937 Metro-Cammell-bodied Daimler COG5, part of the extensive collection of vehicles to be found at the Transport Museum, Wythall. PHILIP LAMB

Registration	Date	Chassis make	Chassis model	Body make	Original operator	Fleet No	Status
O 9926	1913	Tilling Stevens	TTA2	Thomas Tilling	BMMO ('Midland Red')	26	RP
HA 3501	1925	SOS	Standard	Ransomes Sims & Jefferies	BMMO ('Midland Red')	501	A
CN 2870	1927	SOS	Q	Brush	Northern General Transport Co	321	RP
CC 7745	1928	SOS	QL	Brush	Royal Blue of Llandudno		A
OV 4090	1931	Morris Commercial	Dictator	Metro-Cammell	Birmingham Corporation Tramways	90	A
OV 4486	1931	AEC	Regent 661	Metro-Cammell	Birmingham Corporation Tramways	486	A
OC 527	1933	Morris Commercial	Imperial	Metro-Cammell	Birmingham Corporation Tramways	527	A
AHA 582	1935	SOS	DON	Brush	BMMO ('Midland Red')	1703	A
CVP 207	1937	Daimler	COG5	Metro-Cammell	Birmingham City Transport	1107	R
RC 4615	1937	AEC	Regal O662	Willowbrook	Trent Motor Traction Co	714	R
GHA 333	1940	SOS	SON	(chassis only)	BMMO ('Midland Red')	2414	RP
GHA 337	1940	SOS	SON	Brush	BMMO ('Midland Red')	2418	RP
HHA 637	1946	BMMO	S6	Metro-Cammell	BMMO ('Midland Red')	3036	A
FFY 402	1947	Leyland	Titan PD2/3	Leyland	Southport Corporation	85	RP
GUE 247	1948	Leyland	Tiger PS1	Northern Coachbuilders	Stratford-upon-Avon Blue Motors	41	A
HOV 685	1948	Leyland	Titan PD2/1	Brush	Birmingham City Transport	1685	R
JRR 404	1948	Leyland	Titan PD1	Duple	Barton Transport of Chilwell	473	RP
KAL 579	1948	Daimler	CVD6	Massey	W Gash & Sons of Newark	DD2	R
FDM 724	1949	Foden	PVD6	Massey	E. H. Phillips Motor Services of Holywell		A
FJW 616	1949	Sunbeam	F4	Park Royal	Wolverhampton Corporation	616	R
HDG 448	1949	Albion	Venturer CX19	Metro-Cammell	Cheltenham District Traction Co	72	R
HWO 334	1949	Guy	Arab III	Duple	Red & White Services	34	R
JOJ 245	1950	Leyland	Tiger PS2/1	Weymann	Birmingham City Transport	2245	R
JOJ 533	1950	Guy	Arab III special	Metro-Cammell	Birmingham City Transport	2533	R
JUE 349	1950	Leyland	Tiger PS2/3	Northern Counties	Stratford-upon-Avon Blue Motors	33	RP
KFM 775	1950	Bristol	L5G	ECW	Crosville Motor Services	KG126	R
NHA 744	1950	BMMO	S12	Brush	BMMO ('Midland Red')	3744	RP
NHA 795	1950	BMMO	D5B	Brush	BMMO ('Midland Red')	3795	A
ORB 277	1950	Daimler	CVD6	Duple	Tailby & George ('Blue Bus Services') Willington		R
MXX 23	1952	AEC	Regal IV 9821LT RF	Metro-Cammell	London Transport	RF381	R
JOJ 976	1953	Guy	Arab IV	Metro-Cammell	Birmingham City Transport	2976	R
PDH 808	1953	Leyland	Royal Tiger PSU1	Park Royal	Walsall Corporation	808	R
RDH 505	1953	Leyland	Titan PD2/12	Roe	Walsall Corporation	815	RP
SHA 431	1953	Leyland	Titan PD2/12 special	Leyland	BMMO ('Midland Red')	4031	R
FRC 956	1954	Leyland	Titan PD2/12	Leyland	Trent Motor Traction Co	1256	R
UHA 255	1955	BMMO	S14	BMMO	BMMO ('Midland Red')	4255	R

Registration	Date	Chassis make	Chassis model	Body make	Original operator	Fleet No	Status
XHA 482	1956	BMMO	D7	Metro-Cammell	BMMO ('Midland Red')	4482	R
XHA 496	1956	BMMO	D7	Metro-Cammell	BMMO ('Midland Red')	4496	A
SUK 3	1957	Guy	Arab IV	Metro-Cammell	Wolverhampton Corporation	3	R
UTU 596J	1957	Guy	Otter NLLODP	Mulliner	Douglas Corporation	9	R
VVP 911	1958	Bedford	SB3	Duple	Sandwell Motor Co of Birmingham		R
819 HHA	1959	BMMO	C5	BMMO	BMMO ('Midland Red')	4819	RP
WDF 569	1959	Leyland	Tiger Cub PSUC1	Willowbrook	Soudley Valley Coaches of Cinderford		R
871 KHA	1960	BMMO	D9	BMMO	BMMO ('Midland Red')	4871	R
943 KHA	1960	BMMO	D10	BMMO	BMMO ('Midland Red')	4943	R
802 MHW	1961	Bristol	Lodekka FSF6G	ECW	Cheltenham District Traction Co	6037	R
5212 HA	1962	Leyland	Leopard PSU3/4R	Willowbrook	BMMO ('Midland Red')	5212	A
3016 HA	1962	BMMO	D9	BMMO/LPC	BMMO ('Midland Red')	5016	R
5073 HA	1962	BMMO	S15	BMMO	BMMO ('Midland Red')	5073	R
SBF 233	1962	Leyland	Titan PD2/28	Northern Counties	Harper Bros of Heath Hayes	25	R
248 NEA	1963	Daimler	CVG6-30	Metro-Cammell	West Bromwich Corporation	248	R
6545 HA	1964	BMMO	S16	BMMO	BMMO ('Midland Red')	5545	R
BHA 399C	1965	BMMO	D9	BMMO	BMMO ('Midland Red')	5399	R
BHA 656C	1965	BMMO	CM6T	BMMO	BMMO ('Midland Red')	5656	R
BON 474C	1965	Daimler	Fleetline CRG6LX	Marshall	Birmingham City Transport	3474	R
CUV 219C	1965	AEC	Routemaster R2RH/1	Park Royal	London Transport	RCL2219	R
EHA 767D	1966	BMMO	S17	BMMO/Plaxton	BMMO ('Midland Red')	5767	R
GHA 415D	1966	Daimler	Fleetline CRG6LX	Alexander	BMMO ('Midland Red')	6015	R
GRY 60D	1966	Leyland	Titan PD3A/1	Park Royal	Leicester City Transport	60	R
HBF 679D	1966	Leyland	Titan PD2A/27	Metro-Cammell	Harper Bros of Heath Hayes	27	R
JHA 868E	1967	BMMO	S21	BMMO	BMMO ('Midland Red')	5868	R
KHW 306E	1967	Bristol	RELL6L	ECW	Cheltenham District Traction Co	1000	R
NJW 719E	1967	Daimler	Roadliner SRC6	Strachan	Wolverhampton Corporation	719	R
MHA 901F	1968	BMMO	S22	BMMO	BMMO ('Midland Red')	5901	R
KOX 780F	1968	Daimler	Fleetline CRG6LX	Park Royal	Birmingham City Transport	3780	R
NEA 101F	1968	Daimler	Fleetline CRG6LX	MCW	West Bromwich Corporation	101	R
NOV 796G	1968	Daimler	Fleetline CRG6LX	Park Royal	Birmingham City Transport	3796	R
XDH 56G	1968	Daimler	CRC6-36	Northern Counties	Walsall Corporation	56	R
UHA 956H	1969	BMMO	S23	BMMO/Plaxton	BMMO ('Midland Red')	5956	R
XDH 516G	1969	Daimler	Fleetline CRG6LX	Northern Counties	Walsall Corporation	116	R
SOE 913H	1969	Daimler	Fleetline CRG6LX-33	Park Royal	West Midlands PTE	3913	R
SHA 645G	1969	Leyland	Leopard PSU4A/4R	Plaxton	BMMO ('Midland Red')	6145	R
FRB 211H	1970	Bristol	VRTSL2/6LX	ECW	Midland General Omnibus Co	322	R

Registration	Date	Chassis make	Chassis model	Body make	Original operator	Fleet No	Status
UHA 941H	1970	BMMO	S23	BMMO	BMMO ('Midland Red')	5941	A
UHA 981H	1970	BMMO	S23	BMMO/Plaxton	BMMO ('Midland Red')	5981	R
AHA 451J	1971	Leyland	Leopard PSU4B/4R	Plaxton	BMMO ('Midland Red')	6451	R
OWE 271K	1972	Bristol	VRTSL2/6LX	East Lancs	Sheffield Transport	271	R
PDU 135M	1973	Daimler	Fleetline CRG6LX	East Lancs	Coventry City Transport	135	RP
NOB 413M	1974	Bristol	VRTSL6LX	MCW	West Midlands PTE	4413	R
PHA 370M	1974	Ford	R1014	Plaxton/Midland Red	Midland Red Omnibus Co	370	R
JOV 613P	1975	Daimler	Fleetline CRG6LX	Park Royal	West Midlands PTE	4613	R
99-64-HB	1976	Den Oudsten	LOK	Den Oudsten	VAD of Ermele (Netherlands)	5656	A
KON 311P	1976	Leyland	Fleetline FE30 ALR	MCW	West Midlands PTE	6311	R
NOE 544R	1976	Leyland	National 11351A/1R	Leyland National	Midland Red Omnibus Co	544	R
SDA 757S	1977	Leyland	Fleetline FE30AGR	East Lancs	West Midlands PTE	6757	R
WDA 835T	1978	MCW	Metrobus DR102/1	MCW	West Midlands PTE	6835	RP
WDA 956T	1979	Leyland	Fleetline FE30AGR	MCW	West Midlands PTE	1956	R
DOC 26V	1980	Leyland	National NL116L11/1R	Leyland National	West Midlands PTE	1026	R
D553 NOE	1986	Ford	Transit	Carlyle	West Midlands PTE	553	R

Directions by public transport: Infrequent service buses from Birmingham and Solihull. Wythall railway station is on Birmingham-Stratford line and 25 minutes walk to museum. Museum provides buses from Birmingham city centre on the bigger operating days.

Facilities: A B D E G H P R S T

Other information: Frequent services on major operating days. Also journey at 14.30 on Saturdays from May 29 to end of August, and on Sundays and Wednesdays in August.

Above: **Trent 1256 (FRC 956) is the last ever all-Leyland bus built. It currently resides at Wythall.**
PHILIP LAMB

Right: **The Daimler Roadliner was a far from successful bus, and, as a result, only a few have survived into the preservation era. Recently returned to running order at Wythall, with the help of engine manufacturer Cummins, is Strachans-bodied Wolverhampton 719 (NJW 719E), new to the undertaking in 1967.**
PHILIP LAMB

Registration	Date	Chassis make	Chassis model	Body make	Original operator	Fleet No	Status
Unregistered	1902	Rob Blackwell & Co		Horse-drawn tower wagon	Reading Corporation	'William'	A
WW 4688	1927	Garrett	O type	Garrett	Mexborough & Swinton Traction Co	34	A
Unknown	1929	Guy	BTX	Ransomes	Hastings Tramways Co		RP
KW 6052	1929	English Electric	A	English Electric	Bradford Corporation	562	A
TV 4484	1931	Ransomes Sims & Jefferies	D6	(chassis only)	Nottingham City Transport	346	A
1425 P	1932	Fabrique Nationale		Fabrique Nationale	Liege (Belgium)	425	R
TV 9333	1934	Karrier	E6	Brush	Nottingham City Transport	367	RP
ALJ 973	1935	Sunbeam	MS2	Park Royal	Bournemouth Corporation	99	R
CU 3593	1937	Karrier	E4	Weymann	South Shields Corporation	204	R
FW 8990	1937	AEC	661T	Park Royal	Cleethorpes Corporation	54	RP
AVH 470	1938	Karrier	E6	(chassis only)	Huddersfield Corporation	470	A
ARD 676	1939	AEC	661T	Park Royal	Reading Corporation	113	R
FTO 614	1939	AEC	Regent O661	Nottingham City Transport	Nottingham City Transport	802	R
CKG 193	1942	AEC	664T	Northern Counties	Cardiff Corporation	203	R
964 H87	1943	Vetra	CB60	CTL	Limoges (France)	5	R
GHN 574	1944	Karrier	W	East Lancs	Bradford Corporation	792	R
GKP 511	1944	Sunbeam	W	Roe	Maidstone Corporation	56	R
RC 8472	1944	Sunbeam	W	Weymann	Derby Corporation	172	R
CDT 636	1945	Karrier	W	Roe	Doncaster Corporation	375	RP
DKY 706	1945	Karrier	W	East Lancs	Bradford Corporation	706	R
GTV 666	1945	Karrier	W	Brush	Nottingham City Transport	466	RP
RC 8575	1945	Sunbeam	W	Park Royal	Derby Corporation	175	RP
SVS 281	1945	Daimler	CWA6	Duple	Douglas Corporation	52	R
CVH 741	1947	Karrier	MS2	Park Royal	Huddersfield Corporation	541	RP
EDT 703	1947	Leyland	Titan PD2/1	Roe	Doncaster Corporation	94	RP
HKR 11	1947	Sunbeam	W	Northern Coachbuilders	Maidstone Corporation	72	R
JV 9901	1947	AEC	Regent III O961	Roe	Grimsby Corporation	81	A
HYM 812	1948	BUT	9641T	Metro-Cammell	London Transport	1812	R
KTV 493	1948	BUT	9611T	Roe	Nottingham City Transport	493	R

Trolleybus Museum

Sandtoft

Contract address: Belton Road, Sandtoft, Doncaster DN8 5SX

Phone: 01724 711391 (24 hour information line)

E-mail: trolleybusmuseum@sandtoft.org

Website: www.sandtoft.org

Brief description: The Museum hosts the world's largest collection of historic trolleybuses. It has a specially constructed circuit allowing the operation of trolleybus services during operating weekends. There is also a wide selection of trolleybus and trolleybus era memorabilia, artefacts and street furniture.

Events planned in 2010:

3-5 April — Easter Trolley Days

17/18 April — Trolley Days

1-3 May — Extravaganza Weekend

15/16 May — Trolley Days

29-31 May — Weekend Trolleydays

12/13 June — West Yorkshire Weekend

26/27 June — Teddy Bears Picnic

10/11 July — Vintage Bicycle Weekend

24 July — Gathering Preview

25 July — Gathering 2010

14/15 August — Blues and Twos Weekend

28-30 August — Six-wheeler Weekend

18/19 September — Model Weekend

2/3 October — Worldwide Weekend

17 October — St Leger Historic Vehicle Rally

14 November — Twilight Trolleys

11/12 December — Santa Days

Note: Please be aware that vehicles on display can vary from time to time as not all museums display their entire 'fleet'. Visitors wishing to see a particular vehicle should make enquiries prior to their visit.

Opening days/times: 11.00-17.00 on the above dates, except Gathering Preview (11.00-22.00), Gathering 2010 (10.00-18.00), Twilight Trolleys (11.00-18.00) and Santa Days (11.00-16.00)

Directions by car: From M180 junction 2, take A161 southbound to Belton. Turn right and museum is two miles on right-hand side.

Directions by public transport: Please see website or telephone to check operation.

Maidstone Corporation 72 (HKR 11) is a 1947 Sunbeam W with Northern Coachbuilders bodywork turning during the 'Gathering' on 27 July 2008 and showing the impressive overhead erected at the Sandtoft Trolleybus Museum. SIMON GILL

Registration	Date	Chassis make	Chassis model	Body make	Original operator	Fleet No	Status
DRD 130	1949	BUT	9611T	Park Royal	Reading Corporation	144	R
EKU 743	1949	BUT	9611T	Roe	Bradford Corporation	743	A
EKU 746	1949	BUT	9611T	Roe	Bradford Corporation	746	R
EKY 558	1949	Leyland	Titan PD2/3	Leyland	Bradford Corporation	558	RP
GDT 421	1949	Daimler	CVD6	Roe	Doncaster Corporation	112	A
LHN 784	1949	BUT	9611T	East Lancs	Bradford Corporation	834	R
ERD 145	1950	Sunbeam	S7	Park Royal	Reading Corporation	174	R
ERD 152	1950	Sunbeam	S7	Park Royal	Reading Corporation	181	R
FET 618	1950	Daimler	CTE6	Roe	Rotherham Corporation	44	R
GFU 692	1950	BUT	9611T	Northern Coachbuilders	Cleethorpes Corporation	59	A
JWW 375	1950	Sunbeam	F4	East Lancs	Bradford Corporation	845	RP
JWW 376	1950	Sunbeam	F4	East Lancs	Bradford Corporation	846	A
JWW 377	1950	Sunbeam	F4	East Lancs	Bradford Corporation	847	A
KTV 506	1950	BUT	9641T	Brush	Nottingham City Transport	506	R
BDJ 87	1951	BUT	9611T	East Lancs	St Helens Corporation	387	RP
FKU 758	1951	BUT	9611T	Weymann	Bradford Corporation	758	RP
LYR 542	1951	AEC	Regent III 0961	Park Royal	London Transport	RT3323	RP
NDH 959	1951	Sunbeam	F4	Brush	Walsall Corporation	342	R
MDT 222	1953	AEC	Regal III 9621A	Roe	Doncaster Corporation	22	R
OTV 137	1953	AEC	Regent III 9613E	Park Royal	Nottingham City Transport	137	RP
AC-L 379	1956	Henschel	562E	Ludewig	Aachen (Germany)	22	R
KVH 219	1956	BUT	9641T	East Lancs	Huddersfield Corporation	619	R
FYS 839	1958	BUT	9613T	Crossley	Glasgow Corporation	TB78	R
PVH 931	1959	Sunbeam	S7A	East Lancs	Huddersfield Corporation	631	R
XWX 795	1959	AEC	Reliance 2MU3RV	Roe	Felix Motors of Doncaster	40	A
WLT 529	1960	AEC	Routemaster R2RH	Park Royal	London Transport	RM529	R
9629 WU	1960	AEC	Reliance 2MU3RV	Roe	Felix Motors of Doncaster	41	R
VRD 193	1961	Sunbeam	F4A	Burlingham	Reading Corporation	193	R
657 BWB	1962	Leyland	Atlantean PDR1/1	Park Royal	Sheffield Joint Omnibus Committee	1357	R
433 MDT	1963	Leyland	Tiger Cub PSUC1/11	Roe	Doncaster Corporation	33	R

Registration	Date	Chassis make	Chassis model	Body make	Original operator	Fleet No	Status
7830LG69	1964	Vetra	EH87		Lyon France	1704	R
JTF 920B	1964	AEC	Reliance 2MU3RV	East Lancs	Reading Corporation	48	A
66	1967	Lancia		Dalfa	Oporto (Portugal)	140	R
UDT 455F	1968	Leyland	Royal Tiger Cub RTC1/2	Roe	Doncaster Corporation	55	R
WWJ 754M	1973	Daimler	Fleetline CRG6LXB	Park Royal	Sheffield Transport	754	R
8319JD13	1980	Renault	ER100	Renault	Marseilles France	202	R
C45 HDT	1985	Dennis	Dominator DTA1401	Alexander	South Yorkshire PTE	2450	R
D472 OWE	1986	Dennis	Dominator DDA910	Alexander	South Yorkshire PTE	2472	A
D479 OWE	1986	Dennis	Dominator DDA910	Alexander	South Yorkshire PTE	2479	RP

Although the Trolleybus Museum at Sandtoft is a centre of excellent in the preservation of trolleybuses, some motorbuses are also in residence, including this Roe-bodied AEC Regal III saloon, No 22 in the Doncaster fleet. Also in view, and also a Sandtoft resident, is 1960 AEC Reliance/Roe 9629 WU, once No 41 in the Felix Motors fleet. PHILIP LAMB

Ulster Folk & Transport Museum

Cultra

Contract address: Cultra, 153 Bangor Road , Holywood, Co Down, BT18 OEU

Phone: 028 9042 8428

E-mail: info@nmni.com

Website: www.uftm.com

Brief description: A unique collection of wheeled vehicles from cycles to trams, railways, buses and cars. Interpretive exhibitions show the development.

Opening days/times: All the year round but closing for a few days at Christmas time From 10.00 on Weekdays and 11.00 on Sundays (please phone for details)

Directions by car: On A2 Belfast-Bangor Road

Charges: Adult £6 (£7 for special events), Children and concessions £3.50 (£4 for special events)

Registration	Date	Chassis make	Chassis model	Body make	Original operator	Fleet No	Status
FZ 7897	1948	Guy	BTX	Harkness	Belfast Corporation	112	R
EOI 2857	1973	Daimler	Fleetline CRG6LX-33	Alexander (Belfast)	Belfast Corporation	857	R

This Alexander-bodied Daimler Fleetline is a reminder of the many such vehicles, commonplace on the streets of Belfast for many, many years.
PHILIP LAMB

Western Isles Transport Preservation Group

Isle of Lewis

Contact address: 43b Lower Barvas, Isle of Lewis HS2 0QY

Phone: 01851 840294 or 07765 131793

Website: www.witpg.org.uk

Brief description: The collection of vehicles can be visited at any time by prior arrangement. At present stored at a variety of locations, the group is planning to bring the collection to a common site incorporating a working museum.

Events planned: Please see website for details

Directions: By air from Glasgow, Inverness or Aberdeen. By ferry via Ullapool, Uig or Oban

Registration	Date	Chassis make	Chassis model	Body make	Original operator	Fleet No	Status
JS 1972	1924	Ford	T	McLeod	Mackay of Stornaway		R
JS 8089	1948	Bedford	OB	Duple	Mitchell of Stornaway		A
UGB 138H	1970	Bedford	SB5	Duple Midland	Highland Omnibus	10	RP
DSE 980T	1979	Bedford	YRQ	Plaxton	Low of Tomintoul		A
A913 ERM	1984	Bedford	YNT	Plaxton	George T. Irving of Dalston		A
F649 FGE	1988	Mercedes-Benz	507D	Steedrive	Craney of Kilsyth		A

Currently under restoration on the Isle of Lewis is JS 1972, a 1924 Ford Model T with McLeod 8-seat body, new to Mackay of Stornaway.
WESTERN ISLES TRANSPORT PRESERVATION GROUP

Registration	Date	Chassis make	Chassis model	Body make	Original operator	Fleet No	Status
BG 8557	1944	Guy	Arab II	Massey	Birkenhead Corporation	242	RP
BG 9225	1946	Leyland	Titan PD1A	Massey	Birkenhead Corporation	105	RP
HKF 820	1949	AEC	Regent III 9612E	Weymann/LCPT	Liverpool Corporation	A344	RP
AHF 850	1951	Leyland	Titan PD2/1	Metro-Cammell	Wallasey Corporation	54	R
CHF 565	1956	Leyland	Titan PD2/10	Burlingham	Wallasey Corporation	106	RP
FBG 910	1958	Leyland	Titan PD2/40	Massey	Birkenhead Corporation	10	R
FHF 451	1958	Leyland	Atlantean PDR1/1	Metro-Cammell	Wallasey Corporation	1	R
AFM 402A	1962	Bristol	FSG6	ECW	Crosville Motor Services	DFG38	RP
RCM 493	1964	Leyland	Leopard L1	Massey	Birkenhead Corporation	93	R
GCM 152E	1967	Leyland	Titan PD2/37	Massey	Birkenhead Corporation	152	R
UFM 52F	1968	Bristol	RELL6G	ECW	Crosville Motor Services	ERG52	R
CWU 146T	1979	Leyland	Fleetline FE30AGR	Roe	West Yorkshire PTE	7146	R
B926 KWM	1984	Leyland	Atlantean AN68D/1R	Alexander	Merseyside PTE	1070	R
101 CLT	1989	Leyland	Olympian ONCL10/2RZ	Alexander	Lothian Region Transport	362	R

Wirral Transport Museum
Birkenhead

Contact address: 1 Taylor Street, Birkenhead, Merseyside CH41 1BG

Phone: 0151 666 2756

E-mail: one.boroughgroup@googlemail.com

Website: www.wirraltransportmuseum.org

Brief description: The Museum houses a collection of buses, tramcars, motor cycles, cars and a model railway. Local enthusiast groups are restoring some of the trams and buses. Trams operate during weekends and some school holidays.

Opening days/times: Please see website for details

Directions by car: Adjacent to Woodside Ferry Terminal

Directions by public transport: Bus or ferry to Woodside, Train to Hamilton Square railway station

PLACES TO STAY

The Shrewsbury Lodge Hotel
Birkenhead CH43 2JB, 0151 652 4029

Alexia Hotel
Birkenhead CH42 1PJ, 0151 645 8972

The Black Lions Guest House
Birkenhead CH42 1QD, 0151 644 0574

Wallasey Corporation 54 (AHF 850) is a Leyland Titan PD2/1 with Metro Cammell body, new 1951, but looking much older. No 54 is seen outside the museum on 1 October 2006. SIMON GILL

Note: Please be aware that vehicles on display can vary from time to time as not all museums display their entire 'fleet'. Visitors wishing to see a particular vehicle should make enquiries prior to their visit.

YARDLEY WOOD BUS CLUB 1990 – 2010 CELEBRATING 20 YEARS

www.ywbc.co.uk

WE STOCK CORGI, BRITBUS, EFE, OXFORD & CMNL BUS MODELS

ALL PROFIT FROM SALES GO TOWARDS THE RUNNING OF OUR PRESERVED BIRMINGHAM CITY TRANSPORT SINGLE DECK DAIMLER FLEETLINE BUS. FLEET No.3472. Reg No. BON 472C

FORTHCOMING CREATIVE MASTER NORTHCORD MODELS
IE 0005 DUBLIN BUS COASTAL TOUR – VOLVO/ALX400 £25
UK 2017 STAGECOACH IN HULL – PLAXTON PRESIDENT £25
UK 3032 STAGECOACH RIBBLE – DENNIS DART/PLAXTON MPD £25
UK 4017 WEST COAST MOTORS – ALEX. ROYALE (P281 PSX) £27
UK 4018 WEST COAST MOTORS – ALEX. ROYALE (N401 GSX) £27
UK 5026 ARRIVA THE SHIRES – MERCEDES BENZ CITARO £27
UK 6022 STAGECOACH IN DEVON – ADL ENVIRO 400 £29
UK 6027 WESTERN GREYHOUND – ADL ENVIRO 400 £29
UK 6028 ARRIVA MERSEYSIDE – ADL ENVIRO 400 £29
UK 6029 ADL HYBRID DEMONSTRATOR – ADL ENVIRO 400 £29
6031 LONDON GENERAL – ADL ENVIRO 400 £29
UK 8015 BLUE TRIANGLE – ADL ENVIRO 200 £27
UK 8016 FIRST LONDON – ADL ENVIRO 200 £27
UK 9002 BLUESTAR – SCANIA OMNICITY DOUBLE DECKER £29
UK 9003 METROBUS – SCANIA OMNICITY DOUBLE DECKER £29
UK 9004 THAMES TRAVEL - SCANIA OMNICITY DOUBLE DECKER £29
UK PLUS1005 SOUTHAMPTON – BUS STOP SET £7

FORTHCOMING CORGI MODELS
44116A WILTS & DORSET (POOLE) – OPTARE SOLO £22
44116B WILTS & DORSET (SALISBURY) – OPTARE SOLO £22
45120A METROLINE (NORTH FINCHLEY) – MCW METROBUS Mk1 £22
45102B METROLINE (EDGWARE STATION) – MCW METROBUS Mk1 £22
46208A GREYHOUND (PORTSMOUTH) BILLY JEAN – SCANIA IRIZAR £22
46208B GREYHOUND (LONDON) BILLY JEAN - SCANIA IRIZAR £22
46209A GREYHOUND (SOUTHAMPTON) PEGGY SUE – SCANIA IRIZAR £22
46209B GREYHOUND (LONDON) PEGGY SUE – SCANIA IRIZAR £22
46303 ARRIVA LONDON (SIGHTSEEING TOUR) – RM OPEN TOP £22
46401 NATIONAL EXPRESS (WEMBLEY STADIUM) – CAETANO LEVANTE £22
40102A WOLVERHAMPTON – TROLLEYBUS (No.8 FIGHTING COCKS) £22
40102B WOLVERHAMPTON – TROLLEYBUS (No. 8b DUDLEY Br.) £22
41309 GO NORTH EAST – (X56 METROCENTRE) – WRIGHT SOLAR FUSION £25
44115TY LONDON 2012 SITE TOUR BUS – OPTARE SOLO £12

PLEASE PRE-ORDER TO AVOID DISAPPOINTMENT
FOR A FULL LIST OF SPECIAL OFFERS VISIT www.ywbc.co.uk

POST & PACKAGING IS JUST £1.50 PER MODEL
Please Note: From April 4th 2010
P&P Will Be Increased To £2 per Model
This Is Due To The Rise In Postal Charges

IF YOU CANNOT FIND THE MODEL YOU ARE LOOKING FOR, PLEASE GET IN TOUCH AND WE WILL TRY TO SATISFY YOUR REQUIREMENTS

ALL THE LATEST EFE BUS MODELS ARE STILL ONLY £20 INCLUDING...
EFE 35701 GREENLINE – BET 4 BAY 36' COACH
EFE 996647 BRITISH RAIL & SEALINK with Trailer

CONTACT ADDRESS
YARDLEY WOOD BUS CLUB
PO BOX 14029
BIRMINGHAM
B13 3FN

VISIT OUR SALES STAND AT THE FOLLOWING EVENTS IN THE NEXT FEW MONTHS...
MARCH 14TH ASTON MANOR: **4TH/5TH APRIL WYTHALL MUSEUM:** 11TH APRIL COBHAM:
2ND/3RD MAY WYTHALL MUSEUM: 9TH MAY POTTERIES: **16TH MAY HARBOURSIDE BRISTOL:**
30TH/31ST MAY WYTHALL MUSEUM:
SEE OUR BIRMINGHAM CITY TRANSPORT SINGLE DECK FLEETLINE (3472) BON 472C NOW RESTORED IN
THE ORIGINAL DELIVERY CONDITION- BEING UNVEILED AT WYTHALL MUSEUM THIS EASTER

135 MANCHESTER

The SELNEC Preservation Society has a large collection of post-1974 vehicles including this 1980 Leyland Olympian with Northern Counties bodywork, one of a small number of Olympian prototypes. No1451 (NJA 568W) has been restored in Greater Manchester Transport colours. PHILIP LAMB

Aire Valley Transport Group

Address: The Motor House, 7 Granby Street, Bradford, West Yorkshire. BD4 7AN

Phone: 07957 630102

E-mail: avrg@avtg.co.uk

Website: www.avtg.co.uk

Brief description: The Aire Valley Transport Group was formed in the Spring of 2003 by a group of transport enthusiasts from other societies in the Aire Valley. The aim of the AVTG is to restore vehicles that are of historical importance back to their former glory, and put them on show to the public in order to educate them about the history of road transport. The group now has 70 vehicles in its care, making it one of the largest collections in the area. It also has a collection of road and enamel signs, traffic lights, petrol cans and pumps, and also a collection of bus memorabilia including ticket machines, enamel and cast signs, badges. The group is open to anyone with an interest in transport (with or without a vehicle).

Events planned in 2010:

15/16 May — 1940s Weekend, Haworth

10 October — Yorkshire Dales Running Day, Skipton

Opening days/times: By appointment

Charges: FREE

Registration	Date	Chassis make	Chassis model	Body make	Original operator	Fleet No	Status
KW 1961	1927	Leyland	Lion PLSC3	Leyland	Blythe & Berwick of Bradford		A
J 9567	1935	Morris Commercial	CS11/40	Willowbrook	Safety of Jersey	10	A
CTF 423	1938	Leyland	Tiger TS8	Roe	Lancashire United Transport	114	R
HLW 159	1946	AEC	Regent III O961 RT	Park Royal	London Transport	RT172	R
FWW 596	1947	Bedford	OB	Duple	West Yorkshire Road Car Co	646	R
GWT 630	1947	Albion	Valkyrie CX13	Burlingham	South Yorkshire Motors	61	R
HG 9651	1948	Leyland	Tiger PS1	Brush	Burnley Colne & Nelson	10	R
HOD 30	1948	Bristol	L6A	Beadle	Western National Omnibus Co (Royal Blue)	1228	R
GAM 216	1950	Bristol	L6B	Portsmouth Aviation	Wilts & Dorset Motor Services	297	A
LFM 767	1950	Bristol	LL6B	ECW	Crosville Motor Services	SLB186	RP
NHN 128	1951	Bristol	LL6B	ECW	United Automobile Services	BBE1	A
EHL 335	1952	Leyland	Tiger PS2/13A	Roe	West Riding Automobile Co	724	A
HKW 82	1952	AEC	Regent III 9613E	East Lancs	Bradford Corporation	82	R
LWR 424	1953	Bristol	KSW6G	ECW	West Yorkshire Road Car Co	4044	R
SVS 904	1954	Bristol	LS6G	ECW	Southern National Omnibus Co	1381	R
SYG 561	1957	Bedford	SBG	Duple	Walton & Helliwell of Mytholmroyd		A
DHD 177	1959	AEC	Regent V 2LD3RA	Metro-Cammell	Yorkshire Woollen District Transport Co	797	RP
GHD 215	1961	Ford	570E	Duple	Yorkshire Woollen District Transport Co	871	RP
574 CNW	1962	Daimler	CVG6	Roe	Leeds City Transport	574	A
BUF 267C	1965	Leyland	Titan PD3/4	Northern Counties	Southdown Motor Services	267	R
OWT 776M	1974	Bristol	RELL6G	ECW	West Yorkshire Road Car Co	1403	R
MUA 45P	1976	Bristol	LHS6L	ECW	West Yorkshire PTE	45	R
RWU 534R	1977	Leyland	Leopard PSU4D/4R	Plaxton	West Yorkshire PTE	8534	RP
B818 YKR	1985	Freight Rover	Sherpa	Dormobile	Dormobile		A

An historically significant vehicle in the Aire Valley Transport Group's collection is Lancashire United 114 (CTF 423), a dual-purpose 1938 Roe-bodied Leyland Tiger TS8, seen here as it might have looked during World War 2. PHILIP LAMB

Above: **The Aire Valley Transport Group is varied, but mainly features vehicles built before 1960, such as the ensemble featured here. From left to right we see former West Yorkshire Road Car Bristol KSW6G LWR 424, now converted into a recovery vehicle, Burlingham-bodied Albion Valkyrie South Yorkshire 61 (GWT 630), Western National Bristol L6A/Beadle 1224 (HOD 30) in Royal Blue livery and West Yorkshire Bedford OB/Duple CP1 (FWW 596).** PHILIP LAMB

Left: **This former Southdown Northern Counties-bodied Leyland PD3/4, now with the Aire Valley Transport Group, spent sometime with coaching giant Wallace Arnold, with which it was converted to open-top.**
PHILIP LAMB

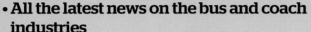

Registration	Date	Chassis make	Chassis model	Body make	Original operator	Fleet No	Status
OT 8283	1928	Dennis	E	(chassis only)	Aldershot & District Traction Co	D210	A
OT 8592	1928	Dennis	E	Strachan & Brown	Aldershot & District Traction Co	D217	A
OT 8898	1928	Dennis	E	Strachan & Brown	Aldershot & District Traction Co	D226	A
OT 8902	1928	Dennis	E	Dennis	Aldershot & District Traction Co	D235	A
BOT 303	1937	Dennis	Lancet II	(chassis only)	Aldershot & District Traction Co	709	A
GAA 580	1948	Dennis	Lancet III	Strachans	Aldershot & District Traction Co	944	A
GAA 616	1948	Dennis	Lancet III	Strachans	Aldershot & District Traction Co	980	RP
GOU 845	1950	Dennis	Lance K3	East Lancs	Aldershot & District Traction Co	145	R
HOU 904	1950	Dennis	Lancet J10	Strachans	Aldershot & District Traction Co	178	R
LAA 231	1953	Dennis	Lancet J10C	Strachans	Aldershot & District Traction Co	196	RP
LOU 48	1954	Dennis	Lance K4	East Lancs	Aldershot & District Traction Co	220	R
MOR 581	1954	AEC	Reliance MU3RV	MCW	Aldershot & District Traction Co	543	R
POR 428	1956	Dennis	Falcon P5	Strachans	Aldershot & District Traction Co	282	R
SOU 456	1958	Dennis	Loline	East Lancs	Aldershot & District Traction Co	348	RP
SOU 465	1958	Dennis	Loline	East Lancs	Aldershot & District Traction Co	357	R
XHO 370	1960	AEC	Reliance 2MU3RV	Weymann	Aldershot & District Traction Co	370	R
462 EOT	1962	Dennis	Loline III	Alexander	Aldershot & District Traction Co	462	RP
488 KOT	1964	Dennis	Loline III	Weymann	Aldershot & District Traction Co	488	R
AAA 503C	1965	Dennis	Loline III	Weymann	Aldershot & District Traction Co	503	R
AAA 506C	1965	Dennis	Loline III	Weymann	Aldershot & District Traction Co	506	R
AAA 508C	1965	Dennis	Loline III	Weymann	Aldershot & District Traction Co	508	RP
CCG 296K	1971	Bristol	RESL6G	ECW	Aldershot & District Traction Co	651	RP
KCG 627L	1973	Leyland	National 1151/1R/0402	Leyland National	Alder Valley	127	R

Aldershot & District Bus Interest Group

Contact address: 111 Park Barn Drive, Guildford, Surrey. GU2 6ER

E-mail: billtutty@ntlworld.com

Website: www.adbig.co.uk

Brief description: The group was formed in 1994 to consolidate the collection of preserved ex-Aldershot & District vehicles and other related artefacts that had been saved over the years, and to provide a focal point for individuals with an interest in every aspect of the old Aldershot & District Traction Co Ltd. The vehicles, all of which remain in private ownership, range from 1920s Dennis E-types through to Dennis, AEC and Bristol buses which entered service with A&D in the 1950s, 1960s and 1970s at the very end of the company's existence. The group works closely with the Dennis Bus Owners Association.

Events planned in 2010:

30 May — Farnham Running day

Other information: Monthly meetings, regular outings and events using the preserved buses. Regular working parties. New members always welcome

The Aldershot & District Bus Interest Group exhibited a number of its vehicles at the 2009 Tilford Rally and Running Day. A pair of Weymann-bodied Dennis Loline IIIs, 488 (488 KOT) of 1964 and 1965-built 503 (AAA 503C), bask in the May sunshine alongside 1954 AEC Reliance 543 (MOR 581), rebodied by Metro-Cammell in 1967. DAVID JUKES

Angus Transport Group

Address: Unit 5, Bridgend, Bridge Street, Montrose, Angus. DD10 8AJ

Contact address: Mr A. D. J. Greenan, Secretary, 7 Woodlands Ave, Noranside by Forfar. DD8 3RD

Phone: 01307 650304

E-mail: agreenan@angustransportgroup.co.uk

Website: www.angustransportgroup.co.uk

Brief description: A small collection of road transport vehicles with (on the whole) links to Scotland.

Events planned in 2010

25 July, 1/8 August — The Basin Rambler, a free bus service linking Montrose High Street and railway station with local tourist attractions on the following dates — full details on our website.

12/13 June, 10/11 July, 17/18 July, 28/29 August — Day Out with Thomas™ free bus service. Full details on website www.caledonianrailway.com.

Opening days/times: By prior arrangement.

Registration	Date	Chassis make	Chassis model	Body make	Original operator	Fleet No	Status
XSA 620	1963	AEC	Reliance 2MU3RA	Plaxton	Burnett of Mintlaw	7	R
EWG 22L	1973	Leyland	Leopard PSU3/3R	Alexander	W. Alexander & Sons (Midland)	MPE152	RP
JSA 102V	1980	Leyland	Leopard PSU3F/4R	Alexander	Northern Scottish	NPE102B	R
RRM 634X	1982	Leyland	Leopard PSU3G/4R	ECW	National Cumberland Motor Services	634	R
XSS 43Y	1982	Leyland	Leopard PSU3G/4R	Alexander	W. Alexander & Sons (Northern)	NPE43	RP
B97 PKS	1985	MCW	Metrobus DR102/47	Alexander	W. Alexander & Sons (Midland)	MRM97	A
E640 BRS	1987	Leyland	TRCTL11/3RH	Alexander	Northern Scottish	NCT40M	RP

Directions by car: From the south: A92 into Montrose, across the bridge over the River Southesk, pass the Shell filling station, just after filling station take the next left sign posted Hospital and the garage is at the bottom of the road on the left.

From the north. A92 south, sign posted Arbroath, towards the southern end of the town look out for sign post Hospital (Shell filling station on the right) and then turn right.

Directions by public transport: Stagecoach Strathtay 30, 39 and 47. Montrose railway station is 800 metres away, the 47 stops at the Railway station, and the 30 and 39 in the High Street, a 5-minute walk from the station.

Charges: None but donations may be made.

The Angus Transport Group, based in Montrose, includes this fine Plaxton Highway-bodied AEC Reliance, new to Burnett of Mintlaw, and later AC145 in the Alexander (Northern) fleet.
ANGUS TRANSPORT GROUP

Aycliffe & District Bus Preservation Society

Contact address: c/o 35 Lowther Drive, Newton Aycliffe, Co Durham. DL5 4UL

Phone: 01325 317657

E-mail: ianwiggett@uwclub.net

Website: www.aycliffebus.org.uk

Brief description: A working collection of five North East buses and a tow truck

Events planned in 2010: Please refer to website

Registration	Date	Chassis make	Chassis model	Body make	Original operator	Fleet No	Status
FHN 923	1940	Bristol	K5G		United Automobile Services	BDO23	A
GHN 189	1942	Bristol	K5G	ECW	United Automobile Services	BGL29	R
LHN 860	1950	Bristol	L5G	ECW	United Automobile Services	BG413	R
304 GHN	1958	Bristol	LS6B	ECW	United Automobile Services	BUC4	RP
AHN 451B	1964	Daimler	CCG5	Roe	Darlington Corporation	7	R
NDL 769G	1969	Bristol	LHS6L	Marshall	Southern Vectis Omnibus Co	833	R

Opening days/times: Please refer to website

Directions by car: Telephone for details

Directions by public transport: Telephone for details

Facilities: Limited but available

Former United Automobile Services 1950 Eastern Coach Works-bodied Bristol L5G BG413 (LHN 860), part of the Aycliffe & District Bus Preservation Society collection, was a frequent visitor to 'Aidensfield' — home to the television programme 'Heartbeat' which featured the Bristol in a number of episodes.
PHILIP LAMB

Registration	Date	Chassis make	Chassis model	Body make	Original operator	Fleet No	Status
EO 9051	1949	Leyland	Titan PD2/3	Park Royal	Barrow in Furness Corporation	124	A
EO 9177	1950	Leyland	Titan PD2/3	Roe	Barrow in Furness Corporation	147	A
CEO 956	1958	Leyland	Titan PD2/40	Park Royal	Barrow in Furness Corporation	169	RP
CEO 957	1958	Leyland	Titan PD2/40	Park Royal	Barrow in Furness Corporation	170	R
BLV 755A	1963	Leyland	Leopard L1	East Lancs	Barrow in Furness Corporation	72	RP
SEO 209M	1974	Leyland	National 11351/1R	Leyland National	Barrow in Furness Corporation	9	RP
CEO 720W	1981	Leyland	National 2 NL116L11/1R	Leyland National	Barrow Borough Transport	20	RP
CEO 723W	1981	Leyland	National 2 NL116L11/1R	Leyland National	Barrow Borough Transport	23	RP
LEO 734Y	1983	Leyland	Atlantean AN68D/1R	Northern Counties	Barrow Borough Transport	104	R
VIL 8730	1988	Talbot	Pullman	Talbot	Barrow Borough Transport	100	RP
G571 BHP	1990	Talbot	Pullman	Talbot	Charity use in Coventry		R

Barrow Transport Museum Trust Ltd

Contact: 2 Greengate Lane, Kendal, Cumbria. LA9 5LQ
Phone: 07970 549889
E-mail: dave.caton@talktalk.net
Brief description: The group has a collection of vehicles previously operated by Barrow-in-Furness Corporation. The aim of the group being to establish a museum of transport history relating to the Furness and South Cumbria area in its own accessible premises.
Directions by car: Please contact for details

Bolton Bus Group

Contact address: 69 Hereford Road, Heaton, Bolton. BL1 4NU

Brief description: A small group of enthusiasts formed to preserve examples of Bolton's buses. Some of the vehicles are displayed at Bury Transport Museum.

Registration	Date	Chassis make	Chassis model	Body make	Original operator	Fleet No	Status
NBN 436	1959	Leyland	Titan PD3/4	East Lancs	Bolton Corporation	128	RP
UBN 902	1962	Leyland	Titan PD3A/2	East Lancs	Bolton Corporation	169	RP
UWH 185	1963	Leyland	Atlantean PDR1/1	East Lancs	Bolton Corporation	185	R
FBN 232C	1965	Leyland	Atlantean PDR1/1	East Lancs	Bolton Corporation	232	R
KUS 607E	1967	Leyland	Atlantean PDR1/1	Alexander	Glasgow Corporation	LA352	RP
TWH 807K	1971	Leyland	Atlantean PDR2/1	East Lancs	SELNEC PTE	6807	A
TWH 809K	1971	Leyland	Atlantean PDR2/1	East Lancs	SELNEC PTE	6809	RP

Bounty Country Buses

E-mail: gerald@emerton.org.uk

Brief description: A carefully assembled and unique collection of country buses, representing the great number of independent operators which established a network of country bus services from the 1920s through to the most profitable years of the 1940s and 1950s and beyond. A tribute to their pioneering spirit of taking the country to the town and the town to the countryside, put together by the Emerton family of Nantwich, Cheshire.

Opening days/times: Viewing by prior arrangement only

Registration	Date	Chassis make	Chassis model	Body make	Original operator	Fleet No	Status
EC 8852	1929	Vulcan	Duchess	Vulcan	Fawcett of Milnthorpe	7	R
WX 2658	1929	Dennis	30cwt	Short	Jackson of Westgate on Sea		R
AG 6470	1931	Reo	FB	Emcol	Liddell of Auchinleck		R
ABH 358	1933	Leyland	Cub KP3	Duple	Oborne of Aylesbury		R
WP 6114	1934	Commer	Centaur B40	Carmichael	Burnhams of Worcester		R
HL 7538	1936	Leyland	Cub KPZ2/1	Roe	West Riding Automobile Co	464	R
ETA 280	1937	Dennis	Ace	Dennis	Hydro Hotel Torquay		R
DDM 652	1947	Maudslay	Marathon II	Duple	Rhyl United Coachways	4	R
GDL 33	1949	Crossley	SD42/7	Whitson	Nash of Ventnor		R
JP 7538	1949	Crossley	SD42/7	Duple	Liptrot of Bamfurlong		R
KTB 672	1949	Crossley	SD42/7	Burlingham	Warburton of Bury		RP
HUY 655	1950	Bedford	OB	Duple	Ketley of Stourport		RP
NKR 529	1950	Crossley	SD42/7	Brockhouse	Molins Saunderton		R
HDM 473	1951	Bedford	SB1	Duple	Owen (Rhyl United)		A
SVA 438	1958	Bedford	C5Z1	Duple Midland	Hutchison of Overtown		RP
TEC 599N	1974	AEC	Reliance 6MU4R	Plaxton	Jackson of Kirkby Stephen		R

Left: The Bounty Country Buses collection includes JP 7538, an immaculate 1949 Crossley SD42/7 with 1955 Duple bodywork. PHILIP LAMB

Right: ABH 358 is a 1933 Leyland Cub KP3 with Duple 20-seat coach body, which started its operating life in Aylesbury, and is Gerald Emerton's latest restoration for the Bounty Country Buses collection. GERALD EMERTON

Registration	Date	Chassis make	Chassis model	Body make	Original operator	Fleet No	Status
RU 2266	1925	Shelvoke & Drewry	Tramocar	(chassis only)	Bournemouth Corporation	9	A
LJ 500	1929	Karrier	WL6/1	Hall Lewis	Bournemouth Corporation	33	RP
VH 6217	1934	AEC	Regent 661	Lee Motors	Huddersfield Corporation	120	R
DKY 711	1944	Karrier	W	East Lancs (1960)	Bradford Corporation	711	A
DKY 712	1944	Karrier	W	East Lancs (1960)	Bradford Corporation	712	A
FRU 224	1944	Guy	Arab II		Bournemouth Corporation	40	A
JLJ 403	1949	Leyland	Tiger PS2/3	Burlingham	Bournemouth Corporation	46	R
KEL 110	1949	Leyland	Titan PD2/3	Weymann	Bournemouth Corporation	110	R
NNU 234	1949	BUT	9611T	Weymann	Nottinghamshire & Derbyshire Traction Co	353	RP
KEL 133	1950	Leyland	Titan PD2/3	Weymann	Bournemouth Corporation	247	R
KLJ 346	1950	BUT	9641T	Weymann	Bournemouth Corporation	212	R
NLJ 268	1953	Leyland	Royal Tiger PSU1/13	Burlingham	Bournemouth Corporation	258	R
NLJ 272	1953	Leyland	Royal Tiger PSU1/13	Burlingham	Bournemouth Corporation	262	R
RRU 904	1955	Leyland	Tiger Cub PSUC1/1	Park Royal	Bournemouth Corporation	267	R
YLJ 147	1959	Leyland	Titan PD3/1	Weymann	Bournemouth Corporation	147	R
8154 EL	1960	Leyland	Titan PD3/1	Weymann	Bournemouth Corporation	154	R
8156 EL	1960	Leyland	Titan PD3/1	Weymann	Bournemouth Corporation	156	R
297 LJ	1962	Sunbeam	MF2B	Weymann	Bournemouth Corporation	297	R
6167 RU	1963	Leyland	Titan PD3A/1	Weymann	Bournemouth Corporation	167	R
AEL 170B	1964	Leyland	Atlantean PDR1/1	Weymann	Bournemouth Corporation	170	R
ALJ 340B	1964	Daimler	Fleetline CRG6LX	M H Cars	Bournemouth Corporation	40	R
CRU 103C	1965	Leyland	Leopard PSU3/2R	Weymann	Bournemouth Corporation	103	R
CRU 180C	1965	Daimler	Fleetline CRG6LX	Weymann	Bournemouth Corporation	180	R
CRU 197C	1965	Daimler	Fleetline CRG6LX	Weymann	Bournemouth Corporation	197	R
KRU 55F	1967	Daimler	Roadliner SRC6	Willowbrook	Bournemouth Corporation	55	R
ORU 230G	1969	Leyland	Atlantean PDR1A/1	Alexander	Bournemouth Corporation	230	R
XRU 277K	1972	Leyland	Atlantean PDR1A/1	Alexander	Bournemouth Corporation	277	RP
DLJ 116L	1973	Daimler	Fleetline CRL6	Alexander	Bournemouth Corporation	116	R
FEL 105L	1973	Leyland	Leopard PSU3B/4R	Plaxton	Bournemouth Corporation	105	RP

Bournemouth Heritage Transport Collection

Phone: 01202 621581

Brief description: The collection comprises vehicles mainly from Bournmouth Corporation or the Bournemouth area that were built between 1928 and 1980. Most are owned by the Bournemouth Passenger Transport Association Ltd, which is registered charity.

Events planned in 2010: Please see the enthusist press for details

Opening days/times: Owing to storage relocation, the collection is not currently open to the public.

Former Bournemouth Corporation Burlingham-bodied Leyland Tiger 46 (JLJ 403) has long been part of the Bournemouth Heritage Transport Collection. It is one of a trio built in 1949 for Bournemouth, all of which survive in preservation, and is seen on Southsea seafront. PHILIP LAMB

Bristol Omnibus Vehicle Collection

Contact address: c/o Combe Barton, High Street, Dinder, Wells, Somerset. BA5 3FL

Phone: 01749 673319

E-mail: drmichaelwalker@hotmail.com

Website: www.bristolbuses.co.uk

Brief description: A collection of former Bristol Omnibus/Bristol Tramways vehicles, artefacts and memorabilia Vehicles are not all housed under one roof and not available for public wiew. However, as many are roadworthy will attend the two Bristol rallies in May and August. Up to 17 were present at Brislington in 2009.

Registration	Date	Chassis make	Chassis model	Body make	Original operator	Fleet No	Status
HW 6634	1929	Bristol	B	Bristol Tramways	Bristol Tramways & Carriage Co	559	A
JHT 802	1946	Bristol	K6A	ECW	Bristol Tramways & Carriage Co	C3386	RP
KHW 630	1947	Leyland	Titan PD1	ECW	Bristol Tramways & Carriage Co	C4019	RP
LHY 976	1949	Bristol	L5G	ECW	Bristol Tramways & Carriage Co	C2736	R
MHU 49	1949	Bedford	OB	Duple	Bristol Tramways	207	A
MHU 193	1949	Bedford	OB	Mulliner	Clifton College Bristol		R
NAE 3	1950	Bristol	L6B	ECW	Bristol Tramways & Carriage Co (Greyhound)	2467	R
NHU 2	1950	Bristol	LSX5G	ECW	Bristol Tramways & Carriage Co	2800	R
NHY 947	1951	Bristol	LWL6B	ECW	Bristol Tramways & Carriage Co (Greyhound)	2815	R
OHY 938	1952	Bristol	KSW6B	ECW	Bath Tramways Motor Co	L8089	R
UHY 360	1955	Bristol	KSW6B	ECW	Bristol Tramways & Carriage Co	C8320	R
UHY 384	1955	Bristol	KSW6G	ECW	Bristol Tramways & Carriage Co	8336	R
924 AHY	1958	Bristol	MW5G	ECW	Bristol Omnibus Co	2934	R
969 EHW	1959	Bristol	Lodekka LD6G	ECW	Bristol Omnibus Co	L8515	R
972 EHW	1959	Bristol	Lodekka LD6B	ECW	Bristol Omnibus Co	LC8518	RP
869 NHT	1961	Bristol	Lodekka FS6G	ECW	Bristol Omnibus Co	L8579	R
BHU 92C	1965	Bristol	MW6G	ECW	Bristol Omnibus Co (Greyhound)	2138	R
CHY 419C	1965	Bristol	Lodekka FLF6G	ECW	Bristol Omnibus Co	C7201	RP
FHU 59D	1966	Bristol	Lodekka FLF6B	ECW	Bristol Omnibus Co	C7246	R
FHW 156D	1966	Bristol	MW6G	ECW	Bristol Omnibus Co (Greyhound)	2150	R
OAE 954M	1973	Bristol	RELL6L	ECW	Bristol Omnibus Co	1332	R
AFB 592V	1980	Bristol	LH6L	ECW	Bristol Omnibus Co	461	R
A952 SAE	1983	Bristol	Olympian ONLXB/1R	Roe	Bristol Omnibus Co	9552	A
A954 SAE	1983	Bristol	Olympian ONLXB/1R	Roe	Bristol Omnibus Co	9554	R

Left: **NHU 2 is the prototype Bristol LSX5G built in 1950. It has been restored to original dual-door condition as Bristol Tramways No 2800 by the Bristol Omnibus Vehicle Collection.** PHILIP LAMB

Right: **Former Bristol Omnibus 1965 Bristol MW6G 2138 (BHU 92C) has been restored by the Bristol Omnibus Vehicle Collection to original Bristol Greyhound condition. The Eastern Coach Works body unusually consists of a bus shell fitted with a full coach interior.**
NIGEL APPLEFORD

Registration	Date	Chassis make	Chassis model	Body make	Original operator	Fleet No	Status
FAE 60	1938	Bristol	L5G		Bristol Omnibus Co	W75	A
JEL 257	1949	Bristol	K5G	ECW	Hants & Dorset Motor Services	1238	A
LHW 918	1949	Bristol	L5G	ECW	Bristol Tramways & Carriage Co	2410	RP
NFM 67	1952	Bristol	KSW6B	ECW	Crosville Motor Services	MW435	A
UHY 359	1955	Bristol	KSW6B	ECW	Bristol Tramways & Carriage Co	C8319	A
980 DAE	1959	Bristol	MW5G	ECW	Bristol Omnibus Co	2960	A
904 OFM	1960	Bristol	SC4LK	ECW	Crosville Motor Services	CSG655	R
507 OHU	1962	Bristol	Lodekka FLF6G	ECW	Bristol Omnibus Co	7062	RP
GYC 160K	1971	Bristol	LH6L	ECW	Hutchings & Cornelius Services of South Petherton		RP
HAX 399N	1975	Bristol	LHS6L	Duple	R I Davies & Son of Tredegar		RP
KHU 326P	1976	Bristol	LH6L	ECW	Bristol Omnibus Co	376	RP
KOU 791P	1976	Bristol	VRT/SL3/6LXB	ECW	Bristol Omnibus Co	5505	A
EWS 746W	1981	Bristol	VRT/SL3/0680	ECW	Bristol Omnibus Co	5538	RP
C416 AHT	1986	Ford	Transit	Carlyle	Bristol Omnibus Co	7416	A
C511 BFB	1986	Ford	Transit	Dormobile	Badgerline	4511	A

Bristol Road Transport Collection

Contact: c/o W. Staniforth, 'Green Bank', Windsoredge Lane, Nailsworth, Stroud, Glos. GL6 0NP

Phone: 07941 615 333

E-mail: william.staniforth@virgin.net

Website: www.bristolbusevents.co.uk

Brief description: Collection of mainly Bristol built buses and other vehicles with connections to the Bristol and Gloucestershire area.

Events planned in 2010:

16 May — Bristol Harbourside Rally and Running Day

Left: **An attractive vehicle in the Bristol Road Transport Collection is this former Crosville SC4LK restored in Crosville's black and cream coaching livery.** BRTC

Above: **Also owned by William Staniforth is this former Eastern National Bristol FLF6G, originally a double-deck coach, but subsequently converted by its owner for sea-front services.** BRTC

Bristol Vintage Bus Group

Contact address: 74 Ridgeway Lane, Whitchurch, Bristol. BS4 5JJ

Website: www.bvbg.org.uk

Brief description: The collection houses over 15 vehicles either built or operated in the Bristol area together with an extensive collection of artefacts and archives relating to the area and the Bristol commercial vehicle manufacturing organisation.

Events planned in 2010

28 March — BVBG Open Day at Flowers Hill

15 August — BVBG / Avon Valley Railway Open Day and Rally at Brislington Park & Ride

31 October — BVBG Open Day at Flowers Hill

Opening days/times: At any time by prior arrangement if someone is available. Archives available for study by prior appointment

Direction by car: Flowers Hill Road is of the A4 Bath Road, right on the City boundary near the Park & Ride

Directions by public transport: Main bus service to Bath from bus station and Temple Meads railway station stops near Flowers Hill

Charges: No admission charge for viewing or special events. Donations welcome

Facilities: B(e) D P R T

Registration	Date	Chassis make	Chassis model	Body make	Original operator	Fleet No	Status
AHU 803	1934	Bristol	J5G	Brislington Body Works	Bristol Tramways & Carriage Co	2355	R
GHT 154	1940	Bristol	K5G	ECW	Bristol Tramways & Carriage Co	C3336	R
GHT 127	1941	Bristol	K5G	ECW	Bristol Tramways & Carriage Co	C3315	R
FTT 704	1945	Bristol	K6A	ECW	Western National Omnibus Co	353	R
LAE 13	1948	Leyland	Titan PD1A	ECW	Bristol Tramways & Carriage Co	C4044	RP
EMW 284	1949	Bristol	L6B	Beadle	Wilts & Dorset Motor Services	279	R
JXC 323	1949	Leyland	Tiger PS1	Mann Egerton	London Transport	TD130	A
KLB 721	1950	AEC	Regent III O961 RT	Park Royal	London Transport	RT1599	R
KLJ 749	1950	Bristol	LL6G	Portsmouth Aviation	Hants & Dorset Motor Services	779	R
MOD 978	1952	Bristol	LS6G	ECW	Southern National Omnibus Co (Royal Blue)	1291	RP
YHY 80	1957	Bristol	LS6G	ECW	Bristol Omnibus Co	3004	RP
363 CLT	1962	AEC	Routemaster	Park Royal	London Transport	RM1363	R
CWN 629C	1965	Bristol	MW6G	ECW	United Welsh Services	134	A

Oldest vehicle in the Bristol Vintage Bus Group's collection is former Bristol Tramways 2355 (AHU 803), a 1934 Brislington Body Works-bodied Bristol J5G.
NIGEL APPLEFORD

Registration	Date	Chassis make	Chassis model	Body make	Original operator	Fleet No	Status
RD 7127	1935	AEC	Regent O661	Park Royal	Reading Corporation	47	R

Contact address: 2 Josephine Court, Southcote Road, Reading. RG30 2DG.

Phone: 0118 958 3974

E-mail: wiltshireman@aol.com

Website: www.britishtrolley.org.uk

British Trolleybus Society

Brief description: The British Trolleybus Society studies the development of the trolleybus and keeps up with current developments. It owns about a dozen trolleybuses, one motorbus and a horse-drawn tower wagon. It is affiliated to The Trolleybus Museum at Sandtoft.

Registration	Date	Chassis make	Chassis model	Body make	Original operator	Fleet No	Status
DKY 704	1945	Karrier	W	East Lancs	Bradford Corporation	704	A
EBO 919	1949	BUT	9641T	Bruce	Cardiff Corporation	262	RP
KBO 961	1955	BUT	9641T	East Lancs	Cardiff Corporation	243	RP
DHW 293K	1972	Bristol	LH6L	ECW	Bristol Omnibus Co	353	A

Cardiff & South Wales Trolleybus Project

Contact address: 211 Hillrise, Llanedeyrn, Cardiff. CF23 6UQ

Website: www.cardiff-trolleybus.co.uk

Brief description: The only trolleybus preservation group in the principality of Wales. A regular newsletter is issued, and new members are always welcome, presently £12.50 per annum. Visits to the workshop can be arranged by writing to the above address for details.

Former Bristol Omnibus Company 353 (DHW 293K), a 1972 Eastern Coach Works-bodied Bristol LH6L carries Thomas Bros livery — its last operator prior to preservation by members of the Cardiff & South Wales Trolleybus Project. NIGEL APPLEFORD

Cardiff Transport Preservation Group

Contact address: 10 Ger Nant, Ystrad Mynach, Hengoed. CF82 7FE

E-mail: mikeystrad73@btinternet.com

Website: www.ctpg.co.uk

Brief description: The CTPG is based at the former Western Welsh depot in Barry, the group is run entirely by volunteers and is always looking for more help with looking after its growing collection of Welsh buses. The collection is not regularly open to the public, but viewing can be arranged via the address above.

Events planned in 2010

6 June — Barry Island

5 September — Merthyr Tydfil

The Cardiff Transport Preservation Group collection includes former Jones of Aberbeeg 98 (889 AAX), a 1961 Weymann bodied Leyland Tiger Cub PSUC1/3.
PHILIP LAMB

Registration	Date	Chassis make	Chassis model	Body make	Original operator	Fleet No	Status
HWO 323	1950	Leyland	Tiger PS1/1	Lydney	Red & White Services	C350	R
LNY 903	1951	Leyland	Titan PD2/12	Leyland	Caerphilly Corporation	3	A
LKG 678	1956	AEC	Regent V MD3RV	Park Royal	Western Welsh Omnibus Co	678	A
964 DTJ	1958	Leyland	Tiger Cub PSU1/1	Weymann	Merthyr Tydfil UDC	100	R
TAX 235	1958	Bristol	Lodekka LD6G	ECW	Red & White Services	L358	R
XNY 416	1958	Guy	Arab LUF	Longwell Green	Aberdare UDC	14	A
TUH 13	1960	Albion	Nimbus NS3	Harrington	Western Welsh Omnibus Co	13	RP
889 AAX	1961	Leyland	Tiger Cub PSUC1/3	Weymann	Jones of Aberbeeg	98	R
XUH 368	1961	Leyland	Titan PD2A/30	Metro Cammell	Cardiff Corporation	368	A
408 DBO	1963	AEC	Regent V 2D3RA	East Lancs	Cardiff Corporation	408	RP
ABO 434B	1964	Guy	Arab V	East Lancs Neepsend	Cardiff Corporation	434	R
GNY 432C	1965	Leyland	Titan PD3/4	Massey	Caerphilly UDC	32	RP
EDV 505D	1966	Bristol	MW6G	ECW	Western National Omnibus Co (Royal Blue)	1423	R
EDW 68D	1966	Leyland	Atlantean PDR1/1	Alexander	Newport Corporation	68	R
KNY 495D	1966	AEC	Regent V 2MD3RA	Northern Counties	Rhondda Transport	495	R
JKG 497F	1968	Daimler	Fleetline CRG6	Park Royal	Cardiff Corporation	497	RP
MBO 512F	1968	AEC	Swift MP2R	Alexander	Cardiff Corporation	512	RP
PAX 466F	1968	Leyland	Titan PD3/4	Massey	Bedwas & Machen UDC	6	R
OUH 177G	1969	Leyland	Leopard PSU3A/4R	Plaxton	Western Welsh Omnibus Co	177	RP
PKG 532H	1969	Daimler	Fleetline CRG6LX	Willowbrook	Cardiff Corporation	532	A
UTG 313G	1969	AEC	Regent V 2MD3RA	Willowbrook	Pontypridd UDC	8	RP
TKG 518J	1971	Leyland	Leopard PSU4A/2R	Willowbrook	Western Welsh Omnibus Co	1518	A
WUH 585K	1972	Daimler	Fleetline CRL6	MCW	Cardiff Corporation	585	RP
NNY 817L	1973	Bedford	YRT	Plaxton	Davies of Pen y Graig		RP
GHB 148N	1974	Bristol	RESL6L	ECW	Cynon Valley	15	R
PKG 587M	1974	Bristol	VRT/SL6G	ECW	Cardiff Corporation	587	A
LUH 105P	1976	Bristol	LHS6L	ECW	Cardiff Corporation	105	RP
OJD 45R	1976	Bristol	LH6L	ECW	London Transport	BL45	A
NDW 407X	1982	Volvo Ailsa	B55-10	Northern Counties	Cardiff Corporation	407	A
C42 CKG	1986	Leyland	Tiger TRCTL11	East Lancs	Islwyn Borough Transport	42	A
C101 HKG	1986	Ford	Transit 190	Robin Hood	National Welsh Omnibus Services	1	RP
G258 HUH	1990	Leyland	Lynx LX2R11C15Z4R	Leyland	Cardiff City Transport	258	A
N143 PTG	1996	Optare	Metrorider	Optare	Cardiff City Transport	143	A
P164 TNY	1996	Mercedes	711D	Plaxton	Rhondda Buses Ltd	164	A

Registration	Date	Chassis make	Chassis model	Body make	Original operator	Fleet No	Status
VV 5696	1937	Bristol	JO5G	ECW	United Counties Omnibus Co	450	R
MPU 21	1948	Bristol	K6B	ECW	Eastern National Omnibus Co	3960	RP
KFM 766	1949	Bristol	L5G	ECW	Crosville Motor Services	KG117	A
FRP 692	1950	Bristol	KS5G	ECW	United Counties Omnibus Co	692	R
FRP 828	1950	Bristol	LL5G	ECW	United Counties Omnibus Co	828	A
ONO 995	1950	Bristol	LL5G	ECW	Eastern National Omnibus Co	4081	RP
CNH 860	1952	Bristol	LWL6B	ECW	United Counties Omnibus Co	426	R
CNH 862	1952	Bristol	LWL6B	ECW	United Counties Omnibus Co	428	R
HWV 294	1952	Bristol	KSW5G	ECW	Wilts & Dorset Motor Services	365	A
KNV 337	1954	Bristol	KSW6B	ECW	United Counties Omnibus Co	964	R
RFU 689	1958	Bristol	SC4LK	ECW	Lincolnshire Road Car Co	2611	R
HAH 537L	1972	Bristol	LH6P	ECW	Eastern Counties Omnibus Co	LH537	R

Chelveston Preservation Group

Contact address: 9 Station Road, Hampton in Arden, Solihull, West Midlands. B92 0BJ

Brief description: A private collection owned by a few members has evolved to represent most types of Bristol chassis from a range of former Tilling Group companies.

Registration	Date	Chassis make	Chassis model	Body make	Original operator	Fleet No	Status
OJO 727	1950	AEC	Regal III 9621A	Willowbrook	City of Oxford Motor Services	727	RP
191 AWL	1956	AEC	Regent V MD3RV	Weymann	City of Oxford Motor Services	L191	R
975 CWL	1958	AEC	Regent V LD3RA	Park Royal	City of Oxford Motor Services	H975	RP
312 MFC	1961	AEC	Bridgemaster 2B3RA	Park Royal	City of Oxford Motor Services	312	R
332 RJO	1963	AEC	Renown 3B3RA	Park Royal	City of Oxford Motor Services	332	RP
OFC 902H	1970	Bristol	VRTSL2/6LX	ECW	City of Oxford Motor Services	902	RP
AUD 310J	1971	Leyland	Leopard PSU3B/4R	Plaxton	O A Slatter & Sons of Long Hanborough	40	A
TJO 56K	1971	AEC	Reliance 6MU4R	Marshall	City of Oxford Motor Services	56	A
YWL 134K	1972	Leyland	Leopard PSU3B/4R	Plaxton	R Jarvis & Sons of Middle Barton		A
NUD 105L	1973	Bristol	VRTSL2/6LX	ECW	City of Oxford Motor Services	105	RP
RBW 87M	1974	Bristol	RELH6L	ECW	City of Oxford Motor Services	87	A
PWL 999W	1980	Leyland	Olympian B45 ONTL11/2R	Alexander	Leyland (prototype)	OBC999	A
VJO 201X	1982	Leyland	Olympian ONLXB/1R	ECW	City of Oxford Motor Services	201	RP
VUD 30X	1982	Leyland	Leopard PSU3G/4R	ECW	City of Oxford Motor Services	30	RP
C729 JJO	1986	Ford	Transit 190D	Carlyle	City of Oxford Motor Services	729	RP

Cherwell Bus Preservation Group

Contact address: 32 Mill Street, Kidlington. OX5 2EF

Brief description: A collection of mainly ex-City of Oxford vehicles housed undercover.

Events planned: The operational vehicles will attend a few events during the rally season.

This pair of former City of Oxford Motor Services Leyland Olympians are part of the Cherwell Bus Preservation Group collection. No 201 (VJO 201X) was new to COMS in 1982 and carries Eastern Coach Works dual-door bodywork. 999 (PWL 999W) is a 1980 Alexander-bodied Leyland prototype, originally operated by Singapore Bus Services. It was acquired by COMS in 1987 and fitted with an ECW dash panel. PHILIP LAMB

City of Portsmouth Preserved Transport Depot

Contact address: Friends of CPPTD, Jasmine Cottage, Dodds Lane, Swanmore, Southampton. SO32 2PX

Email address: friendschairman@cpptd.co.uk

Website address: www.cpptd.co.uk

Brief description: A collection comprising a range of veteran and vintage buses, most of which spent their working lives in the South of England. Vehicles are housed in premises near Portsmouth that are presently not open to the public (please see the website or enthusiast press for latest developments). The collection's vehicles operate free bus services, and attend running days, rallies, carnivals and other events.

Registration	Date	Chassis make	Chassis model	Body make	Original operator	Fleet No	Status
Unregistered	1876	Horse bus			G Wheeler of Fawley		RP
RV 4649	1934	AEC	661T	English Electric	Portsmouth Corporation	201	RP
RV 6367	1935	Leyland	Titan TD4	English Electric	Portsmouth Corporation	7	RP
CTP 200	1944	Bedford	OWB	Duple (replica)	Portsmouth Corporation	170	RP
DTP 823	1947	Leyland	Titan PD1	Weymann	Portsmouth Corporation	189	RP
EHV 65	1951	Bedford	OB	Duple	East Ham Borough Council		R
AHC 442	1951	AEC	Regent III 9613A	Bruce	Eastbourne Corporation	42	R
LRV 996	1956	Leyland	Titan PD2/12	Metro Cammell	Portsmouth Corporation	4	R
ORV 989	1958	Leyland	Titan PD2/40	Metro Cammell	Portsmouth Corporation	112	R
BBK 236B	1964	Leyland	Atlantean PDR1/1	Metro Cammell	Portsmouth Corporation	236	R
BTR 361B	1964	AEC	Regent V 2D3RA	East Lancs Neepsend	Southampton Corporation	361	R
GTP 175F	1967	Leyland	Panther Cub PSURC1	MCW	Portsmouth Corporation	175	A
TBK 190K	1971	Leyland	Atlantean PDR2/1	Pennine	Portsmouth Corporation	190	RP
K916 VDV	1994	Iveco	59-12	Mellor	Blue Admiral of Portsmouth	2040	A

Colin Billington Collection

Phone: 07990 505373

E-mail: royal_blue@lineone.net

Brief description: A private collection of vehicles, formerly operated by the Western and Southern National Omnibus Companies, their predecessors and successors, spanning the years 1927 to 1985, many of which have undergone extensive restoration. A particular feature is a collection of Royal Blue coaches which can be regularly seen recreating bygone coach travel to the West Country along the old coach routes.

Events planned in 2010:

2-4 July — Royal Blue coach run Stevenage to Minehead

18 September — Kingsbridge 7ft 6in Vintage Bus Running Day

Vehicles regularly attend rallies and running days

Registration	Date	Chassis make	Chassis model	Body make	Original operator	Fleet No	Status
VW 203	1927	Leyland	Lion PLSC3	Mumford	National Omnibus & Transport Co	2407	RP
YF 714	1927	Guy	FBB	Vickers	Great Western Railway	1268	RP
RU 8805	1929	AEC	Reliance	Beadle	Elliot Bros Royal Blue		A
FJ 8967	1933	Bristol	H	Brislington Body Works	Western National Omnibus Co	137	R
BTA 59	1934	Dennis	Mace	Eastern Counties	Southern National Omnibus Co	668	R
FTA 634	1941	Bristol	K5G	ECW	Western National Omnibus Co	345	RP
JUO 983	1948	Bristol	LL6B	ECW	Southern National Omnibus Co	1218	RP
LTA 748	1950	Bedford	OB	Duple	Southern National Omnibus Co (Royal Blue)	1409	RP
LTA 946	1950	Bristol	KS6B	ECW	Southern National Omnibus Co	1836	RP
LTA 729	1951	Bristol	LL6B	Duple	Western National Omnibus Co (Royal Blue)	1250	R
MOD 973	1952	Bristol	LS6G	ECW	Southern National Omnibus Co (Royal Blue)	1286	RP
OTT 85	1954	Bristol	LS6G	ECW	Southern National Omnibus Co	1376	RP
RTT 996	1954	Bristol	Lodekka LD6B	ECW	Southern National Omnibus Co	1876	A
519 BTA	1960	Bristol	Lodekka FS6G	ECW	Western National Omnibus Co	1967	A
672 COD	1960	Bristol	SUS4A	ECW	Western National Omnibus Co	600	R
468 FTT	1960	Bristol	Lodekka FLF6G	ECW	Western National Omnibus Co	1969	R
JVS 293	1961	Bristol	MW6G	ECW	Western National Omnibus Co	2266	A
286 KTA	1962	Bristol	SUL4A	ECW	Southern National Omnibus Co	1234	R

Registration	Date	Chassis make	Chassis model	Body make	Original operator	Fleet No	Status
BOD 25C	1965	Bristol	Lodekka FLF6B	ECW	Southern National Omnibus Co	2065	RP
EDV 555D	1966	Bristol	SUL4A	ECW	Southern National Omnibus Co	692	RP
HDV 624E	1967	Bristol	RELH6G	ECW	Western National Omnibus Co (Royal Blue)	2365	R
MOD 823P	1976	Leyland	National 11351A/1R	Leyland National	Western National Omnibus Co	2823	R
AFJ 708T	1978	Leyland	National 11351A/1R	Leyland National	Western National Omnibus Co	2869	R
AFJ 729T	1979	Bristol	LH6L	Plaxton	Western National Omnibus Co	3309	A
FDV 790V	1979	Bristol	LHS6L	ECW	Western National Omnibus Co	1560	R
FDV 803V	1980	Leyland	Leopard PSU3E/4R	Plaxton	Western National Omnibus Co	3547	R
LFJ 847W	1980	Bristol	VRT/SL3/6LXB	ECW	Western National Omnibus Co	1203	RP
A686 KDV	1983	Bristol	Olympian ONLXB/1R	ECW	Devon General Ltd	1814	R
C862 DYD	1985	Ford	Transit 190D	Dormobile	Southern National Ltd	300	R

Opening days/times: View by prior arrangements only

Charges: Donations welcome

Facilities: A B(e) E P R T

Other information: Affiliations NARTM, Thames Valley & Great Western Omnibus Trust, WHOTT

The latest restoration by Colin Billington is FJ 8967, a former Western National 1933 Bristol H6G with 1942 Brislington Bus Works bodywork. NIGEL APPLEFORD

County Durham Bus Preservation Group

Contact: 17 Ringlet Close, Rosewood Park, Gateshead, Tyne and Wear. NE11 9NF

Phone: 07966 155987

E-mail: enquiries.cdbpg@hotmail.co.uk

Website: www.cdbpg.fotopic.net

Brief description: The County Durham Bus Preservation Group consists of a number of vehicle owners collectively maintaining a building storing over 20 buses and coaches. The collection is the largest under one roof in the North East of England and includes unique restored examples from the 1940s to the 1980s.

Below: **Away from its normal territory, but close to where it was built, ex-Northern Metrobus 5307 UTN 501Y is seen in Birmingham city centre on a free service between Aston Manor Transport Museum and the city centre on Sunday 14 March 2010 as part of an event organised by the museum to commemorate the withdrawal of Metrobuses from regular service.**
DAVID GAMBLES

Registration	Date	Chassis make	Chassis model	Body make	Original operator	Fleet No	Status
BTN 113	1934	Daimler	COS4	Northern Coachbuilders	Newcastle Corporation	173	A
HHN 202	1947	Bristol	L5G	ECW	Bells of Westerhope	DB216	R
HUP 236	1948	Albion	Valiant CX39N	ACB	Economic Bus Services of Whitburn	W7	R
LVK 123	1948	Leyland	Titan PD2/1	Leyland	Newcastle Corporation	123	A
NVK 341	1950	AEC	Regent III 9612A	Northern Coachbuilders	Newcastle Corporation	341	R
344 XUK	1954	AEC	Reliance MU3RV	Roe	Roe Demonstrator		R
TUP 859	1956	AEC	Regent V MD3RV	Roe	Hartlepool Corporation	4	RP
YPT 796	1958	AEC	Reliance MU3RV	Roe	Economic Bus Services of Whitburn	W3	R
780 HUP	1960	AEC	Reliance 2MU3RV	Park Royal	Venture of Consett	215	A
221 JVK	1962	Leyland	Atlantean PDR1/1	Alexander	Newcastle Corporation	221	R
EUP 405B	1964	AEC	Routemaster 3R2RH	Park Royal	Northern General Transport Co	2105	R
FBR 53D	1966	Leyland	Panther PSUR1/1R	Strachan	Sunderland Corporation	53	R
VOD 101K	1971	Bristol	RELL6G	ECW	Western National Omnibus Co	2758	RP
ETY 91L	1972	Daimler	Fleetline CRL6	ECW	Tyneside Omnibus	91L	A
GBB 524K	1972	Leyland	Atlantean PDR2/1	Alexander	Tyne & Wear PTE	688	RP
GGR 103N	1974	Leyland	Atlantean AN68/2R	Northern Counties	OK Motor Services		RP
VPT 598R	1977	Leyland	National 11351A/1R	Leyland National	Northern General Transport Co	4598	RP
JPT 901T	1978	Bristol	VRT/SL3/501	ECW	Northern General Transport Co	3401	R
JPT 906T	1979	Bristol	VRT/SL3/501	ECW	Northern General Transport Co	3406	RP
SGR 935V	1979	Bristol	VRT/SL3/501	ECW	Northern General Transport Co	3435	RP
SPT 963V	1980	Leyland	Leopard PSU3E/4R	Plaxton	OK Motor Services		RP
AUP 369W	1980	Leyland	Atlantean AN68B/1R	Roe	Northern General Transport Co	3469	RP
ANA 564Y	1982	Leyland	Atlantean AN68D/1R	Northern Counties	Greater Manchester PTE	8564	
UTN 501Y	1983	MCW	Metrobus DR102/37	MCW	Northern General Transport Co	3501	RP
B207 GNL	1985	Ford	Transit	Alexander	Northern General Transport Co	207	A
C771 OCN	1986	MCW	Metrobus DR102/55	MCW	Northern General Transport Co	3771	A

Left: **Newcastle Corporation's yellow and cream livery is shown to best advantage by its former No 221 (221 JVK), a 1962 Alexander-bodied Leyland Atlantean, part of the County Durham Bus Preservation Group's collection.** PHILIP LAMB

Registration	Date	Chassis make	Chassis model	Body make	Original operator	Fleet No	Status
GNF 10V	1979	Leyland	Titan TNLXB/1R	Park Royal	Greater Manchester PTE	4010	R
UWW 7X	1982	Leyland	Olympian ONLXB/1R	Roe	West Yorkshire PTE	5007	R
B11 CTB	1982	Leyland	Olympian ONTL11/1R	ECW	Leyland (development vehicle)	102	R
D5 CTB	1985	Leyland	Olympian ONTL11/2Rsp	ECW	Leyland (demonstrator)	105	R
E48 TYG	1987	Leyland	Royal Tiger Doyen	Leyland	West Riding Automobile Co	48	R
J139 YRM	1991	Leyland	Olympian ON2R50C13Z4	Leyland	Capital Citybus	139	A
ET 778	1991	Leyland	Olympian ON3R49C18Z4	Alexander	Citybus Hong Kong	152	RP

Dave Rogers Collection

E-mail: citybusdave@aol.com

Brief description: Located near Swindon, the collection represents a passion for Leyland buses and coaches of the 1980s and for vehicles from Hong Kong.

Registration	Date	Chassis make	Chassis model	Body make	Original operator	Fleet No	Status
CC 8671	1929	Dennis	GL	Roberts	Llandudno UDC	2	R
MJ 4549	1932	Dennis	Lancet I	Short	Smith of Westoning		R
TJ 836	1933	Dennis	Dart	Duple	Entwhistle of Morecambe		R
DL 9015	1934	Dennis	Ace	Harrington	Southern Vectis Omnibus Co	405	RP
YD 9533	1934	Dennis	Ace	Dennis	Southern National Omnibus Co	3560	R
JA 5506	1935	Dennis	Lancet I	Eastern Counties	North Western Road Car Co	706	RP
JG 8720	1937	Dennis	Lancet II	Park Royal	East Kent Road Car Co		R
FUF 181	1939	Dennis	Falcon	Harrington	Southdown Motor Services	81	A
CFN 154	1948	Dennis	Lancet III	Park Royal	East Kent Road Car Co		R
CFN 121	1949	Dennis	Lancet III	Park Royal	East Kent Road Car Co		R
EFN 568	1950	Dennis	Falcon P3	Dennis	East Kent Road Car Co		R
EFN 584	1950	Dennis	Lancet III	Park Royal	East Kent Road Car Co		A
JDC 599	1958	Dennis	Loline	Northern Counties	Middlesbrough Corporation	99	R
RDB 872	1964	Dennis	Loline III	Alexander	North Western Road Car Co	872	RP
GRD 576D	1966	Dennis	Loline III	East Lancs	Reading Corporation	76	R
EBB 846W	1980	Dennis	Dominator SD	Angloco	Tyne & Wear Metropolitan Fire Brigade	A07	R
C41 HDT	1985	Dennis	Domino SDA	Optare	South Yorkshire PTE	41	RP
C877 JWE	1985	Dennis	Dominator DDA	Alexander	South Yorkshire PTE	2877	RP
Unregistered	1989	Dennis	Dart 9SDL	Duple	Duple Test Vehicle		A
L116 YVK	1994	Dennis	Dart Mk 2	Northern Counties	Arriva London	DRN116	R

Dennis Bus Owners Association

E:mail: secretary@dennisbusowners.co.uk

Website: www.dennisbusowners.co.uk

Brief description: The association is the focal point for owners and enthusiasts offering advice and information to assist in the preservation and restoration of buses built by Dennis Bros of Guilford. The vehicles listed are some of those which are preserved. Other Dennis vehicles are listed in the collections of the Aldershot & District Bus Interest Group, Amberley Working Museum, Bounty Country Buses, Buckland Omnibus Co, Cobham Bus Museum, Dover Transport Museum, East Kent Road Car Heritage Trust, Leicester Corporation Bus Preservation Group, Oxford Bus Museum, SELNEC collection, the TH Collection, the Trolleybus Museum at Sandtoft and others. Membership is open to all Dennis bus owners and others interested in the make.

The Dennis Bus Owners' Association collection includes this immaculate former East Kent Road Car Company CFN 154, a 1948 Dennis Lancet III bodied by Park Royal. PHILIP LAMB

Devon General Society

Contact address: 23 Barrack Road, Exeter. EX2 5ED

Phone: 07850 165686

Website address: www.devongeneral.org.uk

Brief description: The Devon General Society was formed in 1982 to promote interest in the former Devon General company and its successors, also to stimulate the preservation of all aspects of the company's past for the benefit of future generations. Approximately 35 former Devon General vehicles are currently preserved privately by society members. The society actively assists them and regularly stages events in Devon, where these vehicles can be enjoyed.

Events planned in 2010: Please see website

Devon General Omnibus & Touring Company DR661 (NTT 661), a 1952 Weymann bodied AEC Regent III, is one of many privately owned vehicles once in this fleet whose continued preservation is actively supported by the Devon General Society.
PHILIP LAMB

Registration	Date	Chassis make	Chassis model	Body make	Original operator	Fleet No	Status
OD 7497	1934	AEC	Regent O661	Short	Devon General	DR210	R
ETT 995	1937	AEC	Regent O661 rebuild	Saunders Roe	Devon General	DR705	RP
HTT 487	1946	AEC	Regal I O662	Weymann	Devon General	SR487	R
KOD 585	1949	AEC	Regent III 9612E	Weymann	Devon General	DR585	R
LTA 629	1950	AEC	Regal III 9621A	Duple	Devon General (Grey Cars)	TCR629	R
NTT 661	1952	AEC	Regent III 9613A	Weymann	Devon General	DR661	R
NTT 679	1952	AEC	Regent III 9613S	Weymann	Devon General	DR679	R
DDV 446	1953	AEC	Regent III	Weymann	Devon General	DR716	A
ROD 765	1956	AEC	Regent V MD3RV	Metro Cammell	Devon General	DRD765	R
UFJ 296	1957	Guy	Arab IV	Park Royal	Exeter City Transport	56	R
VDV 798	1957	AEC	Reliance MU3RA	Weymann	Devon General	SR798	RP
VDV 817	1957	AEC	Regent V MD3RV	Metro Cammell	Devon General	DR817	R
VDV 818	1957	AEC	Regent V MD3RV	Metro Cammell	Devon General	DR818	R
XTA 839	1958	Albion	Nimbus NS3N	Willowbrook	Devon General	SN839	R
XUO 721	1958	Bristol	MW6G	ECW	Western National Omnibus Co (Royal Blue)	2238	R
872 ATA	1959	Leyland	Atlantean PDR1/1	Metro Cammell	Devon General	DL872	A
913 DTT	1960	Leyland	Atlantean PDR1/1	Roe	Devon General	DL913	R
928 GTA	1961	Leyland	Atlantean PDR1/1	Metro Cammell	Devon General	DL928	RP
931 GTA	1961	Leyland	Atlantean PDR1/1	Metro Cammell	Devon General	DL931	R
932 GTA	1961	Leyland	Atlantean PDR1/1	Metro Cammell	Devon General	DL932	R
935 GTA	1961	AEC	Reliance 2MU3RV	Willowbrook	Devon General (Grey Cars)	TCR935	R
MSJ 499	1961	Leyland	Atlantean PDR1/1	Metro Cammell	Devon General	DL925	R
ABV 669A	1961	Leyland	Atlantean PDR1/1	Metro Cammell	Devon General	DL927	RP
960 HTT	1962	AEC	Reliance 2MU3RV	Willowbrook	Devon General (Grey Cars)	TCR960	R
1 RDV	1964	AEC	Reliance 2MU3RA	Harrington	Devon General (Grey Cars)	1	R
4 RDV	1964	AEC	Reliance 2MU3RA	Harrington	Devon General (Grey Cars)	4	A
9 RDV	1964	AEC	Reliance 2MU3RA	Marshall	Devon General	9	R
503 RUO	1964	AEC	Regent V 2D3RA	Willowbrook	Devon General	503	RP
CTT 23C	1965	AEC	Reliance 2MU3RA	Park Royal	Devon General	23	R
CTT 513C	1965	AEC	Regent V 2D3RA	Park Royal	Devon General	513	R
CTT 518C	1965	AEC	Regent V 2MD3RA	Willowbrook	Devon General	518	R
EOD 524D	1966	AEC	Regent V 2D3RA	MCW	Devon General	524	R
NDV 537G	1968	Leyland	Atlantean PDR1/2	MCW	Devon General	537	R
TUO 74J	1970	AEC	Reliance 6MU3R	Willowbrook	Devon General	74	R
VOD 542K	1971	Bristol	VRT/SL2/6LX	ECW	Western National Omnibus Co	542	A
VOD 545K	1971	Bristol	VRT/SL2/6LX	ECW	Western National Omnibus Co (Devon General)	545	RP

VOD 550K	1971	Bristol	VRT/SL2/6LX	ECW	Western National Omnibus Co (Devon General)	550	RP
VOD 88K	1972	Bristol	LHS6L	Marshall	Western National Omnibus Co (Devon General)	88	R
ATA 563L	1973	Bristol	VRT/SL2/6LX	ECW	Western National Omnibus Co (Devon General)	563	R
VDV 123S	1978	Bristol	VRT/SL3/6LXB	ECW	Western National Omnibus Co (Devon General)	584	A
A680 KDV	1983	Bristol	Olympian ONLXB/1R	ECW	Devon General Ltd	1804	R
C526 FFJ	1986	Ford	Transit 190D	Carlyle	Devon General Ltd (Bayline)	526	R
C760 FFJ	1986	Ford	Transit 190D	Carlyle	Devon General Ltd	760	R

Memories of summers past are brought to life by this 1964 7ft 6in-wide Harrington Grenadier-bodied AEC Reliance, originally Devon General (Grey Cars) No 1 — another immaculately restored vehicle supported by the Devon General Society. PHILIP LAMB

Dewsbury Bus Museum

Address: Foundry Street, Ravensthorpe, near Dewsbury. WF13 3HW

Contact address: PO Box 297, Dewsbury WF13 9AZ

Phone:: 0844 504 0085

Fax: 0844 504 0085

Email: admin@dewsburybusmuseum.co.uk

Website: www.dewsburybusmuseum.co.uk

Brief description: The Museum houses around 15 buses and coaches from the West Riding area, and is actively engaged in restoration. Members' meetings are held monthly. Vehicles are rallied at various events.

Events planned in 2010:

14 March — Open Day. A free shuttle service will operate from Dewsbury bus station

23 May — Arriva Tour. Tour of all five Arriva-Yorkshire depots, raising funds for Sick Children's Trust. Organised by one of our members, supported by one of our vehicles

14 November — Open Day. A free shuttle service will operate from Dewsbury bus station

Opening days/times: Open Days only. Visits at other times can be made by prior arrangement

Charges: £1 all classes on Open Days.

Directions by car: From M62 (west), junction 25 follow A644 to North Road (Netto store). From M62 (east), junction 28 follow A653 to Dewsbury Ring Road, then A644 to North Road. From M1, junction 40 follow A638 to Dewsbury Ring Road, then A644 to North Road.

Directions by public transport: Arriva 202, 203, 253, 262, 278.

Huddersfield Bus Co. 262. Longstaff's 205 (not Sundays)

All of these services stop outside the Museum

Facilities: Level access. Toilet facilities in adjacent public house.

The Dewsbury Bus Museum collection includes former Todmorden Joint Omnibus Committee 9 (NWW 89E), a 1967 Willowbrook-bodied Leyland Leopard L1. PHILIP LAMB

Registration	Date	Chassis make	Chassis model	Body make	Original operator	Fleet No	Status
CCX 801	1945	Guy	Arab II	Roe	County Motors of Lepton	70	A
BHL 682	1948	Leyland	Titan PD2/1	Leyland	West Riding Automobile Co	640	RP
TWY 8	1950	Albion	CX39N	Roe	South Yorkshire Motors	81	RP
EHL 344	1952	Leyland	Tiger PS2/12A	Roe	West Riding Automobile Co	733	R
JHL 708	1956	AEC	Reliance MU3RV	Roe	West Riding Automobile Co	808	RP
LEN 101	1960	Guy	Wulfrunian	(chassis only)	Bury Corporation	101	A
UCX 275	1961	Guy	Wulfrunian	Roe	County Motors of Lepton	99	RP
PJX 35	1962	Leyland	Leopard L1	Weymann	Halifax Corporation	35	R
WHL 970	1963	Guy	Wulfrunian	Roe	West Riding Automobile Co	970	RP
CUV 208C	1965	AEC	Routemaster R2RH	Park Royal	London Transport	RM2208	R
JJD 524D	1966	AEC	Routemaster R2RH1	Park Royal	London Transport	RML2524	RP
NWW 89E	1967	Leyland	Leopard L1	Willowbrook	Todmorden Joint Omnibus Committee	9	R
LHL 164F	1967	Leyland	Panther PSUR1/1	Roe	West Riding Automobile Co	164	R
MCK 229J	1971	Leyland	Panther PSUR1B/1R	Pennine	Preston Corporation	229	RP
WEX 685M	1973	AEC	Swift 3MP2R	ECW	Great Yarmouth Corporation	85	R
XUA 73X	1982	Leyland	National 2 NL116AL11/1R	Leyland National	West Riding Automobile Co	73	RP
D901 MWR	1987	Volkswagen	LT55	Optare	Yorkshire Rider	1700	R

Registration	Date	Chassis make	Chassis model	Body make	Original operator	Fleet No	Status
CJG 959	1947	Leyland	Titan PD1A	Leyland	East Kent Road Car Co		A
EFN 592	1950	Dennis	Lancet III	Park Royal	East Kent Road Car Co		R
FFN 399	1951	Guy	Arab III	Park Royal	East Kent Road Car Co		R
MLL 570	1951	AEC	Regal IV 9821LT RF	Metro Cammell	London Transport	RF183	RP
GFN 273	1952	Leyland	Titan TD5	Beadle	East Kent Road Car Co		R
KFN 239	1955	AEC	Reliance MU3RV	Weymann	East Kent Road Car Co		RP
MFN 898	1956	Guy	Arab IV	Park Royal	East Kent Road Car Co		RP
PFN 867	1959	AEC	Regent V 2LD3RA	Park Royal	East Kent Road Car Co		R
6801 FN	1961	AEC	Regent V 2D3RA	Park Royal	East Kent Road Car Co		R
YJG 807	1962	AEC	Bridgemaster 2B3RA	Park Royal	East Kent Road Car Co		R
AFN 780B	1963	AEC	Regent V 2D3RA	Park Royal	East Kent Road Car Co		R
AFN 488B	1964	AEC	Reliance 2MU4RA	Duple	East Kent Road Car Co		RP
DJG 619C	1965	AEC	Reliance 2U3RA	Park Royal	East Kent Road Car Co		A
OFN 721F	1968	AEC	Reliance 6U3ZR	Marshall	East Kent Road Car Co		R
VJG 187J	1970	AEC	Swift 5P2R	Marshall	East Kent Road Car Co		R
EFN 178L	1973	Leyland	National 1151/1R/2402	Leyland National	East Kent Road Car Co		R
NFN 84R	1977	Leyland	National 11351A/1R	Leyland National	East Kent Road Car Co	1084	RP
RVB 977S	1978	Bristol	VRT/SL3/6LXB	Willowbrook	East Kent Road Car Co	7977	R
TFN 980T	1978	Bristol	VRT/SL3/6LXB	Willowbrook	East Kent Road Car Co	7980	R
SKL 681X	1981	Bristol	VRT/SL3/6LXB	ECW	East Kent Road Car Co	7681	R

East Kent Road Car Heritage Trust

Contact address: 33 Alfred Road, Dover, Kent. CT162AD

Phone: 01304 204612

E-mail: colinsmith1950@aol.com

Brief description: The Trust exists to collect together and preserve for future generations, all items pertaining to the former East Kent Road Car Co. from tickets to vehicles. While suitable premises are sought, the vehicles are shown to the public at outside events where our travelling museum can also be found.

Above: **Canterbury bus station plays host to a pair of former East Kent Road Car Company vehicles that are part of the East Kent Road Car Heritage Trust collection. 1963 Park Royal bodied AEC Regent V AFN 780B is about to be passed by 1952 Leyland-Beadle GFN 273.** PHILIP LAMB

Left: **The East Kent Road Car Heritage Trust has two Willowbrook-bodied Bristol VRTSL3/6LXBs including now open-topped RVB 977S, originally No 7977 in the East Kent fleet.** DAVID JUKES

Eastern Transport Collection Society

Attleborough

Contact address: The Chairman, 78 Park Road, Spixworth, Norwich. NR10 3PJ

Phone: 01603 891284

E-mail: richard.dixon@easterntransportcollection.org.uk

Website address: www.easterntransportcollection.org.uk

Brief description: The Society owns six ex-Eastern Counties buses, the earliest dates from 1950. Other members' vehicles are also stored on site. A small museum area houses bus and railway memorabilia. Meetings held monthly in Norwich and there are also working parties on the vehicles.

Events planned in 2010:

5 September — Norwich Bus Rally (sponsored by Konectbus of Dereham) at the Norfolk Gala Day, Norfolk Showground, Easton, Norwich. Approx 50 vehicles attend, plus stalls and vehicle rides

Opening days/times: By prior arrangement

Charges: Donations welcome, but entry fee for Norwich Bus Rally

Registration	Date	Chassis make	Chassis model	Body make	Original operator	Fleet No	Status
KNG 718	1950	Bristol	LL5G	ECW	Eastern Counties Omnibus Co	LL718	R
NAH 941	1952	Bristol	KSW5G	ECW	Eastern Counties Omnibus Co	LKH341	RP
MXX 481	1953	AEC	Regal IV 9821LT	Metro Cammell	London Transport	RF504	R
OVF 229	1954	Bristol	Lodekka LD5G	ECW	Eastern Counties Omnibus Co	LKD229	R
KDB 696	1957	Leyland	Tiger Cub PSUC1/1	Weymann	North Western Road Car Co	696	R
5789 AH	1959	Bristol	MW5G	ECW	Eastern Counties Omnibus Co	LS789	R
675 OCV	1962	Bedford	SB3	Duple	Crimson Tours		R
M00 177	1962	Bristol	MW6G	ECW	Eastern National Omnibus Co	556	RP
KVF 658E	1967	Bristol	RESL6G	ECW	Eastern Counties Omnibus Co	RS658	R
PBJ 2F	1967	Leyland	Titan PD2/47	Massey	Lowestoft Corporation	12	RP
OCK 988K	1972	Bristol	VRTSL2/6G	ECW	Ribble Motor Services	BT988	RP
RRM 148M	1974	Leyland	National 1151/1R/2308	Leyland National	Leyland Demonstrator		R
NAH 135P	1976	Bristol	VRT/SL3/501	ECW	Eastern Counties Omnibus Co	VR172	RP
RGS 598R	1976	Bedford	YMT	Duple	Tricentrol Coaches Ltd		RP
CVF 31T	1986	Bristol	VRT/SL3/6LXB	ECW	Great Yarmouth Corporation	31	RP
H74 ANG	1990	Dennis	Condor DDA1810	Duple Metsec	China Motor Bus	DM17	R

Ensign Bus Museum

Contact address: Ensignbus, Jubilee Close, Purfleet. RM15 4YF

Phone: 01708 865656

E-mail: info@ensign-museum.com

Website: www.ensignbus.com

Brief description: The collection is bsed on ex-London types, the emphasis being to keep vehicles in Class 6 MoT condition, enabling regular operation on heritage services and private hire. A number of buses have been successfully repatriated from overseas and Ensign continues to seek rare or unusal ex-London types.'

Registration	Date	Chassis make	Chassis model	Body make	Original operator	Fleet No	Status
ED 6141	1930	Leyland	Titan TD1	Massey	Warrington Corporation	22	A
KR 1728	1930	Leyland	Titan TD1	Short	Maidstone & District Motor Services	321	A
KJ 2578	1931	Leyland	Titan TD1	Weymann	Redcar Motor Services of Tunbridge Wells		A
KR 8385	1931	Leyland	Tiger TS2	Burlingham	Maidstone & District Motor Services	665	A
BXD 628	1935	Leyland	Cub KP03	Short	London Transport	C4	RP
DLU 92	1937	AEC	Regent 0661	LPTB	London Transport	STL2093	A
ELP 223	1938	AEC	Regal 0662	LPTB	London Transport	T499	RP
FXT 183	1940	AEC	Regent III 0661 RT	LPTB	London Transport	RT8	RP
HLJ 44	1948	Bristol	K6A	ECW	Hants & Dorset Motor Services	TD895	R
JXC 432	1948	AEC	Regent III 0961 RT	Weymann	London Transport	RT624	R
JXC 194	1949	AEC	Regent III 0961 RT	Cravens	London Transport	RT1431	R
JXN 370	1949	Leyland	Titan 7RT	Park Royal	London Transport	RTL47	RP

Registration	Date	Chassis make	Chassis model	Body make	Original operator	Fleet No	Status
KGK 758	1949	AEC	Regent III 0961 RT	Cravens	London Transport	RT1499	R
KXW 435	1949	Leyland	Titan 6RT	Leyland	London Transport	RTW335	RP
KGK 708	1950	AEC	Regent III 0961 RT	Saunders Roe	Londom Transport	RT1239	A
KYY 961	1950	AEC	Regent III 0961 RT	Weymann	London Transport	RT3232	R
839 XUJ	1951	Leyland	Tiger PS1/1	Guerseybus	Jersey Motor Transport Co	49	R
840 XUJ	1951	Leyland	Tiger PS1/1	Guerseybus	Jersey Motor Transport Co	44	R
MXX 261	1952	AEC	Regent III 9613E	Weymann	London Transport	RLH61	R
MLL 735	1953	AEC	Regal IV 9822E	Park Royal	British European Airways		A
NXP 775	1954	AEC	Regent III 0961 RT	Weymann	London Transport	RT4421	R
5280 NW	1959	Leyland	Titan PD3/5	Roe	Leeds City Transport	280	R
VLT 25	1959	AEC	Routemaster	Park Royal	London Transport	RM25	R
WLT 371	1959	AEC	Routemaster	Park Royal	London Transport	RM371	R
WLT 882	1961	AEC	Routemaster	Park Royal	London Transport	RML882	R
LDS 279A	1959	AEC	Routemaster	Park Royal	London Transport	RM54	R
485 CLT	1962	AEC	Routemaster	Park Royal	London Transport	RMC1485	R
VYJ 808	1962	AEC	Routemaster	Park Royal	London Transport	RM1361	R
CRU 184C	1965	Daimler	Fleetline CRG6LX	Weymann	Bournemouth Corporation	184	A
CUV 220C	1965	AEC	Routemaster	Park Royal	London Country Bus Services	RCL2220	R
KTJ 204C	1965	Leyland	PD2	East Lancs	Lancaster Corporation	204	R
CUV 226C	1966	AEC	Routemaster	Park Royal	London Transport	RCL2226	RP
JJD 405D	1966	AEC	Routemaster	Park Royal	London Transport	RML2405	R
NMY 634E	1967	AEC	Routemaster	Park Royal	British European Airways	8241	R
EGP 33J	1970	Daimler	Fleetline CRG6LXB	Park Royal	London Transport	DMS33	R
THX 101S	1978	MCW	Metrobus DR101/3	MCW	London Transport	M1	R
THX 646S	1978	Leyland	Fleetline FE30ALR B20	Park Royal	London Transport	DMS2646	R
A249 SVW	1983	Leyland	Tiger TRCTL11/3RP	Duple	Southend Transport	249	A
A250 SVW	1983	Leyland	Tiger TRCTL11/3RP	Duple	Southend Transport	250	R
B115 ORU	1984	MCW	Metroliner DR130/3	MCW	Shamrock & Rambler	3115	A
F292 NHJ	1988	MCW	Metrobus DR102/71	MCW	Ensignbus	192	A

Top right: Ensign Bus Museum's former London Transport Green Line coach RMC 1485, a 1962 AEC Routemaster, wears the red and gold livery carried when operated by East London on its X15 service. DAVID JUKES

Right: The Ensign Bus Museum collection includes former London Transport RT3232 (KYY 961), a 1950 Weymann-bodied AEC Regent III 0961. The bus is seen operating a heritage service through Romford. DAVID JUKES

Friends of King Alfred Buses

Contact address: 40 Norbury Close, Chandlers Ford, Eastleigh. SO53 1PZ

Phone: 023 8026 7084

E-mail: info@fokab.org.uk

Website: www.fokab.org.uk

Brief description: FoKAB was founded in 1985 to assist James Freeman in the preservation of two KAMS buses that he had purchased — 104 and 591 (since scrapped). Since then further ex-KAMS buses have been rescued, including two repatriated from the USA. FoKAB became a registered charity in 2001 and has nearly 300 members. It maintains nine buses and two coaches in roadworthy condition and is currently restoring 708, the rare 1950 Leyland Olympic.

Events planned in 2011:

1 January 2011 — Winchester Buses Running Day.

Other information: FoKAB welcomes groups to view its maintenance facility at Winchester by prior arrangement.

Registration	Date	Chassis make	Chassis model	Body make	Original operator	Fleet No	Status
OU 9286	1931	Dennis	30cwt	Short	King Alfred Motor Services		R
JAA 708	1950	Leyland	Olympic HR40	Weymann	King Alfred Motor Services		RP
POU 494	1956	Leyland	Titan PD2/24	East Lancs	King Alfred Motor Services		R
WCG 104	1959	Leyland	Tiger Cub PSUC1/1	Weymann	King Alfred Motor Services		R
326 CAA	1961	Bedford	SB3	Harrington	King Alfred Motor Services		R
595 LCG	1964	AEC	Renown 3B2RA	Park Royal	King Alfred Motor Services		R
596 LCG	1964	AEC	Renown 3B2RA	Park Royal	King Alfred Motor Services		R
BHO 543C	1965	Bedford	CAL230	Martin Walker	Richmond of Epsom		A
CCG 704C	1965	Bedford	VAL14	Plaxton	King Alfred Motor Services		R
HOR 590E	1967	Leyland	Atlantean PDR1/2	Roe	King Alfred Motor Services		R
HOR 592E	1967	Leyland	Atlantean PDR1/2	Roe	King Alfred Motor Services		R
UOU 417H	1970	Leyland	Panther PSUR1A/1R	Plaxton	King Alfred Motor Services		R
UOU 419H	1970	Leyland	Panther PSUR1A/1R	Plaxton	King Alfred Motor Services		R
NKJ 849P	1976	Commer	Karrier KC6055	Rootes	Enham Village Disabled Transport		R

Glasgow Vintage Vehicle Trust

Museum Address: Bridgeton Bus Garage, 76 Fordneuk Street, Glasgow. G40 3AH

Contact address: Chairman, Iain Macgregor, 19 Poplar Avenue, Bishopton PA7 5AD

Phone: 0141 554 0544

E-mail: info@gvvt.org

Website: www.gvvt.org

Brief description: Around 100 buses and coaches, a few commercials and one tram — dating from pre-World War 2 to 1980s; mostly, but not exclusively, from Scottish fleets.

Registration	Date	Chassis make	Chassis model	Body make	Original operator	Fleet No	Status
ES 5150	1922	Albion	C20	Harvey	Tighanloan Hotel at Fearnan		R
WG 2373	1934	Leyland	Lion LT5B	Burlingham	W Alexander & Sons	P169	R
WG 4445	1937	Leyland	Tiger TS7	Alexander	Alexander	P331	A
BUS 181	1938	AEC	Regent O661	Scottish Commercial	Glasgow Corporation	AR292	R
CRG 811	1947	Daimler	CVD6	Alexander	Aberdeen Corporation	11	A
CRS 834	1948	Daimler	CVD6	Walker / Aberdeen CT	Aberdeen Corporation	14	A
GUS 926	1949	Maudslay	Marathon III	Park Royal	MacBrayne	136	R
CHL 772	1950	Daimler	CVD6	Willowbrook	Bullock of Featherstone		R
FVA 854	1950	Albion	Valiant CX39N	Duple	Hutchisons of Overtown		R
HGG 359	1950	Thornycroft	HF/ER4	Croft	MacBrayne	149	R
522 XUT	1953	Ford	ET7	Barbara	Malta		R
GM 6384	1954	Leyland	Titan PD2/10	Leyland	Central SMT Co	L484	R
6769	1955	Albion	Victor FT39AN	Heaver	Guernsey Railway Co	55	RP

Registration	Date	Chassis make	Chassis model	Body make	Original operator	Fleet No	Status
NSF 757	1956	Leyland	Titan PD2/20	Metro Cammell	Edinburgh Corporation	757	A
KAG 856	1957	Leyland	Titan PD2/20	Alexander	Western SMT Co	D1375	A
YTS 916A	1957	AEC	Reliance MU3RV	Alexander	Alexander	AC102	A
JPA 82V	1957	Albion	Victor FT39KAN	Heaver	Guernsey Motor Co	72	RP
FYS 999	1958	Daimler	CVD6-30	Alexander	Glasgow Corporation	D217	R
SGD 65	1958	Leyland	Titan PD2/24	Alexander	Glasgow Corporation	L163	R
TVS 367	1958	Bristol	Lodekka LD6G	ECW	Central SMT Co	B87	A
FYS 8	1959	Leyland	Titan PD2/24	Glasgow Corporation	Glasgow Corporation	L108	R
MSD 407	1959	Leyland	Titan PD3/3	Alexander	Western SMT Co	D1543	R
MSD 408	1959	Leyland	Titan PD3/3	Alexander	Western SMT Co	D1544	R
NMS 358	1960	AEC	Reliance 2MU3RV	Alexander	Alexander	AC147	R
YYS 174	1960	Bedford	C5Z1	Duple	David MacBrayne of Glasgow	54	R
198 CUS	1961	AEC	Reliance 2MU3RA	Duple Midland	MacBrayne	63	R
RAG 400	1961	Bristol	Lodekka LD6G	ECW	Western SMT Co	B1634	A
SGD 448	1961	Leyland	Titan PD3/2	Alexander	Glasgow Corporation	L446	R
SGD 500	1961	AEC	Regent V 2D2RA	Alexander	Glasgow Corporation	A350	RP
EDS 288A	1961	AEC	Routemaster	Park Royal	London Transport	RM910	RP
BJX 848C	1965	Bedford	VAS1	Duple	Abbeyways of Halifax		A
CUV 121C	1965	AEC	Routemaster	Park Royal	London Transport	RM2121	R
DMS 348C	1965	Leyland	Leopard PSU3/3R	Alexander	Alexander (Midland)	MPE62	R
GYS 896D	1966	Leyland	Atlantean PDR1/1	Alexander	Glasgow Corporation	LA320	R
HGA 983D	1966	Bedford	VAS1	Willowbrook	David MacBrayne of Glasgow	210	R
GRS 334E	1967	Albion	Viking VK43AL	Alexander	Alexander (Northern)	NNV34	A
HFR 501E	1967	Leyland	Titan PD3A/1	MCW	Blackpool Corporation	501	R
JMS 452E	1967	Albion	Viking VK43AL	Alexander	Alexander (Midland)	MNV37	R
VMP 8G	1968	Albion	Viking VK43AL	Alexander	Road Transport Industry Training Board	16	RP
NDL 375G	1969	Bedford	VAM70	Duple	Paul of Ryde	12	R
NRG 26H	1969	AEC	Swift 2MP2R	Alexander	Aberdeen Corporation	26	A
VMP 10G	1969	AEC	Reliance 6U3ZR	Alexander	Road Transport Industry Training Board		R
XGA 15J	1970	Leyland	Atlantean PDR1A/1	Alexander	Glasgow Corporation	LA517	RP
WSD 756K	1972	Leyland	Leopard PSU3/3R	Alexander	Western SMT Co	L2366	R
XGM 450L	1972	Leyland	Leopard PSU3/3R	Alexander	Central SMT Co	T150	R
NMS 576M	1973	Leyland	Leopard PSU3/3R	Alexander	Alexander (Midland)	MPE176	A
CST 703N	1974	Ford	R1114	Alexander	Highland Omnibuses	T93	RP
SCS 335M	1974	Leyland	Leopard PSU3/3R	Alexander	Western SMT Co	L2466	R
VSB 164M	1974	Bedford	YRT	Plaxton	Craig West Coast Motors of Campbeltown		RP
JGA 189N	1975	Leyland	Atlantean AN68/1R	Alexander	Greater Glasgow PTE	LA907	R

Events planned in 2010:

3 May — Vintage Voyages to Tall Ships Event

27 June — West End Vintage Bus Service, West End of Glasgow

10 October — Annual Open Day, Bridgeton Bus Garage

Charges: Open Day: Adult £5, Concession £3, Family (2+2) £12.

Directions by car: From M74 Junction 2 west on London Road towards Bridgeton Cross.

Directions by public transport: First Glasgow 43 and 64 to road end, or 16, 18, 46 and 263 to Bridgeton Cross (short walk eastward). SPT Rail to Bridgeton (short walk eastward).

Facilities: B(e) D R(e) T

Former Blackpool Corporation 501 (HFR 501E), a 1967 MCW-bodied Leyland Titan PD3A/1, resides with the Glasgow Vintage Vehicle Trust. PHILIP LAMB

Above: **This attractive version of Kelvin Scottish's yellow and two-tone blue livery is carried by immaculate 1985 Alexander RL-bodied MCW Metrobus 1669 (B100 PKS), part of the Glasgow Vintage Vehicle Trust collection.** PHILIP LAMB

Below: **Seen inside the Glasgow Vintage Vehicle Trust's Bridgeton base are former W. Alexander & Sons (Fife) FPE 194 (RSC 194Y), a 1982 Alexander T-bodied Leyland Leopard, and ex-Paul's Tours of Ryde (Isle of Wight) 12 (NDL 375G), a 1969 Duple Viceroy-bodied Bedford VAM70.** PHILIP LAMB

Registration	Date	Chassis make	Chassis model	Body make	Original operator	Fleet No	Status
JUS 774N	1975	Leyland	Atlantean AN68/1R	Alexander	Greater Glasgow PTE	LA927	RP
MSF 122P	1975	Leyland	Leopard PSU3C/4R	Alexander	Lothian Region Transport	122	A
MSJ 385P	1976	Seddon	Pennine VII	Alexander	Western SMT Co	S2579	RP
OJD 903R	1977	Leyland	National 10351A/1R	Leyland National	London Transport	LS 103	R
RSD 973R	1977	Seddon	Pennine VII	Alexander	Western SMT Co	S2670	RP
SSN 248S	1977	Volvo Ailsa	B55-10	Alexander	Tayside Regional Council	248	RP
XUS 575S	1977	Leyland	Atlantean AN68A/1R	Alexander	Greater Glasgow PTE	LA1204	RP
EFS 229S	1978	Leyland	Leopard PSU3E/4R	Alexander	Lothian Region Transport	229	R
TSJ 47S	1978	Leyland	Leopard PSU3D/4R	Alexander	Western SMT Co	L2747	A
VHB 678S	1978	Bristol	VRT/SL3/501	ECW	National Welsh Omnibus Services	HR4378	A
EMS 362V	1980	Leyland	Leopard PSU3E/4R	Alexander	Alexander (Midland)	MPE362	R
FSL 615W	1980	Bedford	YMQ	Plaxton	Henderson Coaltown of Markinch		R
GCS 50V	1980	Leyland	Leopard PSU3E/4R	Alexander	Western SMT Co	L50	R
GSO 80V	1980	Leyland	Leopard PSU3E/4R	Alexander	Alexander (Northern)	NPE80	R
HSD 73V	1980	Leyland	Fleetline FE30AGR	Alexander	Western SMT Co	R73	R
HSD 86V	1980	Leyland	Fleetline FE30AGR	Alexander	Western SMT Co	R86	R
KSD 103W	1980	Volvo Ailsa	B55-10	Alexander	Western SMT Co	A103	RP
LMS 168W	1980	Leyland	Fleetline FE30AGR	Alexander	Alexander (Midland)	MRF168	R
UHG 141V	1980	Leyland	Atlantean AN68A/2R	Alexander	Preston Bus	141	R
RMS 400W	1981	Leyland	Leopard PSU3G/4R	Alexander	Alexander (Midland)	MPE400	R
SSA 5X	1981	Leyland	Olympian ONLXB/1R	Alexander	Alexander (Northern)	NL05	R
UGB 196W	1981	Leyland	Atlantean AN68A/1R	Alexander	Strathclyde Transport	LA1443	RP
FGE 423X	1982	Dennis	Dominator DD	Alexander	Central SMT Co	D23	RP
KYV 781X	1982	MCW	Metrobus DR101/14	MCW	London Transport	M781	R
TSO 16X	1982	Leyland	Olympian ONLXB/1R	ECW	Alexander (Northern)	NL016	R
FLD 447Y	1982	Bedford	YMP	Plaxton	Bonas of Coventry		RP
RSC 194Y	1982	Leyland	Leopard PSU3G/4R	Alexander	Alexander (Fife)	FPE194	R
ALS 102Y	1983	Leyland	Tiger TRBTL11/2R	Alexander	Alexander (Midland)	MPT102	A
MNS 10Y	1983	Leyland	Tiger TRBTL11/2R	Alexander	Central SMT Co	LT10	A
A735 PSU	1983	Volvo Ailsa	B55-10 Mk III	Alexander	Strathclyde PTE	A109	A
47638	1984	Ford	R1015	Wadham Stringer	Jersey Motor Transport Co	23	A
A25 VDS	1984	Leyland	Tiger TRBLXB/2RH	Alexander	Central SMT Co	LT25	A
B177 FFS	1985	Volvo	Citybus B10M-50	Alexander	Alexander (Fife)	977	A
B100 PKS	1985	MCW	Metrobus DR132/6	Alexander	Alexander (Midland)	MRM100	R
D902 CSH	1987	Leyland	Olympian ONTL11/1RH	Alexander	Lowland Scottish	902	A
E186 BNS	1988	MCW	Metrorider MF154/12	MCW	Strathclyde Buses	M89	R
G545 RDS	1990	Volvo	Citybus B10M-50	Alexander	Strathclyde Buses	AH101	A
G571 PNS	1990	Leyland	Roadrunner 9-13R	Wright	Strathclyde Regional Council	23189	R

Registration	Date	Chassis make	Chassis model	Body make	Original operator	Fleet No	Status
Unregistered	1922	Karrier		(unknown)	(unknown)		A
WT 9156	1925	Karrier	JH	Strachan & Brown	Premier Transport of Keighley		RP
DY 5029	1928	Karrier	JKL	London Lorries	A Timpson & Son of Catford	117	A
TE 5780	1928	Karrier	WL6	English Electric	Ashton-under-Lyne Corporation	8	RP
VH 2088	1929	Karrier	ZA	(unknown)			RP
RB 4757	1932	Commer	Centaur	Reeve & Kenning	H G Fox of Alfreton		R
JC 5313	1938	Guy	Wolf	Waveney	Llandudno UDC		R
14 PKR	1961	Karrier	BFD	Plaxton	W Davis & Sons of Sevenoaks		A

Golcar Transport Collection

Contact address: 45 Cowlersley Lane, Cowlersley, Huddersfield. HD4 5TZ

Phone: 01484 654133

Brief description: A unique collection of Karrier vehicles, most of which are long-term restoration projects. The collection includes a WL6 six-wheeled saloon with clerestory-roofed body built by English Electric.

Opening days/times; Collection opens to coincide with craft weekends at the Colne Valley Museum; can be opened at other times by prior arrangement.

Registration	Date	Chassis make	Chassis model	Body make	Original operator	Fleet No	Status
FOI 1629	1973	Bristol	LH6L	Alexander (Belfast)	Ulsterbus	1629	R
OSJ 620R	1977	Leyland	Leopard PSU3C/3R	Alexander (Falkirk)	Western SMT Co	1886	R
SOI 3591	1978	Leyland	Leopard PSU3A/4R	Alexander (Belfast)	Ulsterbus	1591	R
VOI 8415	1980	Bristol	RELL6G	Alexander (Belfast)	Belfast Citybus	2415	R
AXI 2259	1982	Leyland	Leopard PSU3E/4R	Wright	Ulsterbus	259	R
BXI 2583	1982	Bristol	RELL6G	Alexander (Belfast)	Ulsterbus	2583	R
BXI 339	1984	Leyland	Leopard PSU3F/4R	Alexander (Belfast)	Ulsterbus	339	R
DXI 3343	1984	Leyland	Tiger TRBTL11/2RP	Alexander (Belfast)	Ulsterbus	343	R

Irish Transport Trust

Contact address: 3, Donegal Drive, Whitehead, Co. Antrim, BT38 9LT

Website: www.ith.org.uk

Brief description: Formed in 1969, the trust provides for the preservation recording exchange on all aspects pertaining to road transport history current and future matters. A number of vehicles both pre-and postwar have been restored by Trust members and the Trust it self has eight vehicles from more time which are typical of those operated by Ulsterbus and Citybus over most of their existance. After a number of false starts the trust is currently in the process of obtaining both limited company and charitable status, leading to the ultimate ambition of establishing a museum dedicated to road passenger transport in Northern Ireland.

Events planned in 2010:

17 April — Annual Bus & Coach Rally at Cultra

The Irish Transport Trust's former Ulsterbus 1982 Alexander (Belfast)-bodied Leyland Leopard 339 (BXI 339) arrives at its 2007 event at Cultra.
PHILIP LAMB

John Shearman Collection

Phone: 01892 534067

E-mail: johnshearmanbuses@hotmail.com

Brief description: A private collection which includes vehicles representing traditional British double-deckers designed for export markets.

Opening days/times: Vehicles attend rallies every summer

Registration	Date	Chassis make	Chassis model	Body make	Original operator	Fleet No	Status
LEV 917	1946	Leyland	Titan PD1/1	Alexander	City Coach Company of Brentwood	LD1	R
KSV 102	1954	AEC	Regent III 9631E	Weymann	Carris of Lisbon	255	R
ABW 225D	1966	AEC	Regent V 2D2RA	Metal Sections	Kowloon Motor Bus	A165	R

Kelvin Amos Collection

Contact address: 30 Blandford Close, Nailsea, Bristol. BS48 2QQ

E-mail: ka92@blueyonder.co.uk

Brief description: The vehicles in the collection are regularly shown and run on free bus services.

Registration	Date	Chassis make	Chassis model	Body make	Original operator	Fleet No	Status
LHT 911	1948	Bristol	L5G	Brislington Body Works	Bristol Tramways	2388	R
KED 546F	1968	Leyland	Panther Cub PSURC1	East Lancs	Warrington Corporation	92	R
PWS 492S	1977	Leyland	Leopard PSU3E/4R	Plaxton	Bristol Omnibus Co	2098	R

Kent Heritage Bus Collection

Contact address: 6 Chelsfield House, Queen's Ave, Maidstone. ME16 OEP

Brief description: From its beginings in 1967, the main emphasis has been to secure for preservation a good cross-sction of the important passenger models constructed by Tilling-Stevens of Maidstone backed by a general archive of their activites. Local body builders, Short Bros of Rochester and Beadle of Dartford, are also represented. The early years of Maidstone & District Motor Services are another special inteest. To this end, rare examples operated by the company during its first 50 years (1911-61) have been secured.

Opening days/times: Viewing by prior arrangement only

Registration	Date	Chassis make	Chassis model	Body make	Original operator	Fleet No	Status
KL 7796	1925	Tilling Stevens	TS6 Petrol Electric	Short	Maidstone & District Motor Services	73	RP
DX 7657	1928	Tilling Stevens	B10B2 Express	(chassis only)	Eastern Counties Roadcar Co	P113	R
KO 7311	1928	Tilling Stevens	B9A Express	Short	Maidstone & District Motor Services	461	RP
JG 669	1930	Tilling Stevens	B10C2 Express	Brush	East Kent Road Car Co	669	R
JG 691	1930	Tilling Stevens	B10C2 Express	Brush	East Kent Road Car Co	691	A
OU 7951	1931	Tilling Stevens	B10A2 Express	(chassis only)	Aldershot & District Traction Co	TS15	A
LKT 991	1950	Bristol	L6A	ECW	Maidstone & District Motor Services	SO43	R

Registration	Date	Chassis make	Chassis model	Body make	Original operator	Fleet No	Status
6219 TF	1963	Guy	Arab IV	Northern Counties	Lancashire United Transport	135	RP
HTJ 522B	1964	Guy	Arab V	Northern Counties	Lancashire United Transport	167	R
EIB 8234	1970	Bristol	LH6L	Northern Counties	Lancashire United Transport	335	A
LTE 491P	1976	Leyland	Leopard PSU3C/4R	Plaxton	Lancashire United Transport	440	R
PTD 655S	1978	Leyland	Fleetline FE30GR	Northern Counties	Lancashire United Transport	511	R
TWH 689T	1978	Leyland	Leopard PSU3E/4R	Plaxton	Lancashire United Transport	541	A
124 YTW	1980	Volvo	B58-61	Plaxton	Lancashire United Transport	616	A

Lancashire United Transport Society

Contact address: Secretary, 45 Tarn Drive, Bury, Lancashire. BL9 9QB

E-mail: secretary@lancashireunited.org.uk

Website: www.lancashireunited.org.uk

Brief description: Representing the history of former Lancashire United Transport, once the largest independent operator in the country.

Events planned: Please see website for details.

Registration	Date	Chassis make	Chassis model	Body make	Original operator	Fleet No	Status
GTB 903	1946	Leyland	Titan PD1	Leyland	Lytham St Annes Corporation	19	R
CCK 663	1949	Leyland	Titan PD2/3	Brush	Ribble Motor Services	2687	A
DFV 146	1949	Leyland	Titan PD2/5	Burlingham	Blackpool Corporation	246	A
JCK 530	1956	Leyland	Titan PD2/12	Burlingham	Ribble Motor Services	1455	RP
760 CTD	1957	Leyland	Titan PD2/20	Northern Counties	Lytham St Annes Corporation	61	A
PFR 346	1959	Leyland	Titan PD2/27	Metro Cammell	Blackpool Corporation	346	A
534 RTB	1961	Guy	Arab IV	Metro Cammell	Lancashire United Transport	43	R
561 TD	1962	Daimler	Fleetline CRG6LX	Northern Counties	Lancashire United Transport	97	R
583 CLT	1962	AEC	Routemaster	Park Royal	London Transport	RM1583	R
RRN 405	1962	Leyland	Atlantean PDR1/1	Weymann	Ribble Motor Services	1805	RP
YFR 351	1962	Leyland	Titan PD3/1	Metro Cammell	Blackpool Corporation	351	A
CTF 627B	1964	Leyland	Titan PD2A/27	Massey	Lytham St Annes Corporation	70	R
CUV 290C	1965	AEC	Routemaster	Park Royal	London Transport	RML2290	R
HFR 512E	1967	Leyland	Titan PD3A/1	MCW	Blackpool Corporation	512	R
HFR 516E	1967	Leyland	Titan PD3A/1	MCW	Blackpool Corporation	516	R
SMK 734F	1967	AEC	Routemaster	Park Royal	London Transport	RML2734	R
LFR 529F	1968	Leyland	Titan PD3/11	MCW	Blackpool Corporation	529	R
LFR 540G	1968	Leyland	Titan PD3/11	MCW	Blackpool Corporation	540	A
PFR 554H	1970	AEC	Swift MP2R	Marshall	Blackpool Corporation	554	R
ATD 281J	1971	Leyland	Atlantean PDR1A/1	Northern Counties	Lytham St Annes Corporation	77	R
OCK 995K	1972	Bristol	VRTSL6LX	ECW	Ribble Motor Services	1995	RP
OCK 997K	1972	Bristol	VRTSL6LX	ECW	Ribble Motor Services	1997	RP
STJ 847L	1972	Seddon	RU	Pennine	Lytham St Annes Corporation	47	A

Lancastrian Transport Trust

Contact address: 1 Beverley Grove, Blackpool. FY4 2BG

Phone : 07815 983885

E-mail: paul@ltt.org.uk

Website: www.ltt.org.uk

Brief description: Collection of buses and trams from Blackpool and the Fylde coast.

Events planned in 2010

11 April — Open Day, Brinwell Road Depot, FY4 4QU 12.00-16.00

27 June — Totally Transport, New South Promenade, Blackpool 11.00-16.00

31 October — Open Day, Brinwell Road Depot, FY4 4QU 12.00-16.00

Free bus service during open days

Opening days/times: 11 April and 31 October only (see events)

Charges: £1

Directions by car: See website

Directions by public transport: Lines 3, 6 and 16 serve the depot

Below: One of the newer vehicles in the Lancashire Transport Trust collection is former Blackpool Corporation 334 (AHG 334V), a 1980 East Lancs-bodied Leyland Atlantean. PHILIP LAMB

Below right: The Lancashire Transport Trust collection includes former Blackpool Corporation 529 (LFR 529F), a 1968 MCW bodied Leyland Titan PD3/11, carrying the mainly cream variant of Blackpool's livery in which it was new. PHILIP LAMB

Registration	Date	Chassis make	Chassis model	Body make	Original operator	Fleet No	Status
OFR 970M	1974	AEC	Swift 3MP2R	Marshall	Blackpool Corporation	570	R
HRN 99N	1975	Leyland	Atlantean AN68/1R	Northern Counties	Fylde Borough Transport	79	RP
NRN 397P	1976	Leyland	Atlantean AN68/1R	Park Royal	Ribble Motor Services	1397	RP
OJI 4371	1977	Leyland	Atlantean AN68A/1R	Northern Counties	Fylde Borough Transport	85	R
AHG 334V	1980	Leyland	Atlantean AN68A/2R	East Lancs	Blackpool Transport	331	RP
NKU 214X	1982	Dennis	Dominator DDA	Alexander	South Yorkshire PTE	2214	R
F575 RCW	1988	Volkswagen LT55	City Pacer	Optare	Blackpool Transport	575	R

Legionnaire Group

Contact address: 66 Montfort Road, Strood, Rochester, Kent. ME2 3EX

E-mail: bob.wingrove@btinternet.com

Brief description: The group aims to restore at least one of each combination of chassis/Legionnaire so that Harrington's last body style is represented in preservation.

Registration	Date	Chassis make	Chassis model	Body make	Original operator	Fleet No	Status
SPU 985	1951	Leyland	Olympic HR44	Weymann	Jennings Coaches of Ashen		RP
72 MMJ	1964	Bedford	VAL14	Harrington	Reliance Coaches of Meppershall	72	RP
CDK 409C	1965	Bedford	VAL14	Harrington	Yelloway Motor Services of Rochdale		A
JNK 681C	1965	Ford	Thames 36 676E	Harrington	SP Coaches of Sutton		RP

Registration	Date	Chassis make	Chassis model	Body make	Original operator	Fleet No	Status
FJF 193	1950	Leyland	Titan PD2/1	Leyland	Leicester City Transport	154	R
GAY 171	1950	Leyland	Tiger PS1/1	Willowbrook	Allen of Mountsorrel	43	RP
OJF 191	1956	Leyland	Tiger Cub PSUC1/1	Weymann	Leicester City Transport	191	A
TBC 163	1958	Leyland	Titan PD3/1	Park Royal	Leicester City Transport	163	RP
217 AJF	1961	AEC	Bridgemaster B3RA	Park Royal	Leicester City Transport	217	RP
90 HBC	1964	Leyland	Titan PD3A/1	East Lancs	Leicester City Transport	90	RP
DBC 190C	1965	AEC	Renown 3B3RA	East Lancs	Leicester City Transport	190	R
FJF 40D	1966	AEC	Renown 3B3RA	East Lancs	Leicester City Transport	40	RP
GRY 48D	1966	Leyland	Titan PD3A/1	MCW	Leicester City Transport	48	RP
PBC 98G	1968	Leyland	Atlantean PDR1A/1	ECW	Leicester City Transport	98	A
PBC 113G	1969	Leyland	Atlantean PDR1A/1	Park Royal	Leicester City Transport	113	A
TRY 122H	1969	Bristol	RELL6L	ECW	Leicester City Transport	122	RP
ARY 225K	1972	Scania	BR111MH	MCW	Leicester City Transport	225	R
GJF 301N	1975	Scania	Metropolitan BR111DH	MCW	Leicester City Transport	301	R
UFP 175S	1977	Scania	Metropolitan BR111DH	MCW	Leicester City Transport	175	A
UFP 233S	1977	Dennis	Dominator DD	East Lancs	Leicester City Transport	233	A
TBC 50X	1982	Dennis	Dominator DDA	East Lancs	Leicester City Transport	50	RP
C100 UBC	1986	Dennis	Dominator	East Lancs	Leicester Citybus	100	RP

Leicester City Transport 190 (DBC 190C) is an AEC Renown with East Lancs highbridge body, one of three delivered in 1965. It is associated with the Leicester Transport Heritage Trust and depicted on the forecourt of the now demolished Abbey Park Road depot in Leicester on 10 June 2009. SIMON GILL

Leicester Transport Heritage Trust

Address: 13 Warren Road, Enderby, Leicester. LE19 2DR.

Phone: 07891 071908

E-mail: lctbusgroup@aol.com

Website: www.ltht.org.uk

Brief description: The Leicester Transport Heritage Trust was formed in 2007 and has been a charitable trust since May 2008. The Trust is an educational charity designed to bring together a wide variety of people with specialist or general transport interest relating to Leicester and Leicestershire.

Events planned in 2010

12 September — Leicester Bus Running Day at Abbey Pumping Station Museum, Corporation Road, Leicester. LE4 5PX

Facilities: B(e)

Leyland National Group

Contact Address: 4 Westwey, 29 Byfleet Road, New Haw. KT15 3JQ

Email: secretary@leylandnationalgroup.org

Telephone: 01932 852603 07816 597317

Website: www.leylandnational.co.uk

Brief description: The group aims to promote the preservation of the Leyland National bus alongside supporting vehicle owners, where possible, with help and advice with their preservation projects. We also have an interest in maintaining a history of this type of vehicle.

Registration	Date	Chassis make	Chassis model	Body make	Original operator	Fleet No	Status
MLL 763	1952	AEC	Regal IV 9821LT	Metro Cammell	London Transport	RF226	R
NLE 534	1952	AEC	Regal IV 9821LT	Metro Cammell	London Transport	RF534	R
MXX 292	1953	AEC	Regal IV 9821LT	Metro Cammell	London Transport	RF404	RP
NLE 636	1953	AEC	Regal IV 9821LT	Metro Cammell	London Transport	RF636	
GP 14 ST	1956	Leyland	Royal Tiger Worldmaster	Verhuil			
UNB 524	1958	Leyland	Titan PD2/40	Metro Cammell	Manchester Corporation	3524	R
VLT 8	1958	AEC	Routemaster	Park Royal	London Transport	RM8	
CUV 51C	1965	Daimler	Fleetline CRG6LX	Park Royal	London Transport	XF1	
JJD 508D	1966	AEC	Routemaster	Park Royal	London Transport	RML2508	
KGJ 621D	1966	AEC	Routemaster	Park Royal	British European Airways	8228	
AML 97H	1970	AEC	Swift 4MP2R	Park Royal	London Transport	SMD97	
YHT 802J	1970	Bristol	RESL6L	ECW	Bristol Omnibus Co	516	
UEL 564J	1971	Bristol	RELL6G	ECW	Hants & Dorset Motor Services	8116	RP
YHY 592J	1971	Bristol	RELL6L	ECW	Bristol Omnibus Co	1212	R
JGF 753K	1971	AEC	Swift 4MP2R	MCW	London Transport	SMS753	
FRM 499K	1972	Leyland	National 1151/2R/0401	Leyland National	Leyland Research Fleet		A
HOR 413L	1972	Leyland	National 1151/2R/0403	Leyland National	Gosport & Fareham Omnibus Co	13	RP
JPA 121K	1972	AEC	Reliance 6U2R	Park Royal	London Country Bus Services	RP121	
NPD 108L	1972	Leyland	National 1151/2R/0402	Leyland National	London Country Bus Services	LN8	R
JIL 2157	1973	Leyland	National 1151/1R/0402	East Lancs National Greenway	London Country	LNC42	
NUD 106L	1973	Bristol	VRTSL2/6LX	ECW	City of Oxford Motor Services	106	
SPK 203M	1973	AEC	Reliance 6U3ZR	Plaxton	London Country Bus Services	P3	
WEX 687M	1973	AEC	Swift 3MP2R	ECW	Great Yarmouth Corporation	87	RP
XRB 415L	1973	Leyland	National 1151/2R/0403	Leyland National	Midland General Omnibus Co	415	
OTO 547M	1973	Leyland	Atlantean AN68/1R	East Lancs	Nottingham City Transport	547	
THM 601M	1973	Daimler	Fleetline CRL6	MCW	London Transport	DMS1601	
OCN 744M	1974	Leyland	National 1151/1R/0401	Leyland National	Venture Transport	144M	
UPE 203M	1974	Leyland	National 1051/1R/0402	Leyland National	London Country Bus Services	SNB103	A
WPG 217M	1974	Leyland	National 10351/1R/SC	Leyland National	London Country Bus Services	SNC117	A
YFY 4M	1974	Leyland	National 1151/2R/0402	Leyland National	Southport Corporation	4	
GNU 568N	1974	Leyland	National 11351/1R	Leyland National	Trent Motor Traction Co	421	
GNU 569N	1974	Leyland	National 11351/1R	Leyland National	Trent Motor Traction Co	422	R
JMY 120N	1974	Leyland	National 11351/1R/EXC	Leyland National	National Travel		A
UMO 180N	1974	Leyland	National 11351/1R	Leyland National	Alder Valley	180	R
GHV 2N	1974	Daimler	Fleetline CRL6	Park Royal	London Transport	DM1002	A
AL.8765	1975	Leyland	National 11351/2R	Leyland National	MTT Tasmania	636	
GLJ 681N	1975	Leyland	National 11351/1R/SC	Leyland National	Hants & Dorset Motor Services	3645	

Registration	Date	Chassis make	Chassis model	Body make	Original operator	Fleet No	Status
GPC 731N	1975	Leyland	National 11351/1R	Leyland National	Alder Valley	182	
GVV 887N	1975	Leyland	National 11351/1R	Leyland National	United Counties Omnibus Co	496	
HFM 186N	1975	Leyland	National 11351/1R/SC	Leyland National	Crosville Motor Services	ENL930	
HPF 318N	1975	Leyland	National 10351/1R/SC	Leyland National	London Country Bus Services	SNC168	R
KPA 369P	1975	Leyland	National 11351/1R	Leyland National	Alder Valley	218	RP
687 NKY	1976	Leyland	National 10951/2R	Leyland National	Blackstone of Booval		
6691 PH	1976	Bedford	YMT	Plaxton	King of the Road Worthing		
JOX 506P	1976	Leyland	National 11351A/1R	Leyland National	Midland Red Omnibus Co	506	
KHT 122P	1976	Leyland	National 11351/1R	Leyland National	Bristol Omnibus Co	G3024	
KJD 507P	1976	Leyland	National 11351A/2R	Leyland National	London Transport	LS7	A
KJD 524P	1976	Leyland	National 11351A/2R	Leyland National	London Transport	LS24	
KJD 530P	1976	Leyland	National 10351A/2R	Leyland National	London Transport	LS30	
KJD 535P	1976	Leyland	National 10351A/2R	Leyland National	London Transport	LS35	
KRE 279P	1976	Leyland	National 11351/1R	Leyland National	Potteries Motor Traction Co	279	RP
KSO 74P	1976	Leyland	National 10351/2R	Leyland National	Grampian Regional Transport	74	
MDL 880R	1976	Leyland	National 11351A/1R	Leyland National	Southern Vectis Omnibus Co	880	A
NPJ 472R	1976	Leyland	National 11351A/1R	Leyland National	Alder Valley	251	R
NPK 250R	1976	Leyland	National 11351A/1R	Leyland National	London Country Bus Services	SNB250	
NPK 257R	1976	Leyland	National 10351A/1R	Leyland National	London Country Bus Services	SNB257	
MAN 32N	1977	Leyland	National 11351A/1R	Leyland National	Isle of Man Road Services	32	
OJD 879R	1977	Leyland	National 10351A/2R	Leyland National	London Transport	LS79	
OJD 898R	1977	Leyland	National 10351A/2R	Leyland National	London Transport	LS98	
PCD 80R	1977	Leyland	National 11351A/1R	Leyland National	Southdown Motor Services	34	A
PRR 454R	1977	Leyland	National 11351A/1R	Leyland National	Trent Motor Traction Co	454	
SKR 556R	1977	Leyland	National 11351A/1R	Leyland National	Maidstone & District Motor Services	3556	
UHG 736R	1977	Leyland	National 11351A/2R	East Lancs National Greenway	Ribble Motor Services	736	
UPB 308S	1977	Leyland	National 11351A/1R	Leyland National	London Country Bus Services	SNB308	A
UPB 312S	1977	Leyland	National 10351A/1R	Leyland National	London Country Bus Services	SNB312	R
UPB 340S	1977	Leyland	National 10351A/1R	Leyland National	London Country Bus Services	SNB340	
VKE 566S	1977	Leyland	National 11351A/1R	Leyland National	Maidstone & District Motor Services	3566	R
PTD 673S	1978	Leyland	National 11351A/1R	Leyland National	Lancashire United Transport	536	RP
SBK 740S	1978	Leyland	National 11351/2R	Leyland National	Gosport & Fareham Omnibus Co	40	
THX 217S	1978	Leyland	National 10351A/2R	Leyland National	London Transport	LS217	
THX 220S	1978	Leyland	National 10351A/1R	Leyland National	London Transport	LS220	RP
TOF 702S	1978	Leyland	National 11351A/1R	Leyland National	Midland Red Omnibus Co	702	
TPE 159S	1978	Leyland	National 11351A/1R	Leyland National	Alder Valley	283	
AFJ 707T	1978	Leyland	National 11351A/1R	Leyland National	Western National Omnibus Co	2868	A

Far left above: **London Country SNC168 (HPF 318N) is seen on the Leyland National Group's March 2010 Running Day at the site of the former Leatherhead garage.** MICHAEL BERG

Far left below: **At Alton in 2008, we see Hastings & District-liveried VKE 566S. When new this bus was No 3566 in the Maidstone & District fleet, and has subsequently been fitted with a Volvo engine.** MICHAEL BERG

Above: **New to Alder Valley in 1975 as its No 218 (KPA 369P), this Leyland National is seen in Wokingham on the occasion of the Leyland National Group 2009 Annual General Meeting.** MICHAEL BERG

Below: **Former Provincial 76 (WFX 257S), seen here in an experimental version of People's Provincial livery in 2008, has now left the group to return to service with Thompson's Travel of Christchurch.** MICHAEL BERG

Top: Formerly LNC42, this Greenway conversion is now JIL 2157, and is still in service with Tanat Valley Coaches. MICHAEL BERG

Above: Latterly a People's Provincial vehicle, RUF 37R was new as Southdown 37 — the identity in which it is preserved. MICHAEL BERG

Registration	Date	Chassis make	Chassis model	Body make	Original operator	Fleet No	Status
AYJ 100T	1978	Leyland	National 11351A/1R	Leyland National	Southdown Motor Services	100	RP
DAR 120T	1978	Leyland	National 11351A/1R	Leyland National	Eastern National Omnibus Co	1898	RP
GFR 799W	1978	Leyland	National 2 NL116690/1R	Leyland National	Ribble Motor Services	799	
AYJ 97T	1979	Leyland	National 11351/1R	Leyland National	Southdown Motor Services	97	
AYR 339T	1979	Leyland	National 10351/2R	Leyland National	London Transport	LS339	
AYR 343T	1979	Leyland	National 10351/2R	Leyland National	London Transport	LS343	
BPL 469T	1979	Leyland	National 10351B/1R	Leyland National	London Country Bus Services	SNB469	RP
BRC 837T	1979	Bristol	VRT/SL3/6LXB	ECW	Trent Motor Traction Co	837	
GMB 390T	1979	Leyland	National 11351/1R	Leyland National	Crosville Motor Services	SNL390	
WYV 6T	1979	Leyland	Titan TNLXB	Park Royal	London Transport	T 6	
YPL 433T	1979	Leyland	National 10351B/1R	Leyland National	London Country Bus Services	SNB433	R
YPL 449T	1979	Leyland	National 10351B/1R	Leyland National	London Country Bus Services	SNB449	A
AWN 815V	1979	Leyland	National 11351/1R	Leyland National	South Wales Transport	815	
BUH 239V	1979	Leyland	National 2 NL106L11/1R	Leyland National	National Welsh Omnibus Services	NS8011	A
EPD 511V	1979	Leyland	National 10351B/1R	Leyland National	London Country Bus Services	SNB511	A
EPD 543V	1979	Leyland	National 10351B/1R	Leyland National	London Country Bus Services	SNB543	A
FDV 827V	1979	Leyland	Leopard PSU3E/4R	Willowbrook	Western National Omnibus Co	3536	
FDV 829V	1979	Leyland	National 2 NL116L/1R	Leyland National	Western National (Devon General)	2883	R
JHJ 150V	1979	Leyland	National 11351/1R	Leyland National	Eastern National Omnibus Co	1924	
TRN 810V	1979	Leyland	National 10351B/1R	Leyland National	Ribble Motor Services	810	RP
AAE 647V	1980	Leyland	National 2 NL116L11/1R	Leyland National	Bristol Omnibus Co	3503	
AAE 650V	1980	Leyland	National 2 NL116L11/1R	Leyland National	Bristol Omnibus Co	3506	
AAE 658V	1980	Leyland	National 2 NL116L11/1R	Leyland National	Bristol Omnibus Co	3514	
BHY 997V	1980	Leyland	National 2 NL116L11/1R	Leyland National	Bristol Omnibus Co	3523	
BHY 998V	1980	Leyland	National 2 NL116L11/1R	Leyland National	Bristol Omnibus Co	3524	
BUH 240V	1980	Leyland	National 2 NL106L11/1R	Leyland National	National Welsh Omnibus Services	NS8012	
BVP 765V	1980	Leyland	National 11351/1R	Leyland National	Midland Red Omnibus Co	765	
BVP 811V	1980	Leyland	National 2 NL116L11/1R	Leyland National	Midland Red Omnibus Co	811	
CJH 123V	1980	Bristol	VRT/SL3/6LXB	ECW	Alder Valley	983	
DOC 37V	1980	Leyland	National 2 NL116L11/1R	Leyland National	West Midlands PTE	7037	
FWA 450V	1980	Leyland DAB	Artic LG17575-690/4	Leyland	South Yorkshire PTE	2007	RP
HFG 923V	1980	Leyland	National 2 NL116L11/1R	Leyland National	Southdown Motor Services	123	R
NAT 198V	1980	Leyland	National 2 NL116L11/1R	Leyland National	East Yorkshire Motor Services	198	
RMA 442V	1980	Bristol	VRT/SL3/501	ECW	Crosville Motor Services	DVL442	
APT 117W	1980	Leyland	National 2 NL116L11/1R	Leyland National	United Automobile Services	3117	
GCK 428W	1980	Leyland	National 2 NL116AL11/1R	Leyland National	Fishwick of Leyland	7	
KWA 22W	1980	Leyland	National 2 NL116L11/1R	Leyland National	South Yorkshire PTE	22	
PWY 582W	1980	Leyland	National 2 NL106L11/1R	Leyland National	West Yorkshire	1015	

Left: **Two former London Buses Leyland Nationals are seen together at Alton in 2007 — they are, on the left, LS24 (KJD 524P) with LS98 (OJD 898R) to the right.** MICHAEL BERG

Below: **Leyland Nationals in London service were fitted out with more standing space than was usual. This is the interior of LS98.** MICHAEL BERG

Registration	Date	Chassis make	Chassis model	Body make	Original operator	Fleet No	Status
SVV 587W	1980	Leyland	National 2 NL116L11/1R	Leyland National	United Counties Omnibus Co	587	R
SVV 588W	1980	Leyland	National 2 NL116L11/1R	Leyland National	United Counties Omnibus Co	588	
SVV 589W	1980	Leyland	National 2 NL116L11/1R	Leyland National	United Counties Omnibus Co	589	
SIB 6706	1981	Leyland	National 2 NL106AL11/1R	East Lancs National Greenway	Ribble Motor Services	855	
ERV 115W	1981	Leyland	National 2 NL106AL11/1R	Leyland National	Portsmouth Corporation	115	
EWS 751W	1981	Bristol	VRT/SL3/680	ECW	Bristol Omnibus Co	5543	
GUW 443W	1981	Leyland	National 2 NL106AL11/2R	East Lancs National Greenway	London Transport	LS443	A
GUW 444W	1981	Leyland	National 2 NL106AL11/2R	Leyland National	London Transport	LS444	RP
JCK 852W	1981	Leyland	National 2 NL106AL11/1R	Greenway	Ribble Motor Services	252	RP
JVV 270W	1981	Bristol	VRT/SL3/6LXB	ECW	Southdown Motor Services	270	
LFJ 859W	1981	Bristol	VRT SL3/6LXB	ECW	Western National (Devon General)	1212	
VVV 956W	1981	Bristol	VRT/SL3/6LXB	ECW	United Counties Omnibus Co	956	
CKB 166X	1981	Leyland	National 2 NL116AL11/1R	Leyland National	Merseyside PTE	6169	
KEP 829X	1981	Leyland	National 2 NL116AL11/1R	Leyland National	South Wales Transport	829	
OFV 621X	1981	Leyland	National 2 NL116AL11/1R	Leyland National	Fishwick of Leyland	26	
AXI 2533	1982	Bristol	RELL6G	Alexander (Belfast)	Belfast Citybus	2533	
PSX 188Y	1982	Leyland	Leopard PSU3G/4R	Alexander	W Alexander & Sons (Fife)	FPE188	
PSX 189Y	1982	Leyland	Leopard PSU3G/4R	Alexander	W Alexander & Sons (Fife)	FPE189	RP
PWO 87Y	1982	Leyland	Leopard PSU4G/2R	East Lancs	Rhymney Valley	87	
TWE 263Y	1982	Leyland	National 2 NL116AL11/1R	Leyland National	Yorkshire Traction	263	
BXI 2599	1983	Bristol	RELL6G	Alexander (Belfast)	Ulsterbus	2599	
A301 KJT	1984	Leyland	National 2 NL116TL11/1R	Leyland National	Provincial of Gosport	1	R
B359 LOY	1984	Leyland	National 2 NL116TL11/1R	Leyland National	British Airways	BU395	
B361 LOY	1984	Leyland	National 2 NL116TL11/3R	Leyland National	British Airways	BU397	RP
DXI 3370	1989	Leyland	Tiger TRBLXCT/2RH	Alexander (Belfast)	Ulsterbus	370	

London Transport Museum

Acton

Depot address: 2 Museum Way, 118-120 Gunnersbury Lane, London. W3 9BQ

Contact address: 39 Wellington Street, London WC2E 7BB

Phone: 020 7565 7298

E-mail: enquiries@ltmuseum.co.uk

Website: www.ltmuseum.co.uk

Brief description: The Depot is a working museum store and treasure trove of over 370,000 objects. Attractions include rare road and rail vehicles, station models, signs, ticket machines, posters and original artworks.

Events planned in 2010:

13/14 March — Museum Depot, Acton Open Weekend: London's transport in miniature

16/17 October — Museum Depot, Acton Open Weekend: Family Open Weekend

Opening days/times: Pre-booked guided tours on the last Friday and Saturday of the month

Special Open Weekends please contact for details or see website

Directions by car: Parking on site is reserved for Blue Badge holders and must be requested in advance. Limited parking is available in local area

Directions by public transport: Tube to Acton Town (District & Piccadilly lines). Check www.tfl.gov.uk before you travel

Charges: Adults £10; Senior citizens £8; Students £6*

Accompanied children under 16 FREE

*These prices include a voluntary Gift Aid donation

Facilities: B(e) D F G L R S T

Registration	Date	Chassis make	Chassis model	Body make	Original operator	Fleet No	Status
Unregistered	1888	Horse bus		LGOC	London General Omnibus Co		R
LC 3701	1906	De Dion		(chassis only)	London General Omnibus Co	L7	R
XC 8059	1921	AEC	K	LGOC	London General Omnibus Co	K424	R
MN 2615	1923	Tilling Stevens	TS3A Petrol Electric	(chassis only)	Douglas Corporation	10	R
XM 7399	1923	AEC	S	LGOC	London General Omnibus Co	S742	R
YR 3844	1926	AEC	NS	LGOC	London General Omnibus Co	NS1995	R
GK 3192	1931	AEC	Regent 661	LGOC	London General Omnibus Co	ST821	R
GK 5323	1931	AEC	Renown 663	LGOC	London General Omnibus Co	LT165	R
GK 5486	1931	AEC	Regal 662	Duple	London General Omnibus Co	T219	R
GO 5198	1931	AEC	Renown 664	LGOC	London General Omnibus Co	LT1076	R
HX 2756	1931	AEC	663T	UCC	London United Tramways	1	R
AXM 649	1934	AEC	Regent 661	Chalmers	London Transport	830J	R
AYV 651	1934	AEC	Regent 661	LPTB	London Transport	STL469	R

The London Transport Museum Acton Depot contains vehicles restored to running order that may be ridden on and viewed at some events. AEC Routemaster RM1 (SLT 56) is seen at Wisley airfield in the company of London's numerically last example of the type, RML2760 (SMK 760F), owned and operated by East London. DAVID JUKES

Registration	Date	Chassis make	Chassis model	Body make	Original operator	Fleet No	Status
BXD 576	1935	AEC	Q 0762	Birmingham RC&W	London Transport	Q55	R
CLE 122	1936	Leyland	Cub KP03	Weymann	London Transport	C94	R
HYM 768	1948	BUT	9641T	Metro-Cammell	London Transport	1768	R
MXX 364	1953	Guy	Special NLLVP	ECW	London Transport	GS64	R
NLE 537	1953	AEC	Regal IV 9821LT RF	Metro-Cammell	London Transport	RF537	R
NXP 997	1954	AEC	Regent III O961 RT	Park Royal	London Transport	RT4712	R
OLD 589	1954	AEC	Regent III O961 RT	Park Royal	London Transport	RT4825	R
SLT 56	1956	AEC	Routemaster	Park Royal/LTE	London Transport	RM1	R
SLT 57	1957	AEC	Routemaster	Park Royal/LTE	London Transport	RM2	RP
CUV 229C	1965	AEC	Routemaster R2RH/1	Park Royal	London Transport	RCL2229	R
KGY 4D	1966	AEC	Routemaster FR2R	Park Royal	London Transport	FRM1	R
AML 582H	1969	AEC	Merlin 4P2R	MCW	London Transport	MBA582	R
KJD 401P	1976	Bristol	LH6L	ECW	London Transport	BL1	A
TPJ 61S	1977	Bristol	LHS6L	ECW	London Country Bus Services	BN61	R
NUW 567Y	1982	Leyland	Titan TNLXB/2RR	Leyland	London Transport	T567	R
C526 DYT	1986	Volkswagen	LT55	Optare	London Transport	OV2	R
F115 PHM	1988	Volvo	B10M	Alexander	Grey Green	VA115	R
Unregistered	1993	Optare	MetroRider	Optare	London Transport	MRL242	R

Just some of the many treasures contained within the London Transport Museum Depot. Former London General Omnibus Company 1921 AEC K K424 (XC 8059) and 1926 AEC NS NS1995 (YR 3844) both carry bodywork built in London General's own workshops. DAVID JUKES

Registration	Date	Chassis make	Chassis model	Body make	Original operator	Fleet No	Status
JRX 823	1955	Bristol	KSW6B	ECW	Thames Valley Traction Co	748	R
TDL 998	1960	Bristol	Lodekka FS6G	ECW	Southern Vectis Omnibus Co	565	R
RCP 237	1962	AEC	Regent V 2D3RA	Northern Counties	Hebble Motor Services	619	A
YDL 315	1962	Bristol	Lodekka FS6G	ECW	Southern Vectis Omnibus Co	570	R
KHC 367	1963	AEC	Regent V 2D3RV	East Lancs	Eastbourne Corporation	67	R

Medstead Depot Omnibus Group

Contact address: Hon Secretary, Medstead Depot Omnibus Group, c/o Power House, Windsor Way, Aldershot, Hants. GU11 1JG

Brief description: Vehicles from Medstead Depot Omnibus Group are regularly to be seen at shows and rallies throughout the year. In addition to the vehicles listed, others belonging to members of the Aldershot & District Bus Interest Group and the Southampton & District Transport Heritage Trust are associated with the group and stored on site from time to time. There is an open day once per year, associated with the Mid-Hants Railway and Alton Bus Rally

Events planned in 2010:

2 May, 6 June, 4 July, 1 August, 5 September — Free bus services to Chawton.

Merseyside Transport Trust

Contact: 17 Carlton Street, Liverpool. L3 7ED

E-mail: enquiries@mttrust.co.uk

Website: www.mttrust.co.uk

Brief description: The Merseyside Transport Trust is a charitable trust with a collection of over 30 buses and coaches that represent the development of post war public transport on Merseyside. We organises a number of events each year which give the opportunity to travel on our restored buses. You can also join the Friends of the Merseyside Transport Trust and receive a quarterly newsletter and there is also the opportunity to help at our events.

Events planned in 2010

4 April — Spring Classic Bus Running Day. Frequent free bus services from Liverpool's Pier Head (Mann Island) to Broadway, Norris Green using buses from the 1970s period.

Summer 2010 (exact date to be confirmed) — Southport Routes Tour. Tour of former MPTE routes in the resort using vehicle types synonymous with those used in the town in the 1970s. Date to be confirmed.

7/8 August — Woodvale Rally. Variety of buses used on the Park & Ride service within the show. Further details on the event from http://www.woodvale-rally.org.uk/

12 September — Classic Liverpool Bus Running Day. Frequent free bus services from Liverpool's Pier Head (Mann Island) to Liverpool South Parkway Interchange and other parts of the city using buses from the collection and visiting vehicles

Facilities: B(e)

Registration	Date	Chassis make	Chassis model	Body make	Original operator	Fleet No	Status
GKD 434	1946	AEC	Regent II O661	Weymann/LCPT	Liverpool Corporation	A233	A
JKC 178	1949	Daimler	CVA6	Northern Counties	Liverpool Corporation	D553	A
KMN 501	1949	Leyland	Titan PD2/1	Leyland	Isle of Man Road Services	71	A
KMN 519	1950	Leyland	Comet CP01	Park Royal	Douglas Corporation	21	R
MKB 994	1952	AEC	Regent III 9613A	Crossley	Liverpool Corporation	A801	A
NKD 536	1953	AEC	Regent III 9613S	Crossley	Liverpool Corporation	A36	RP
NKD 540	1954	AEC	Regent III 9613S	Saunders Roe	Liverpool Corporation	A40	RP
RKC 262	1955	Leyland	Titan PD2/20	Alexander	Liverpool Corporation	L161	RP
SKB 168	1956	Leyland	Royal Tiger PSU1/13	Crossley/MCW	Liverpool Corporation	XL171	RP
SKB 224	1956	Leyland	Titan PD2/20	Crossley/LCPT	Liverpool Corporation	L227	RP
VKB 711	1956	Leyland	Titan PD2/20	Crossley	Liverpool Corporation	L255	R
VKB 841	1957	Leyland	Titan PD2/20	Crossley	Liverpool Corporation	L320	A
VKB 900	1957	AEC	Regent V D3RV	Metro Cammell	Liverpool Corporation	A267	R
116 TMD	1958	AEC	Bridgemaster B3RA	Park Royal	Liverpool Corporation	E3	A
371 BKA	1959	AEC	Regent V LD3RA	Park Royal	Liverpool Corporation	E1	R
372 BKA	1959	Leyland	Atlantean PDR1/1	Metro Cammell	Liverpool Corporation	E2	A
BHT 677A	1960	Leyland	Atlantean PDR1/1	Metro Cammell	Wallasey Corporation	15	RP
256 SFM	1961	Bristol	Lodekka FLF6B	ECW	Crosville Motor Services	DFB43	A
875 VFM	1961	Bristol	Lodekka FSF6G	ECW	Crosville Motor Services	DFG65	A
501 KD	1962	Leyland	Atlantean PDR1/1	Metro Cammell	Liverpool Corporation	L501	R
FKF 801D	1966	Leyland	Atlantean PDR1/1	MCW	Liverpool City Transport	L801	A
FKF 835E	1967	Leyland	Atlantean PDR1/1	MCW	Liverpool City Transport	L835	R
FKF 933G	1968	Leyland	Panther PSUR1A/1R	MCW	Liverpool City Transport	1054	R
LCM 159G	1968	Leyland	Atlantean PDR1/2	Northern Counties	Birkenhead Corporation	159	R
SKB 695G	1969	Bristol	RELL6G	Park Royal	Liverpool City Transport	2025	R
UKA 562H	1969	Leyland	Atlantean PDR2/1	Alexander	Liverpool City Transport	1111	R
PFY 72J	1971	Leyland	Panther PSUR1B/1R	Marshall	Southport Corporation	72	A
BKC 236K	1972	Leyland	Atlantean PDR1A/1	Alexander	Merseyside PTE	1236	R
BKC 276K	1972	Leyland	Atlantean PDR1A/1	Alexander	Merseyside PTE	1276	RP
CKC 308L	1972	Daimler	Fleetline CRG6LXB	MCW	Merseyside PTE	3008	A
DKC 330L	1972	Leyland	Atlantean AN68/1R	Alexander	Merseyside PTE	1330	A
VWM 83L	1973	Leyland	Atlantean AN68/1R	Alexander	Southport Corporation	83	R
OLV 551M	1974	Leyland	Atlantean AN68/1R	Alexander	Merseyside PTE	1551	A
GKA 74N	1975	Bristol	VRTSL6G	East Lancs	Merseyside PTE	2122	A
MTJ 771S	1977	Leyland	National 11351A/1R	Leyland National	Merseyside PTE	1771	A
OEM 788S	1978	Leyland	Atlantean AN68A/1R	MCW	Merseyside PTE	1788	A
TWM 220V	1979	Leyland	Atlantean AN68A/1R	East Lancs	Merseyside PTE	1836	R
UKA 23V	1980	MCW	Metrobus DR103/2	MCW	Merseyside PTE	0023	A

Registration	Date	Chassis make	Chassis model	Body make	Original operator	Fleet No	Status
VHF 57V	1980	Bedford	YMT	Plaxton	Toppings Coaches		A
WWM 904W	1980	Dennis	Dominator DD	Willowbrook	Merseyside PTE	0027	RP
XLV 156W	1981	Leyland	National 2 NL116AL11/1R	Leyland National	Merseyside PTE	6156	R
EKA 220Y	1982	Leyland	Tiger TRCTL11/1R	Duple	Merseyside PTE	7020	RP
A135 HLV	1984	Leyland	Atlantean AN68D/1R	Alexander	Merseyside PTE	1055	R
D685 SEM	1986	Dodge	S56	Alexander	Merseyside Transport	7685	RP
F261 YTJ	1989	Leyland	Olympian ONCL10/1/R2	Northern Counties	Merseyside Transport	0261	RP

Left: The eye-catching Merseyside PTE livery is worn by the Merseyside Transport Trust's former Liverpool City Transport 1968 MCW-bodied Leyland Panther 1054 (FKF 933G), seen here in Liverpool city centre. PHILIP LAMB

Right: Merseyside Transport Trust's former Liverpool Corporation L255 (VKB 711) is a 1956 Leyland Titan PD2/20 with Crossley bodywork featuring the operator's distinctive frontal treatment. PHILIP LAMB

Registration	Date	Chassis make	Chassis model	Body make	Original operator	Fleet No	Status
LN 7270	1908	Leyland	X2	Tilling	London Central Motor Omnibus Co	14	R
HE 12	1913	Leyland	S3.30.T	Brush	Barnsley & District Electric Traction Co	5	R
LF 9967	1913	Leyland	S3.30.T	Birch	Wellingborough Motor Omnibus Co	H	R
CC 1087	1914	Leyland	S4.36.T3	Leyland	London & North Western Railway	59	R
BD 209	1921	Leyland	G7	Dodson	United Counties Omnibus Co	B15	R
C 2367	1921	Leyland	G	Phoenix	Todmorden Corporation	14	R
DM 2583	1923	Leyland	SG7	Leyland	Brookes Bros ('White Rose') of Rhyl	27	R
XU 7498	1924	Leyland	LB5	Dodson	Chocolate Express Omnibus Co	B6	R
PW 8605	1926	ADC	415	United	United Automobile Services	E61	A
YG 7831	1934	Leyland	Tiger TS6	Northern Counties	Todmorden Joint Omnibus Committee	15	RP

Mike Sutcliffe Collection

Phone: 01525 221676

E-mail: sutcliffes@leylandman.co.uk

Website: www.mikesutcliffe.com

Brief description: A collection of 15 vehicles, mainly buses of Leyland manufacture from the period 1908 to 1934, this is the most significant collection of early motorbuses in the world, and includes the oldest British-built motorbus. Mike Sutcliffe was awarded the MBE in 2004 for services to Motor Heritage.

Opening days/times: Viewing can be arranged by appointment only

Charges: free

National Museum of Science and Industry

Swindon

Contact address: Science Museum Swindon, Wroughton, Swindon. SW4 9LT

Phone: 01793 846200

E-mail: wroughton.enquiries@nmsi.ac.uk

Website: www.sciencemuseum.org.uk

Brief description: The bus collection is located at Science Museum, Wroughton, near Swindon, Wiltshire.

Opening days/times: Appointment only

Directions by car: On A4361 approximately 4 miles south of Swindon

Directions by public transport: Publicised for open days

Charges: Published for each event

Registration	Date	Chassis make	Chassis model	Body make	Original operator	Fleet No	Status
LMJ 653G	1913	Fiat	52B		(operator unknown) Yugoslavia		RP
JCP 60F	1928	Leyland	Lion PLSC1	Leyland	Jersey Railways & Tramways		A
DR 4902	1929	Leyland	Titan TD1	Leyland	National Omnibus & Transport Co	2849	A
DX 8871	1930	Ransomes Sims & Jefferies	D	Ransomes Sims & Jefferies	Ipswich Corporation	44	A
VO 6806	1931	AEC	Regal 662	Cravens	Red Bus of Mansfield		A
JN 5783	1935	AEC	Q 762	(chassis only)	Westcliff-on-Sea Motor Services		A
CPM 61	1939	AEC	661T	Weymann	Brighton Hove & District	6340	A
HVF 455L	1940	Saurer	CRD		GFM (Switzerland)	52	A
DHR 192	1943	Guy	Arab II	Weymann	Swindon Corporation	51	A
KPT 909	1949	Leyland	Titan PD2/1	Leyland	Weardale Motor Services of Frosterley		R
HET 513	1953	Crossley	DD42/7	Crossley	Rotherham Corporation	213	A
NLP 645	1953	AEC	Regal IV 9822E	Park Royal	British European Airways	1035	A
OTT 55	1953	Bristol	LS5G	ECW	Southern National Omnibus Co	1701	A
504 EBL	1963	Bedford	VAL14	Duple	Reliance Motor Services of Newbury	87	A
Unregistered	1970	Moulton	MD	Moulton	Moulton Development vehicle		A
BCD 820L	1973	Leyland	National 1151/1R/0102	Leyland National	Southdown Motor Services	20	A

North East Bus Preservation Trust Ltd

Contact: c/o R L Kell, Relly Steading, Broom Lane, Durham. DH7 7RJ

Phone: 0191 3845146

E-mail: bob.kell@nebpt.co.uk

Website: www.nebpt.co.uk

Brief description: A selection of Trust vehicles will be on show at our major events as detailed below. Free heritage bus services are provided at all functions.

Events planned in 2010

2 May — Metrocentre, Gateshead

13 June — Durham, Howlands Park & Ride site

18 July — Whitley Bay Seafront

30 August — Seaburn Recreation Park, Sunderland

Registration	Date	Chassis make	Chassis model	Body make	Original operator	Fleet No	Status
CN 4740	1931	SOS	IM4	Short	Northern General Transport Co	540	A
MV 8996	1931	Bedford	WLB	Duple	Howards of West Byfleet		R
CN 6100	1934	Northern General Transport	SE6 (LSE4)	Short	Northern General Transport Co	604	RP
DPT 848	1939	Leyland	Tiger TS8	Roe	Sunderland District	159	R
EF 7380	1942	Leyland	Titan TD7	Roe	West Hartlepool Corporation	36	R
GSR 244	1943	Commer	Q4	Scottish Aviation	Meffan of Kirriemuir		RP
KTJ 502	1947	Leyland	Tiger PS1	Burlingham	Haslingden Corporation	2	RP
ABR 433	1949	Crossley	DD42/7C	Crossley	Sunderland Corporation	100	RP
LYM 729	1951	AEC	Regal IV 9621E	ECW	Tillings Transport		RP
CBR 539	1952	Guy	Arab III	Roe	Sunderland Corporation	139	RP
PHN 831	1952	Bristol	LS5G	ECW	United Automobile Services	BU2	A
DCN 83	1953	AEC Beadle		Beadle	Northern General Transport Co	1483	RP
MWD 908	1953	Bedford	SB	Duple	Hill of Stockingford		RP
SPT 65	1955	Guy	Arab LUF	Weymann	Northern General Transport Co	1665	RP
UUA 212	1955	Leyland	Titan PD2/11	Roe	Leeds City Transport	212	R
JHL 701	1956	Bedford	SBG	Plaxton	Swan of Berwick		R

Registration	Date	Chassis make	Chassis model	Body make	Original operator	Fleet No	Status
UFJ 292	1957	Guy	Arab IV	Massey	Exeter Corporation	52	R
WTS 708A	1957	Bristol	LS5G	ECW	United Automobile Services	BU250	A
AFT 930	1958	Leyland	Titan PD3/4	Metro Cammell	Tynemouth & District	230	RP
8124 WX	1961	Bristol	MW6G	ECW	West Yorkshire Road Car Co	CUG27	R
204 UXJ	1961	AEC	Routemaster	Park Royal	London Transport	RM1058	R
6249 UP	1963	Leyland	Leopard PSU3/3RT	Alexander	Venture Transport Co of Consett	249	RP
ACU 304B	1963	Leyland	Leopard PSU3/3R	Plaxton	Stanhope Motor Services		R
PCN 762	1964	AEC	Routemaster	Park Royal	Northern General Transport Co	2099	R
WBR 248	1964	Atkinson	Alpha PM746HL	Marshall	Sunderland Corporation	48	R
CUV 186C	1965	AEC	Routemaster	Park Royal	London Transport	RM2186	R
ZV 1510	1966	Leyland	Atlantean PDR1/1 Mk2	MCCW	Newcastle Corporation	118	A
JJD 551D	1966	AEC	Routemaster	Park Royal	London Transport	RML2551	R
ECU 201E	1967	Bristol	RESL6L	ECW	South Shields Corporation	1	R
SMK 686F	1967	AEC	Routemaster	Park Royal	London Transport	RML2586	R
SMK 732F	1967	AEC	Routemaster	Park Royal	London Transport	RML2732	R
VVK 149G	1969	Bedford	J6LZ5	Nicolou	Cyprus		R
WHN 411G	1969	Bristol	VRTSL6LX	ECW	United Automobile Services	601	RP
WHA 237H	1970	Leyland	Leopard PSU3A/4R	Plaxton	BMMO ('Midland Red')	6237	RP
GAN 744J	1971	Leyland	Leopard PSU5/4RT	Plaxton	Banfield Coaches		RP
GAN 745J	1971	Leyland	Leopard PSU5/4RT	Plaxton	Banfield Coaches		RP
PCW 203J	1971	Bristol	RESL6L	Pennine	Burnley Colne & Nelson	103	R
SWV 155J	1971	Daimler	Fleetline CRG6LX	Northern Counties	Swindon Corporation	155	RP
JPF 113K	1972	AEC	Swift 3MP2R	Alexander	London Country Bus Services	SMA13	A
MCN 30K	1972	Leyland/NGT	Tynesider	Weymann/ Northern General	Northern General Transport Co	3000	R
NHN 250K	1972	Daimler	Fleetline SRG6LX-36	Roe	Darlington Corporation	50	R
BUP 736L	1973	Leyland	Leopard	Plaxton	Weardale of Stanhope		RP
E901 DRG	1973	Bedford	YRQ	Plaxton	Smith of Durham		RP
JFT 228N	1974	Leyland	Atlantean AN68/1R	Park Royal	Northern General Transport Co		R
TME 134M	1974	AEC	Reliance 6MU4R	Plaxton	Glenton Tours of London		A
GUP 907N	1975	Bristol	LH6L	ECW	United Automobile Services	1623	R
E903 DRG	1975	Ford	R1114	Plaxton	Smith of Durham		RP
PPT 446P	1976	Leyland	Leopard PSU3C/4R	Plaxton	Eden of West Aukland		RP
RFR 424P	1976	Leyland	Atlantean AN68/1R	ECW	Ribble Motor Services	1424	A
OCU 807R	1977	Leyland	Fleetline FE30AGR	Alexander	Tyne & Wear PTE	807	RP
OCU 769R	1977	Scania	BR111DH	MCW	Tyne & Wear PTE	769	RP
RCU 588S	1977	Leyland	Atlantean AN68A/2R	Willowbrook	Tyne & Wear PTE	588	RP
RCU 838S	1978	Daimler	Fleetline FE30AGR	Alexander	Tyne & Wear PTE	838	R

Opening days/times: Events 10.00-16.30
Charges: All events free except Seaburn at £3 per head
Directions by car: Check website
Directions by public transport: Check website
Facilities: B(e) E P R S T

Former West Yorkshire Road Car Company CUG27 (8124 WX), a 1961 Eastern Coach Works-bodied Bristol MW6G, is part of the North East Preservation Trust collection. PHILIP LAMB

Registration	Date	Chassis make	Chassis model	Body make	Original operator	Fleet No	Status
SCN 268S	1978	Leyland	Atlantean AN68A/2R	Alexander	Tyne & Wear PTE	268	R
UVK 290T	1978	Leyland	Atlantean AN68A/2R	Alexander	Tyne & Wear PTE	290	R
EJR 110W	1980	Leyland	Atlantean AN68A/2R	Alexander	Tyne & Wear PTE	110	R
EJR 111W	1980	Leyland	Atlantean AN68A/2R	Alexander	Tyne & Wear PTE	111	R
UPT 681V	1980	Leyland	National 2 NL116L11/1R	Leyland	Northern General Transport Co	4681	RP
FTN 708W	1981	Leyland	National 2 NL116AL11/1R	Leyland	Northern General Transport Co	4708	RP
FTN 710W	1981	Leyland	National 2 NL116AL11/1R	Leyland National	Northern General Transport Co	4710	R
JTY 403X	1981	Leyland	Olympian ONLXB/1R	ECW	Northern General Transport Co	3603	RP
PAJ 829X	1981	Bristol	VRT/SL3/6LXB	ECW	United Automobile Services	829	RP
JFT 413X	1982	Scania	BR112DH	Alexander	Tyne & Wear PTE	413	R
SJR 612Y	1983	Leyland	Olympian	ECW	Northern General Transport Co	3612	RP
C655 LFT	1985	Leyland	Olympian ONLXB/1R	Alexander	Tyne & Wear PTE	655	RP
F107 HVK	1988	Leyland	Lynx	Leyland	Stagecoach	107	RP
K101 KMV	1991	Leyland	Lynx	Leyland	Northern General Transport Co	4999	RP
K715 PCN	1991	Dennis	Dart	Alexander	Tyne & Wear PTE	1715	RP

The North East Bus Preservation Trust looks after this pair of former Sunderland Corporation buses. 1966 Leyland Panther 53(FBR 53D) carries Strachans bodywork to the operator's idiosyncratic trans-Atlantic style of the time, while 1964 Atkinson Alpha 48 (WBR 248) is bodied in more conventional form by Marshall of Cambridge. PHILIP LAMB

This Leyland Atlantean was new to Nottingham City Transport in 1974 as a 9.5m double-decker registered OTO 555M. It was rebodied 20 years later with this East Lancs single-deck body, the chassis being lengthened prior to the fitting of its new bodywork. The Atlantean's original registration number was transferred to another vehicle whilst in Nottingham ownership — RAU 804M is its replacement. PHILIP LAMB

Registration	Date	Chassis make	Chassis model	Body make	Original operator	Fleet No	Status
VLT 108	1959	AEC	Routemaster R2RH	Park Royal	London Transport	RM108	R
80 NVO	1962	Leyland	Titan PD3/4	Northern Counties	South Notts Bus Co of Gotham	80	RP
ETO 452C	1965	Leyland	Atlantean PDR1/2	MCW	Nottingham City Transport	452	RP
STO 526H	1970	Leyland	Atlantean PDR1A/1	Northern Counties	Nottingham City Transport	526	A
VAU 397J	1970	Leyland	Atlantean PDR1/3	Northern Counties	Nottingham City Transport	397	RP
GAU 728L	1973	Leyland	National 1051/2R/0101	Leyland National	Nottingham City Transport	728	R
OTO 540M	1973	Leyland	Atlantean AN68/1R	East Lancs	Nottingham City Transport	540	R
RAU 804M	1974	Leyland	Atlantean AN68/1R	East Lancs (1991)	Nottingham City Transport	555	R
MTV 760P	1976	Leyland	Leopard PSU3C/4R	Duple	Nottingham City Transport	760	RP
UTV 218S	1978	Leyland	Fleetline FE30AGR	Northern Counties	Nottingham City Transport	218	RP
VRC 480S	1978	Leyland	Fleetline FE30ALR	Northern Counties	South Notts Bus Co of Gotham	111	RP
HNN 114V	1980	Leyland	Fleetline FE30ALR	Northern Counties	South Notts Bus Co of Gotham	114	R
RSG 820V	1980	Leyland	National II NL116L11/1R	Leyland National	Fife Scottish	FPN20	A
RNU 433X	1981	Leyland	Atlantean AN68C/1R	Northern Counties	Nottingham City Transport	433	R
RTV 442X	1981	Leyland	Atlantean AN68C/1R	Northern Counties	Nottingham City Transport	442	RP
VRC 611Y	1982	Leyland	Leopard PSU3G/4R	Plaxton	Barton Transport of Chilwell	611	RP
C724 MRC	1985	Leyland	National II NL116TL11/1R	Leyland National	Nottingham City Transport	724	A

Nottingham Heritage Vehicles

Contact address: c/o 49 Valley View, Berry Hill Park, Mansfield, Notts. NG18 4US

Telephone: 07980 943658 or 07971 105491

E-mail: simon@nottinghamheritagevehicles.co.uk

Website: www.nottinghamheritagevehicles.co.uk

Brief description: Nottingham Heritage Vehicles was established in 2001 under the Notts & Derby Heritage Transport Group name. Today, with a small team of dedicated local enthusiasts, we strive to preserve examples of our local transport heritage — namely buses and coaches from the Nottingham area. We exhibit examples from our collection at a number of events throughout the year.

Opening days/times: Visiting by arrangement on Saturdays.

Events planned: The operational vehicles will attend a few events during the rally season.

Registration	Date	Chassis make	Chassis model	Body make	Original operator	Fleet No	Status
DM 6228	1929	Leyland	Lioness LTB1	Burlingham	Brooks Bros of Rhyl	7	
SV 6107	1929	Leyland	Titan TD1	Leyland	Jersey Motor Transport Co	24	

The Rhyl-based fleet of Brookes Bros, which traded as White Rose, included this 1929 normal-control Leyland Lioness now owned by Peter Stanier. Its Burlingham bodywork is fitted with a folding canvas roof to enable operation in open-top form when the British summer allowed.
PHILIP LAMB

Peter Stanier Collection

Phone : 01474 814476

Brief description: A collection of preserved Leyland petrol-engined vehicles with their origins in the island of Jersey.

Opening days/times: Not normally open for viewing. Arrangements to visit can be made, by appointment, telephoning first for details.

Plymouth City Transport Preservation Group

Registration	Date	Chassis make	Chassis model	Body make	Original operator	Fleet No	Status
TCO 537	1960	Leyland	Atlantean PDR1/1	Metro Cammell	Plymouth Corporation	137	R
WJY 758	1962	Leyland	Atlantean PDR1/1	Metro Cammell	Plymouth Corporation	158	R
DDR 201C	1965	Leyland	Atlantean PDR1/1	Metro Cammell	Plymouth City Transport	201	R
NFJ 592M	1973	Bristol	LH6L	ECW	Western National Omnibus Co	1592	A
STK 129T	1979	Leyland	Atlantean AN68A/1R	Park Royal	Plymouth City Transport	129	RP
STK 131T	1979	Leyland	Atlantean AN68A/1C	Park Royal	Plymouth City Transport	131	R
STK 133T	1979	Leyland	Atlantean AN68A/1R	Park Royal	Plymouth City Transport	133	RP
VJY 141V	1980	Leyland	Atlantean AN68A/1R	East Lancs	Plymouth Corporation	141	A
TTT 168X	1981	Leyland	Atlantean AN68C/1R	East Lancs	Plymouth City Transport	168	R
TTT 170X	1981	Leyland	Atlantean AN68C/1R	East Lancs	Plymouth City Transport	170	A
TTT 171X	1981	Leyland	Atlantean AN68C/1R	East Lancs	Plymouth City Transport	171	R

Address: The Tramshed, Milehouse Bus Depot, Milehouse Road, Plymouth, Devon. PL3 4AA

Contact address: Secretary PCTPG, c/o 7 Greenfield Drive, Ivybridge, Devon PL21 0UG

Phone: 01752 691602 or 07779 004813

E-mail: enquiries@plymouthcitytransport.co.uk

Website: www.plymouthcitytransport.co.uk

Brief description: The group was formed in July 2006 by founder members Ralph Delbridge, Gareth Ruby and Ian Byrne. Our aim is to preserve the history of Plymouth City Transport through vehicle preservation, archiving of photos, documents, artefacts and making the vehicles accessible to all. A collection of 11 former Plymouth vehicles have been collected to date. Vehicles used on running days are supported by a group sales/exhibition vehicle.

Opening days/times: Please see website for all information

Charges: Free rides at events.

Directions by car: Plymouth city centre (various locations)

A38 Plymouth Devon

Directions by public transport: Several running days integrate with Plymouth railway station and stop near the City's Bretonside bus station

Facilities: A B(e) S

Other information: Membership forms can be downloaded on line or send a SSAE to the secretary as per contact details. Concession £8, Adult £12, Family £20 for 12 months membership

Plymouth City Transport's predominantly red livery is shown to advantage by its former 201 (DDR 201C), a 1965 Metro-Cammell bodied Leyland Atlantean PDR1/1, now part of the Plymouth City Transport Preservation Group's collection. PHILIP LAMB

Registration	Date	Chassis make	Chassis model	Body make	Original operator	Fleet No	Status
CK 4474	1931	Leyland	Tiger TS3	Leyland	Ribble Motor Services	1117	A
RN 7588	1935	Leyland	Tiger TS7	Burlingham	Ribble Motor Services	209	RP
TJ 6760	1935	Leyland	Lion LT5A	Leyland	Lytham St Annes Corporation	24	RP
RN 7824	1936	Leyland	Cheetah LZ2	Brush	Ribble Motor Services	1568	RP
BTF 25	1937	Leyland	Titan TD4c	Leyland	Lytham St Annes Corporation	45	A
RN 8622	1939	Leyland	Titan TD5	Alexander	Ribble Motor Services	2057	R
ACK 796	1944	Guy	Arab II	Northern Counties / Bond	Ribble Motor Services	2413	A
DRN 289	1950	Leyland	Titan PD2/3	Leyland	Ribble Motor Services	1349	A
MTC 540	1950	AEC	Regent III 9613E	Park Royal	Morecambe & Heysham Corporation	72	RP
ERN 700	1952	Leyland	Royal Tiger PSU1/13	Leyland	Ribble Motor Services	377	RP
FCK 884	1954	Leyland	Tiger Cub PSUC1/1T	Saunders Roe	Ribble Motor Services	452	R
HRN 31	1955	Leyland	Titan PD2/13	Metro Cammell	Ribble Motor Services	1391	A
JFV 527	1955	Commer	TS3	Harrington	Abbott of Blackpool		A
JCK 542	1956	Leyland	Titan PD2/12	Burlingham	Ribble Motor Services	1467	RP
528 CTF	1957	Leyland	Titan PD2/40	Weymann	J Fishwick & Sons of Leyland	5	R
881 BTF	1958	Leyland	Titan PD2/41	East Lancs	Lancaster City Transport	881	A
KCK 869	1958	Leyland	Titan PD3/4	Burlingham	Ribble Motor Services	1523	A
MBN 177	1958	Leyland	Titan PD3/5	East Lancs	Bolton Corporation	122	RP
NRN 586	1960	Leyland	Atlantean PDR1/1	Metro Cammell	Ribble Motor Services	1686	R
SFV 421	1960	Leyland	Atlantean PDR1/1	Weymann	W C Standerwick	25	A
PCK 618	1961	Leyland	Leopard L2	Harrington	Ribble Motor Services	1036	R
PRN 145	1961	Leyland	Atlantean PDR1/1	Metro Cammell	Scout Motor Services of Preston	5	A
PRN 906	1961	Leyland	Titan PD3/4	Metro Cammell	Preston Corporation	14	A
RRN 428	1962	Leyland	Atlantean PDR1/1	Weymann	Ribble Motor Services	1279	RP
RCK 938	1962	Leyland	Titan PD3/5	Metro Cammell	Ribble Motor Services	1793	A
TCK 465	1963	Leyland	Leopard PSU3/1R	Marshall	Ribble Motor Services	465	A
TCK 726	1963	Leyland	Leopard PSU3/3RT	Harrington	Ribble Motor Services	726	A
TRN 731	1964	Leyland	Leopard PSU3/3R	Plaxton	W C Standerwick	731S	R
ARN 811C	1965	Leyland	Leopard PSU3/3RT	Weymann	Ribble Motor Services	811	R
FPT 6G	1969	Leyland	Leopard PSU3/3RT	Plaxton	Weardale Motor Services of Frosterley		A
LRN 321J	1970	Bristol	RESL6L	Marshall	Ribble Motor Services	321	A
NCK 106J	1971	Leyland	Leopard PSU4	Plaxton	Ribble Motor Services	1006	RP
NCK 338J	1971	Bristol	RESL6L	ECW	Ribble Motor Services	338	R
PTF 714L	1972	Bristol	RELH6L	ECW	Ribble Motor Services	1019	A
PTF 718L	1972	Leyland	National 1151/2R/0401	Leyland National	Ribble Motor Services	372	A
PTF 727L	1972	Leyland	National 1151/2R/0401	Leyland National	Ribble Motor Services	386	R

Ribble Vehicle Preservation Trust

Contact: 37 Hall Park, Lancaster. LA1 4SH

E-mail: ray.bignell@btinternet.com

Website: www.rvpt.org

Brief description: Collection of mainly Ribble group vehicles which are regularly displayed and/or used in service at events throughout the year.

Events planned in 2010: No specific RVPT events in 2010. Buses will appear at other events; please see RVPT website for details.

The Saunders-Roe bodywork on this 1954 former Ribble Motor Services Leyland Tiger Cub may be identified by the chrome strips and recessed windscreens. No 452 (FCK 884) is one of a number of preserved ex-Ribble buses and coaches maintained by the Ribble Vehicle Preservation Trust.
PHILIP LAMB

Registration	Date	Chassis make	Chassis model	Body make	Original operator	Fleet No	Status
UTF 732M	1974	Leyland	Leopard PSU3B/4R	Duple	Ribble Motor Services	1052	R
MFR 306P	1976	Leyland	Leopard PSU3C/2R	Alexander	Lancaster City Transport	306	R
XCW 955R	1978	Leyland	National 11351A/1R	Leyland National	J Fishwick & Sons of Leyland	24	R
TRN 481V	1979	Leyland	Atlantean AN68A/1R	ECW	Ribble Motor Services	1481	R
DBV 100W	1980	Leyland	Olympian B45	ECW	Ribble Motor Services	2100	RP
DBV 831W	1980	Leyland	National 2 NL106L11/1R	Leyland National	Ribble Motor Services	831	R
B900 WRN	1983	Leyland	Tiger TRCTL11/2RH	Duple	Ribble Motor Services	900	RP
G186 JHG	1989	Leyland	Olympian ONLXB/2R2	Alexander	Ribble (Stagecoach)	2186	R

Contact address: Fir Tree Farm, The Common, Corley Moor, Coventry. CV7 8AR

Phone: 01676 541802

E-mail: Rogerrbctc@aol.com

Brief description: A collection of post-war touring and express coaches supplemented by Midlands originated historic buses and coaches

Events planned in 2010:

Visiting many UK Bus Rallies and Transport Events around the UK

Opening days/times: Collection open to visitors by prior arrangement.

Facilities: B P T

Registration	Date	Chassis make	Chassis model	Body make	Original operator	Fleet No	Status
VG 5541	1933	Bristol	GJW	Weymann	Norwich Electric Tramways		RP
EVC 244	1940	Daimler	COG5/40	Park Royal	Coventry City Transport	244	A
JYC 855	1947	Leyland	Tiger PS1	Harrington	Scarlet Motors of Minehead		R
GOU 732	1949	Tilling Stevens	K6LA7	Scottish Aviation	Altonian Coaches of Alton		R
FNV 557	1950	Leyland	Tiger PS2/3	Whitson	Church ('Royal Blue') of Pytchley		R
GKV 94	1950	Daimler	CVA6	Metro Cammell	Coventry City Transport	94	RP
LTA 813	1950	Bristol	KS5G	ECW	Western National Omnibus Co	994	R
LTA 898	1951	Bristol	LL6B	Duple	Southern National Omnibus Co	1269	A
NTU 125	1951	Foden	PVRF6	Metalcraft	Hollinshead of Biddulph		R
EHL 336	1952	Leyland	Tiger PS2/13A	Roe	West Riding Automobile Co	725	R
NXL 847	1953	AEC	Regal III 6821A	Duple	Eastern Belle of Bow London		R
OTT 43	1953	Bristol	LS6G	ECW	Western National Omnibus Co (Royal Blue)	2200	R
WKJ 787	1956	Beadle-Commer		Beadle	Beadle Demonstrator		R
780 GHA	1959	BMMO	C5	BMMO	BMMO ('Midland Red')	4780	R
56 GUO	1961	Bristol	MW6G	ECW	Western National Omnibus Co (Royal Blue)	2267	RP
5056 HA	1962	BMMO	S15	BMMO	BMMO ('Midland Red')	5056	R
EHA 424D	1966	BMMO	D9	BMMO/Willowbrook	BMMO ('Midland Red')	5424	R
OTA 640G	1969	Bristol	RELH6G	ECW	Southern National Omnibus Co (Royal Blue)	2380	R
PHA 505G	1969	BMMO	S22	BMMO	Midland Red Omnibus Co	5905	A

Underfloor-engined single-deck coaches were finding favour with operators the length and breadth of the country when front-engined NXL 847 was delivered to Eastern Belle of Bow, London in 1953. This Duple-bodied AEC Regal III, owned by Roger Burdett is unusual in being 30-foot long. PHILIP LAMB

Registration	Date	Chassis make	Chassis model	Body make	Original operator	Fleet No	Status
CET 613	1943	Sunbeam	MS2c	East Lancs	Rotherham Corporation	88	RP
FET 617	1950	Daimler	CTE6	Roe	Rotherham Corporation	37	R

Rotherham Trolleybus Group

Contact address: 113 Tinker Lane, Walkley, Sheffield. S6 5EA

Phone: 0114 266 3173

Brief description: This group is open to all with an interest in Rotherham area trolleys, the vehicles and the system. Active restoration of the vehicles takes place and the group works closely with the Trolleybus Museum at Sandtoft.

Registration	Date	Chassis make	Chassis model	Body make	Original operator	Fleet No	Status
KGK 529	1949	Leyland	Titan 6RT	Leyland	London Transport	RTW29	R
KGK 575	1949	Leyland	Titan 6RT	Leyland	London Transport	RTW75	R
KLB 881	1949	Leyland	Titan 6RT	Leyland	London Transport	RTW151	A
KLB 908	1949	Leyland	Titan 6RT	Leyland	London Transport	RTW178	R
KLB 915	1949	Leyland	Titan 6RT	Leyland	London Transport	RTW185	R
LLU 957	1950	Leyland	Titan 6RT	Leyland	London Transport	RTW467	R
LLU 987	1950	Leyland	Titan 6RT	Leyland	London Transport	RTW497	R

RTW Bus Group

Contact address: 7 Oldbury Close, St Mary Cray. BR5 3TH

Brief description: The group was formed in 1999, and comprises the owners of the preserved RTW vehicles and those interested in the type. The vehicles appear at rallies from time to time. A DVD on the history of the RTW is available from the Group.

Above: **An RTW bus group get-together at Alton last year, marking the 60 anniversary of the type's entry into service, sees five of the seven group members together.**
NIGEL APPLEFORD

Left: **Resplendent former London Transport RTW185 (KLB 915), a 1949 all-Leyland 6RT, is one of seven preserved examples owned by members of the RTW Bus Group.**
PHILIP LAMB

SELNEC Preservation Society

Contact address: 267 Rivington Crescent, Pendlebury, Swinton, Manchester. M27 8TQ

Phone: 0161 736 9899 or 0161 736 9898

Email: webmaster@selnec.org.uk

Website: www.selnec.org.uk

Brief description: A collection of buses from the SELNEC era, including the SELNEC Standard, Mancunian and a range of vehicles operated throughout central Manchester.

Events planned in 2010: Will visit a number of local rallies, road runs and shows in the North West of England.

Greater Manchester PTE 3001 (ANA 1Y), a 1982 Northern Counties-bodied Leyland Olympian, was numerically the first production example of the type for this operator, and an exhibit at the 1982 Motor Show. The SELNEC Preservation Society has restored the bus to as-new condition. PHILIP LAMB

Registration	Date	Chassis make	Chassis model	Body make	Original operator	Fleet No	Status
EN 9965	1950	Leyland	Titan PD2/4	Weymann	Bury Corporation	165	RP
DNF 708C	1965	Daimler	Fleetline CRG6LX	Metro Cammell	Manchester Corporation	4708	A
END 832D	1966	Leyland	Atlantean PDR1/2	Metro Cammell	Manchester Corporation	3832	RP
GNB 518D	1966	Bedford	VAL14	Plaxton	Manchester Corporation	205	A
LNA 166G	1968	Leyland	Atlantean PDR2/1	Park Royal	Manchester City Transport	1066	R
NNB 547H	1969	Leyland	Atlantean PDR2/1	East Lancs	Manchester City Transport	1142	A
NNB 589H	1970	Daimler	Fleetline CRG6LXB	Park Royal	SELNEC PTE	2130	A
ONF 865H	1970	Leyland	Atlantean PDR2/1	Park Royal	SELNEC PTE	1177	A
PNF 941J	1971	Leyland	Atlantean PDR1A/1	Northern Counties	SELNEC PTE	EX1	R
RNA 220J	1971	Daimler	Fleetline CRG6LXB	Park Royal	SELNEC PTE	2220	A
TNB 759K	1972	Daimler	Fleetline CRG6LXB	Northern Counties	SELNEC PTE	EX19	A
VNB 132L	1972	Leyland	Atlantean AN68/1R	Park Royal	SELNEC PTE	7032	R
VNB 173L	1972	Leyland	Atlantean AN68/1R	Northern Counties	SELNEC PTE	7147	A
VNB 177L	1972	Daimler	Fleetline CRG6LXB	Northern Counties	SELNEC PTE	7206	R
VNB 203L	1972	Daimler	Fleetline CRG6LXB	Northern Counties	SELNEC PTE	7232	R
WBN 955L	1972	Leyland	Atlantean AN68/1R	Park Royal	SELNEC PTE	7077	R
YDB 453L	1972	Seddon	Pennine IV-236	Seddon	SELNEC PTE	1700	R
AJA 408L	1973	Bristol	VRTSL2/6LXB	ECW	SELNEC Cheshire Bus Co	408	R
WWH 43L	1973	Daimler	Fleetline CRG6LXB	Park Royal	SELNEC PTE	7185	R
XJA 534L	1973	Leyland	Atlantean AN68/1R	Park Royal	SELNEC PTE	7143	A
XVU 341M	1973	Seddon	Pennine IV-236	Seddon	SELNEC PTE	1711	A
YNA 321M	1973	Daimler	Fleetline CRG6LXB	Northern Counties	SELNEC PTE	7366	A
XVU 363M	1974	Seddon	Pennine IV-236	Seddon	Greater Manchester PTE	1733	A
BNE 729N	1974	Seddon	Pennine IV-236	Seddon	Greater Manchester PTE	1735	A
BNE 751N	1974	Leyland	Atlantean AN68/1R	Northern Counties	Greater Manchester PTE	7501	A
BNE 764N	1974	Bristol	LH6L	ECW	Greater Manchester PTE	1321	A
HNB 24N	1975	Leyland	National 10351/1R	Leyland National	Greater Manchester PTE	105	R
OBN 502R	1977	Leyland	Fleetline FE30GR	Northern Counties	Lancashire United Transport	485	A
PTD 640S	1977	Leyland	Fleetline FE30GR	Northern Counties	Lancashire United Transport	496	A
XBU 1S	1978	Leyland	Fleetline FE30GR	Northern Counties	Greater Manchester PTE	8001	R
ANE 2T	1979	Leyland	Titan TNLXB1RF	Park Royal	Greater Manchester PTE	4002	R
BNC 960T	1979	Leyland	Atlantean AN68A/1R	Park Royal	Greater Manchester PTE	7960	R
GBU 1V	1979	MCW	Metrobus DR101/6	MCW	Greater Manchester PTE	5001	R
GNF 15V	1980	Leyland	Titan TNTL11/1RF	Park Royal	Greater Manchester PTE	4015	A
GNF 16V	1980	Leyland	Fleetline FE30GR	Northern Counties	Greater Manchester PTE	8141	RP
HDB 116V	1980	Leyland	Fleetline FE30GR	Northern Counties	Greater Manchester PTE	8116	R
MNC 525W	1980	Leyland	Atlantean AN68A/1R	Northern Counties	Greater Manchester PTE	8325	A
NJA 568W	1980	Bristol	Olympian B45/TL11/1R	Northern Counties	Greater Manchester PTE	1451	R

Registration	Date	Chassis make	Chassis model	Body make	Original operator	Fleet No	Status
DWH 706W	1981	Leyland	Fleetline FE30GR	Northern Counties	Lancashire United Transport	613	R
SND 455X	1981	Leyland	Atlantean AN68B/1R	Northern Counties	Greater Manchester PTE	8455	A
SND 460X	1981	Leyland	Atlantean AN68B/1R	Northern Counties	Greater Manchester PTE	8460	R
ANA 1Y	1982	Leyland	Olympian ONTL11/1R	Northern Counties	Greater Manchester PTE	3001	R
SND 501X	1982	Leyland	Atlantean AN68B/1R	Northern Counties	Greater Manchester PTE	8501	A
WRJ 448X	1982	Volvo Ailsa	B55-10	Northern Counties	Greater Manchester PTE	1448	A
ANA 10Y	1983	Bristol	Olympian ONTL11/1R	Northern Counties	Greater Manchester PTE	3010	A
ANA 601Y	1983	Leyland	Atlantean AN68D/1R	Northern Counties	Greater Manchester PTE	8601	A
ANA 645Y	1983	Leyland	Atlantean AN68D/1R	Northern Counties	Greater Manchester PTE	8645	R
FWH 461Y	1983	Scania	BR112DH	Northern Counties	Greater Manchester PTE	1461	A
A700 HNB	1984	Leyland	Atlantean AN68D/1R	Northern Counties	Greater Manchester PTE	8700	RP
A472 HNC	1984	Dennis	Falcon V DD	Northern Counties	Greater Manchester PTE	1472	A
A701 LNC	1984	Leyland	Atlantean AN68D/1R	Northern Counties	Greater Manchester PTE	8701	A
A765 NNA	1984	Leyland	Atlantean AN68D/1R	Northern Counties	Greater Manchester PTE	8765	RP
A30 ORJ	1984	Leyland	Olympian ONLXB/1R	Northern Counties	Greater Manchester PTE	3030	RP
B101 SJA	1985	Leyland	Olympian ONLXB/1R	Northern Counties	Greater Manchester PTE	3101	A
B901 TVR	1985	Dennis	Dominator DDA	Northern Counties	Greater Manchester PTE	2001	A
B702 VVR	1985	Leyland	Cub CU435	Reeve Burgess	Greater Manchester PTE	1702	R
C751 YBA	1985	Dennis	Domino SDA	Northern Counties	Greater Manchester PTE	1751	R
C201 CBU	1986	Leyland	Olympian ONLXB/1R	Northern Counties	Greater Manchester PTE	3201	A
C225 CBU	1986	Leyland	Olympian ONLXB/1R	Northern Counties	Greater Manchester PTE	3225	A
C481 CBU	1986	Volvo	Citybus B10M-50	Northern Counties	Greater Manchester PTE	1481	A
C823 CBU	1986	Dodge	S 56	Northern Counties	Greater Manchester PTE	1823	RP
D302 JVR	1986	MCW	Metrobus DR102/51	Northern Counties	Greater Manchester PTE	5302	A
D501 LNA	1986	Leyland	Lynx	Leyland Lynx	Greater Manchester Buses	501	A
D277 JVR	1987	Leyland	Olympian ONLXB/1R	Northern Counties	Greater Manchester Buses	3277	RP
D320 LNB	1987	MCW	Metrobus DR102/51	Northern Counties	Greater Manchester Buses	5320	R
D509 MJA	1987	Iveco	49-10	Robin Hood	Greater Manchester Buses	1509	A
F301 DRJ	1989	Leyland	Olympian ONLXB/1RZ	Northern Counties	Greater Manchester Buses	3301	A
F305 DRJ	1989	Leyland	Olympian ONLXB/1RZ	Northern Counties	Greater Manchester Buses	3305	A
H140 GVM	1991	Dennis	Dominator DDA	Northern Counties	Greater Manchester Buses	2040	A
H467 GVM	1991	Scania	N113 DRB	Northern Counties	Greater Manchester Buses	1467	R

Above right: **The SELNEC Preservation Society has secured many of Greater Manchester PTE's firsts. Its former 5001 (GBU 1V) was numerically the first MCW Metrobus delivered to the operator in 1979.** PHILIP LAMB

Right: **The 1986 deregulation of the country's bus services saw Greater Manchester Buses launch a number of routes on Merseyside using Birkenhead & District-liveried vehicles. This short-lived excursion is recalled by the SELNEC Preservation Society on its 1980 Northern Counties-bodied Leyland Fleetline 4116 (HDB 116V).** PHILIP LAMB

Southampton & District Transport Heritage Trust

Contact address: 104 Oak Tree Road, Southampton. SO18 1PH

Email: chene.arbre@talktalk.net

Brief description: The collection includes a selection of Southampton's fleet from the early 1970s. The small membership carries out restoration work. Several of the vehicles are privately owned by Trust members.

Registration	Date	Chassis make	Chassis model	Body make	Original operator	Fleet No	Status
FTR 511	1949	Guy	Arab III	Park Royal	Southampton Corporation	64	R
LOW 217	1954	Guy	Arab III	Park Royal	Southampton Corporation	71	R
JOW 928	1955	Guy	Arab UF	Park Royal	Southampton Corporation	255	RP
318 AOW	1962	AEC	Regent V 2D3RA	Park Royal	Southampton Corporation	318	RP
335 AOW	1963	Leyland	Titan PD2A/27	Park Royal	Southampton Corporation	335	RP
370 FCR	1963	AEC	Regent V 2D3RA	East Lancs	Southampton Corporation	350	R
JOW 499E	1967	AEC	Swift MP2R	Strachan	Southampton Corporation	1	RP
KOW 901F	1967	AEC	Regent V 3D2RA	East Lancs Neepsend	Southampton Corporation	393	RP
KOW 910F	1967	AEC	Regent V 3D2RA	East Lancs Neepsend	Southampton Corporation	402	RP
PCG 889G	1968	AEC	Reliance 6MU3R	Plaxton	Coliseum Coaches of Southampton		A
TTR 167H	1970	Leyland	Atlantean PDR1A/1	East Lancs	Southampton Corporation	133	R
HNP 989J	1971	Leyland	Atlantean PDR1A/1	East Lancs	Southampton Corporation	139	R
BCR 379K	1972	Seddon	Pennine RU	Pennine	Southampton Corporation	15	RP
NLP 389V	1979	Leyland	National 2 NL116L11/3R	Leyland National	British Airways	C279	R

Southdown Historic Vehicle Group

Contact address: 73 Cuckfield Crescent, Worthing, West Sussex.

E-mail: southdownqueenmary@ntlworld.com

Website: http://home.fastnet.co.uk/gerrycork/worthingbusrally.htm

Brief description: A private collection of vehicles, most of which operated for Southdown Motor Services or have south coast connections. The collection is not on public view but vehicles are rallied and often appear in service on runnning days.

Events planned in 2010

25 July — Worthing Running Day

Registration	Date	Chassis make	Chassis model	Body make	Original operator	Fleet No	Status
GUF 191	1945	Guy	Arab II	Northern Counties	Southdown Motor Services	451	RP
GFY 406	1950	Leyland	Titan PD2/3	Leyland	Southport Corporation	106	R
LRV 992	1956	Leyland	Titan PD2/12	Metro Cammell	Portsmouth Corporation	2	R
YTG 304	1958	Leyland	Titan PD3/4	Massey	Llynfi Motors	72	A
XUF 141	1960	Leyland	Tiger Cub PSUC1/2	Weymann	Southdown Motor Services	1141	R
70 AUF	1962	Commer	Avenger IV	Harrington	Southdown Motor Services	70	A
XWV 416A	1963	AEC	Regent V 2D3RV	East Lancs	Eastbourne Corporation	68	RP
8859 VR	1964	AEC	Regent V 2D3RA	East Lancs Neepsend	A Mayne & Son of Manchester		RP
972 CUF	1964	Leyland	Titan PD3/4	Northern Counties	Southdown Motor Services	972	R
401 DCD	1964	Leyland	Titan PD3/4	Northern Counties	Southdown Motor Services	401	R
412 DCD	1964	Leyland	Titan PD3/4	Northern Counties	Southdown Motor Services	412	R
416 DCD	1964	Leyland	Titan PD3/4	Northern Counties	Southdown Motor Services	416	R
419 DCD	1964	Leyland	Titan PD3/4	Northern Counties	Southdown Motor Services	419	R
PRX 187B	1964	Leyland	Titan PD3/4	Northern Counties	Southdown Motor Services	415	RP
BUF 122C	1965	Leyland	Leopard PSU3/1RT	Marshall	Southdown Motor Services	122	R
BUF 260C	1965	Leyland	Titan PD3/4	Northern Counties	Southdown Motor Services	260	R
BUF 277C	1965	Leyland	Titan PD3/4	Northern Counties	Southdown Motor Services	277	R
BUF 426C	1965	Leyland	Titan PD3/4	Northern Counties	Southdown Motor Services	426	R
BJK 672D	1966	Leyland	Titan PD2A/30	East Lancs	Eastbourne Corporation	72	R

FCD 294D	1966	Leyland	Titan PD3/4	Northern Counties	Southdown Motor Services	294	R
DHC 784E	1967	Leyland	Titan PD2A/30	East Lancs	Eastbourne Corporation	84	R
KUF 199F	1968	Leyland	Leopard PSU3/1RT	Willowbrook	Southdown Motor Services	199	R
PUF 165H	1969	Leyland	Leopard PSU3/1RT	Northern Counties	Southdown Motor Services	465	R
TCD 374J	1970	Daimler	Fleetline CRG6LX	Northern Counties	Southdown Motor Services	374	R
TCD 383J	1970	Daimler	Fleetline CRG6LX	Northern Counties	Southdown Motor Services	383	RP
TCD 481J	1970	Bristol	RESL6L	Marshall	Southdown Motor Services	481	R
TCD 490J	1970	Bristol	RESL6L	Marshall	Southdown Motor Services	490	RP
UUF 116J	1971	Bristol	VRTSL6LX	ECW	Southdown Motor Services	516	R
UUF 335J	1971	Leyland	Leopard PSU3B/4RT	Plaxton	Southdown Motor Services	1835	R
SCD 731N	1974	Leyland	Atlantean AN68/1R	Park Royal - Roe	Southdown Motor Services	731	R
RUF 37R	1977	Leyland	National 11351A/2R	Leyland National	Southdown Motor Services	37	R
HNP 154S	1978	Leyland	Atlantean AN68A/1R	East Lancs	Brighton Corporation	3	R
ANJ 306T	1978	Leyland	Leopard PSU3E/4RT	Plaxton	Southdown Motor Services	1306	R
OPV 821	1979	Leyland	Leopard PSU3E/4RT	Plaxton	Southdown Motor Services	1321	RP
USV 324	1979	Leyland	Leopard PSU3E/4RT	Plaxton	Southdown Motor Services	1320	RP

Below: **Recently restored Bristol VRTSL6LX Southdown 516 (UUF 116J) is seen in action at the Worthing Running Day in July 2009.** DAVID JUKES

Left: **The former Southdown Northern Counties bodied Leyland Titan PD3/4 is numerically the best-represented vehicle type within the Southdown Historic Vehicle Group collection. Its eldest example is 972 (972 CUF) of 1964, complete with illuminated advertisement panel on its offside.** DAVID JUKES

St Margaret's School Transport Society

Registration	Date	Chassis make	Chassis model	Body make	Original operator	Fleet No	Status
CMS 201	1949	Leyland	Tiger PS1	Alexander	Alexander	PA133	R
GWM 816	1951	Crossley	SD42/7	Crossley	Southport Corporation	116	RP

Contact address: St Margaret's High School, Aigburth Road, Liverpool. L17 6AB

Telephone: 0151 427 1825

Brief description: Formed in 1979, the Society specialises in single deck half-cabs from the 1940s and 1950s. Meetings are held regularly to carry out vehicle restoration. Visitors are welcome but prior appointment is essential. Please contact the address given.

Telford Bus Group

Contact address: Publicity Officer, Telford Bus Group, 2 Clifton Avenue, Brownhills, Walsall, West Midlands . WS8 7DU

Phone: 07968 410306

E-mail: telfordbusgroup@yahoo.co.uk

Website: www.tbg.150m.com

Brief description: The Telford Bus Group was establshed in 1990 to bring together some preserved bus owners and local bus enthusiasts, some of who are actively involved in the upkeep and restoration of Member's vehicles, but most simply support the others' efforts by travelling to the bus rallies or other events around the country in the summer months.

The Telford Bus Group has a number of Bedford VALs within its collection. BHO 670J is a Duple Viceroy 37-bodied VAL70 that was new to Castle Coaches of Waterlooville, Hampshire. It is seen in nearby Horndean during a visit to its former haunts.
PHILIP LAMB

Registration	Date	Chassis make	Chassis model	Body make	Original operator	Fleet No	Status
LFM 404	1950	Bedford	OB	Duple	Crosville Motor Services	SL67	A
386 DD	1961	Bedford	J2	Plaxton	Talbott of Moreton-in-Marsh		RP
3190 UN	1962	Commer	Avenger IV	Plaxton	Wright of Penycae		R
9797 DP	1964	Bedford	VAL14	Duple	Smiths of Reading		RP
CTT 774C	1965	Bedford	VAS1	Duple	Heard of Bideford		A
EHL 472D	1966	Bedford	VAL14	Plaxton	West Riding Automobile Co	3	R
JTH 100F	1968	Bedford	VAM14	Duple	Davies of Pencader		RP
RBC 345G	1969	Bedford	VAL70	Duple	Cook of Dunstable		RP
WWY 115G	1969	Bedford	VAL70	Plaxton	Abbey Coachways of Selby		R
BWP 727H	1970	Bedford	VAM70	Plaxton	Regent Motors of Redditch		A
VBD 310H	1970	Bedford	VAL70	Plaxton	Coales of Woolaston		R
FYG 663J	1970	Bedford	VAL70	Willowbrook	Wigmore of Dinnington		RP
BHO 670J	1971	Bedford	VAL70	Duple	Castle Coaches of Waterlooville		R
RNA 236J	1971	Daimler	Fleetline CRG6LXB-33	Park Royal	SELNEC PTE	2236	R
TUX 906J	1971	Bedford	YRQ	Duple	Corvedale of Ludlow	6	A
CDC 166K	1972	Seddon	Pennine VI	Plaxton	Bob's of Middlesbrough	26	RP
CDC 167K	1972	Seddon	Pennine VI	Plaxton	Bob's of Middlesbrough	27	A
CDC 168K	1972	Seddon	Pennine VI	Plaxton	Bob's of Middlesbrough	28	RP
FAR 724K	1972	Bedford	VAL70	Duple	Langley Coaches of Slough		RP
XUR 290K	1972	Bedford	VAL70	Plaxton	Morgan of Bognor Regis		R
DNT 174L	1973	Bedford	YRQ	Duple	Prince of Newcastle		A
JHA 227L	1973	Leyland	Leopard PSU3B/2R	Marshall	Midland Red Omnibus Co	227	R
HNT 945N	1974	Bedford	VAS	Duple	Corvedale of Ludlow		A
BOK 1V	1979	MCW	Metrobus DR102/12	MCW	West Midlands PTE	2001	RP
UIB 5303	1984	MCW	Metroliner CR126/1	MCW	East Kent Road Car Co	8846	RP
D536 NDA	1986	Freight Rover	Sherpa 350	Carlyle	West Midlands PTE	536	RP

Former SELNEC PTE 2236 (RNA 236J), a 1971 Daimler Fleetline CRG6LXB-33 with Park Royal 'Mancunian' bodywork, has been restored to later Greater Manchester PTE condition by the Telford Bus Group. DAVID JUKES

Registration	Date	Chassis make	Chassis model	Body make	Original operator	Fleet No	Status
KD 5296	1928	Leyland	Tiger TS2	Harrington	Imperial Motor Services of Liverpool		A
VRF 372	1951	Foden	PVRF6	Harrington	Bassett's Coaches of Tittensor		A
JAP 698	1954	Harrington	Contender	Harrington	Audawn Coaches of Corringham		RP
YYB 118	1957	Dennis	Lancet UF	Harrington	Hutchings & Cornelius Services of South Petherton		RP
PFR 747	1959	Bedford	SB3	Harrington	Abbotts of Blackpool		A
487 GFR	1964	AEC	Reliance 2U3RA	Harrington	Abbotts of Blackpool		R

TH Collection

Phone: 01263 834829

E-mail: thcollection@dsl.pipex.com

Website: www.thcoachwork.co.uk

Brief description: A private collection representing coachwork built by Thomas Harrington of Hove. It is believed the vehicles are now all unique examples of the chassis and body combination.

Opening days/times: Appointment only

Three Counties Bus and Commercial Vehicle Museum

Contact address: 18 Greenriggs, Stopsley, Luton, Beds. LU2 9TQ.

Phone: 01582 413200

E-mail: bristol.rell6l@googlemail.com

Website: www.3cbcvm.org.uk

Brief description: A large collection of vehicles, ranging from 1930 to the present day, predominantly from the local area of Hertfordshire, Bedfordshire and Buckinghamshire, and their operators. The group seeks to further the interest and onward preservation of vehicles from the area and encourage education about all aspects of passenger transport within the three counties.

Events planned in 2010:

Attendances by various vehicles from the collection at many rallies in the South East region.

Opening days/times: Contact us for details

Directions by car: Rally attendances only

Directions by public transport: Rally attendances only

Charges: None but donations towards vehicle restoration are always welcome.

Registration	Date	Chassis make	Chassis model	Body make	Original operator	Fleet No	Status
FXT 122	1939	Leyland	Cub REC	LPTB	London Transport	CR16	RP
DBL 154	1946	Bristol	K6A	ECW	Thames Valley Traction Co	446	R
CFN 104	1947	Leyland	Tiger PS1/1	Park Royal	East Kent Road Car Co		R
JWU 307	1950	Bedford	OB	Duple	Lunn of Rothwell		RP
LYR 915	1952	AEC	Regent III O961 RT	Weymann	London Transport	RT3496	R
MXX 434	1952	AEC	Regal IV 9821LT	Metro Cammell	London Transport	RF457	R
MXX 332	1953	Guy	Special NLLVP	ECW	London Transport	GS32	R
MXX 489	1953	AEC	Regal IV 9821LT	Metro Cammell	London Transport	RF512	RP
RSJ 747	1956	Albion	Victor FT39AN	Heaver	Guernsey Motor Co	69	R
VYO 767	1959	Bristol	MW6G	ECW	Tilling		RP
OVL 473	1960	Bristol	Lodekka FS5G	ECW	Lincolnshire Road Car Co	2378	R
EFM 631C	1965	Bristol	Lodekka FS6G	ECW	Crosville Motor Services	DFG182	R
DEK 3D	1966	Leyland	Titan PD2/37	Massey	Wigan Corporation	140	R
KBD 712D	1966	Bristol	Lodekka FS6G	ECW	United Counties Omnibus Co	712	R
KBD 715D	1966	Bristol	Lodekka FS6G	ECW	United Counties Omnibus Co	715	RP
NBD 311F	1967	Bristol	RELL6G	ECW	United Counties Omnibus Co	311	RP
RBD 319G	1968	Bristol	RELL6G	ECW	United Counties Omnibus Co	319	RP
UXD 129G	1968	Bristol	RELL6L	ECW	Luton Corporation	129	RP
UBD 757H	1969	Bristol	VRTSL6LX	ECW	United Counties Omnibus Co	757	A
VLW 444G	1969	AEC	Merlin 4P2R	MCW	London Transport	MBS444	A
VMO 234H	1969	Bristol	LH6L	ECW	Thames Valley Traction Co	214	RP
ANV 775J	1971	Bristol	VRTSL6G	ECW	United Counties Omnibus Co	775	R
WRP 767J	1971	Bristol	VRTSL6G	ECW	United Counties Omnibus Co	767	RP
JPL 153K	1972	Leyland	Atlantean PDR1A/1	Park Royal	London Country Bus Services	AN53	RP
GPD 313N	1974	Bristol	LHS6L	ECW	London Country Bus Services	BN45	RP
RBD 111M	1974	Bedford	YRT	Willowbrook	United Counties Omnibus Co	111	A
HBD 919T	1977	Bristol	VRT/SL3/6LXB	ECW	United Counties Omnibus Co	919	R
SOA 674S	1977	Leyland	Leopard PSU3E/4R	Plaxton	Midland Red Omnibus Co	674	R
SBD 525R	1977	Leyland	National 11351A/1R	Leyland National	United Counties Omnibus Co	525	RP
GCK 279S	1978	Bedford	YLQ	Plaxton	Battersbys Silver Grey Coaches		RP
XPK 51T	1978	AEC	Reliance 6U2R	Duple	London Country Bus Services	RB51	R
TPD 109X	1982	Leyland	Olympian ONTL11/1R	Roe	London Country Bus Services	LR9	A
C24 NVV	1985	Ford	Transit	Carlyle	United Counties Omnibus Co	24	A

1978 Duple Dominant II-bodied AEC Reliance XPK 51T has been restored to original Green Line condition as RB51 by members of the Three Counties Bus & Commercial Vehicle Museum. PHILIP LAMB

Registration	Date	Chassis make	Chassis model	Body make	Original operator	Fleet No	Status
SUG 591M	1974	Leyland	Atlantean AN68/2R	Roe	Leeds City Transport	591	RP
C507 KBT	1985	Leyland	Olympian ONTL11/1R	Optare	West Yorkshire PTE	5507	R
C807 KBT	1986	Leyland	Cub CU435	Optare	West Yorkshire PTE	1807	R
D705 HUA	1986	Freight Rover	350D	Optare	West Yorkshire PTE	1705	RP
D515 HUB	1987	Leyland	Olympian ONTL11/1R	Optare	Yorkshire Rider	5515	RP
D176 NON	1987	Freight Rover	Sherpa 350	Carlyle	Bee Line Buzz Company	176	A
E204 PWY	1987	Mercedes-Benz	811D	Optare	Yorkshire Rider	2204	RP
G254 JYG	1989	DAF	SB220	Optare	Yorkshire Rider	1254	RP

Optare rose from the ashes of Charles Roe in the mid-1980s, with some of its earlier output now joining the ranks of preserved vehicles. The Transport Yorkshire Preservation Group includes two former West Yorkshire PTE vehicles bodied by Optare in Leeds: 1985 Leyland Olympian 5507 (C507 KBT) and 1986 Leyland Cub 1807 (C807 KBT).
TYPG

Transport Yorkshire Preservation Group Ltd

Contact address: Unit 591, 57 Great George Street, Leeds. LS1 3AJ

E-mail: info@typg.org.uk

Website: www.typg.org.uk

Brief description: Collection of preserved vehicles new to West Yorkshire PTE and/or Yorkshire Rider. The vehicles are located in private buildings across the North of England and the Midlands. Our vehicles occasionally operate special services at events (both those organised by ourselves and by others).

Events planned in 2010:

No 2010 events, but a Deregulation 25 event in Leeds is being planned for Summer 2011.

Charges: donations

Facilities: B(e) D P

Registration	Date	Chassis make	Chassis model	Body make	Original operator	Fleet No	Status
RRU 903	1955	Leyland	Tiger Cub PSUC1/1	Park Royal	Bournemouth Corporation	266	R
8159 EL	1960	Leyland	Titan PD3/1	Weymann	Bournemouth Corporation	159	RP
H262 MFX	1991	Dennis	Dominator DDA	East Lancs	Bournemouth Yellow Buses	262	R

Vintage Yellow Buses of Devon
Dartmouth

Contact address: The Chalet, Church Hill, Kingswear, Dartmouth, Devon. TQ6OBX

Brief description: A small collection of privately owned buses from Bournemouth and Devon

Opening days/times: Not normally open, but visitors welcome by appointment only.

West Country Historic Omnibus and Transport Trust

Contact address: 6 Oak Drive, Portishead, Bristol. BS20 6SS

Phone: 01275 843967

E-mail: info@busmuseum.org.uk

Website: www.busmuseum.org.uk

Brief description: To establish and preserve for posterity a representative selection of omnibuses and other vehicles from the counties of Cornwall, Devon, Somerset and Dorset. Provide an archive of material relating to West Country road transport.

Events planned in 2010:

19 September — 8th West Country Historic Bus, Coach & Lorry Gathering, Devon County Showground, Westpoint, Exeter.

Registration	Date	Chassis make	Chassis model	Body make	Original operator	Fleet No	Status
EFJ 92	1938	Bedford	WTB	Heaver	Taylor of Exeter		RP
LTA 772	1951	Bristol	LWL5G	ECW	Western National Omnibus Co	1613	R
OTT 98	1952	Bristol	LS6G	ECW	Royal Blue (Southern National)	1299	R
86 GFJ	1963	Leyland	Titan PD2A/30	Massey	Exeter City Transport	86	R
OTA 632G	1969	Bristol	RELH6G	ECW	Southern National Omnibus Co (Royal Blue)	1460	R
TDV 217J	1970	Leyland	Panther PSUR1B/1R	Marshall	Devon General	217	R
VDV 137S	1977	Bristol	VRT/SL3/6LXB	ECW	Western National Omnibus Co (Devon General)	937	R
AFJ 727T	1979	Bristol	LH6L	Plaxton	Western National Omnibus Co	3307	R
AFJ 764T	1979	Bristol	VRT/SL3/6LXB	ECW	Western National Omnibus Co	1157	R
A927 MDV	1983	Ford	Transit 160D	Carlyle	Western National Omnibus Co (Devon General)	7	R
C705 FFJ	1986	Ford	Transit 160D	Robin Hood	Devon General Ltd	705	RP
C801 FRL	1986	Mercedes	L608D	Reeve Burgess	Western National Ltd	104	A
L929 CTT	1994	Iveco	59-12	Mellor	Devon General Ltd	1000	R
M627 HDV	1994	Iveco	59-12	Wadham Stringer	Devon General Ltd	1029	A

West Midlands Bus Preservation Society

Contact address: Secretary, 22 Beaumont Way, North Canes, Cannock. WS11 9FQ

Brief description: the main core of the collection is of vehicles from the West Midlands PTE in the period 1969 to 1986. Other artefacts are being collected for inclusion in a planned transport museum.

Opening days/times: The vehicles can be viewed by special arrangement — please contact the secretary.

Registration	Date	Chassis make	Chassis model	Body make	Original operator	Fleet No	Status
DUK 278	1946	Guy	Arab II	Roe	Wolverhampton Corporation	378	A
UHY 362	1955	Bristol	KSW6B	ECW	Bristol Tramways	8322	R
NOV 880G	1969	Daimler	Fleetline CRG6LX	Park Royal	Birmingham City Transport	3880	R
TOB 997H	1970	Daimler	Fleetline CRG6LX-33	Park Royal	West Midlands PTE	3997	A
HHA 101L	1972	Leyland	National 1151/1R/2501	Leyland National	Midland Red Omnibus Co	101	RP
TOE 527N	1974	Volvo Ailsa	B55-10	Alexander	West Midlands PTE	4527	R
NOC 600R	1976	Leyland	Fleetline FE30AGR	Park Royal	West Midlands PTE	6600	R
JOV 738P	1976	Volvo Ailsa	B55-10	Alexander	West Midlands PTE	4738	R
TVP 898S	1978	Daimler	Fleetline FE30AGR	MCW	West Midlands PTE	6898	R

Registration	Date	Chassis make	Chassis model	Body make	Original operator	Fleet No	Status
UO 2331	1927	Austin	20 5PL	Tiverton	Sidmouth Motor Co		RP
PSL 234	1931	Maudslay	ML3BC	Thurgood	Church ('Royal Blue') of Pytchley		A
JY 124	1932	Tilling Stevens	B10A2 Express	Beadle	Western National Omnibus Co	3379	RP
OD 5489	1933	Vauxhall	Cadet VY	Mount Pleasant	Davis of Rockbeare		R
OD 5868	1933	Leyland	Lion LT5	Weymann	Devon General	68	A
OD 7500	1934	AEC	Regent O661	Brush	Devon General	DR213	R
ADV 128	1935	Bristol	JO5G	Beadle	Western National Omnibus Co	222	RP
ATT 922	1935	Bristol	JJW6A	Beadle	Western National Omnibus Co	172	RP
AUO 74	1935	Leyland	Lion LT5A	(chassis only)	Devon General	SL79	A
FV 5737	1936	Leyland	Tiger TS7	Duple	Ribble Motor Services	753	R
JK 5605	1936	Leyland	Titan TD4	Leyland	Eastbourne Corporation	95	R
ADR 813	1938	Leyland	Titan TD5c	Leyland	Plymouth Corporation	141	R
BOW 162	1938	Bristol	L5G	Hants & Dorset	Hants & Dorset Motor Services	9081	A
BOW 169	1938	Bristol	L5G		Hants & Dorset Motor Services	TS676	A
EFJ 666	1938	Leyland	Tiger TS8	Cravens	Exeter Corporation	66	R
EFJ 241	1938	Leyland	Titan TD5	Leyland	Exeter Corporation	26	RP
EUF 204	1938	Leyland	Titan TD5	Park Royal	Southdown Motor Services	204	A
DOD 474	1940	AEC	Regal O662	Weymann	Devon General	SR474	RP
ETJ 108	1940	Leyland	Tiger TS11	Roe	Leigh Corporation	79	A
GTA 395	1941	Bristol	LL5G	Brislington Body Works	Southern National Omnibus Co	373	RP
JK 9115	1947	Leyland	Titan PD1	East Lancs	Eastbourne Corporation	17	A
AHL 694	1947	Leyland	Tiger PS1/1	Barnaby	J Bullock & Sons of Featherstone	284	R
KHU 624	1947	Bristol	K6B	ECW	Bristol Omnibus Co	3705	RP
GLJ 957	1948	Leyland	Titan PD1A	ECW	Hants & Dorset Motor Services	PD959	A
JFJ 606	1949	Daimler	CVD6	Brush	Exeter Corporation	43	A
KGU 434	1949	Leyland	Titan 7RT	Park Royal	London Transport	RTL358	RP

West of England Transport Collection

Contact address: 15 Land Park, Chulmleigh, Devon. EX18 7BH

Phone: 01769 580811

Website: www.winkleigh.net

Brief description: A large private collection of vehicles, mainly from West Country major operators. The collection includes buses, coaches and transport memorabilia.

Opening days/times: Viewing by prior arrangement with Colin Shears

Below: **Many vehicles at Winkleigh remain unrestored including this Roe-bodied Leyland-DAB, once no310 (RLN 237W) in the British Airways fleet.**
NIGEL APPLEFORD

Right: **Exeter Corporation specified a cutaway rear entrance on this 1938 Cravens-bodied Leyland Tiger TS8. The former 66 (EFJ 666) is part of the Winkleigh-based West of England Transport Collection.**
NIGEL APPLEFORD

A long term Winkleigh resident is this Hants & Dorset 1948 Leyland PD1A with ECW lowbridge bodywork, one of quite a number of similar Leylands supplied in the early postwar years to Tilling organisations due to a shortage of Bristol K chassis. NIGEL APPLEFORD

Registration	Date	Chassis make	Chassis model	Body make	Original operator	Fleet No	Status
LTV 702	1951	AEC	Regal III 9621E	East Lancs	Nottingham City Transport	702	A
Q995 CPE	1953	AEC	Regent III O961 RT	Park Royal	London Transport	RT4588	A
TFJ 808	1956	Guy	Arab IV	Massey	Exeter Corporation	50	A
WRL 16	1956	Rowe	Hillmaster	Reading	Millbrook Steamboat & Trading Co		A
ONV 425	1957	Bristol	SC4LK	ECW	United Counties Omnibus Co	125	RP
974 AFJ	1960	Guy	Arab IV	Massey	Exeter Corporation	74	R
484 EFJ	1962	Leyland	Titan PD2A/30	Massey	Exeter City Transport	84	A
815 KDV	1963	Bristol	Lodekka FLF6B	ECW	Western National Omnibus Co	2010	A
991 MDV	1963	AEC	Reliance 2MU3RV	Marshall	Devon General	991	A
HDV 626E	1967	Bristol	RELL6G	ECW	Western National Omnibus Co (Royal Blue)	2700	RP
VTY 543J	1970	Leyland	Leopard PSU3A/4R	Plaxton	Tyne Valley of Acomb		A
HTA 844N	1975	Leyland	National 11351/1R	Leyland National	Western National Omnibus Co	2813	
KTT 38P	1975	Bristol	LH6L	ECW	Western National (Devon General)	108	A
MPX 945R	1977	Ford	Transit	Robin Hood	Angela of Bursledon		A
PTT 106R	1977	Bristol	LH6L	Plaxton	Western National Omnibus Co	3406	A
CRM 927T	1979	Leyland/DAB	LG17575-690/4	Leyland	South Yorkshire PTE	2006	A
ATK 154W		Leyland	Atlantean AN68B/1R	East Lancs	Plymouth Citybus		
DBV 43W	1980	Leyland	Leopard PSU4E/4R	East Lancs	Burnley and Pendle	43	A
RLN 237W	1981	Leyland-DAB	6-35-690/4	Roe	British Airways	C310	A
YNW 33X	1982	Leyland	Leopard PSU3E/4R	Plaxton	Shilton of Leeds		R
A749 NTA	1984	Ford	Transit	Ford	Devon County Council		A
K361 LWS	1992	Leyland DAF	400	G & M	Rothwell of Plymouth		A
L512 BOD	1993	Leyland DAF	400	DAF	Okehampton College		RP

Workington Transport Heritage Trust

Contact: 22 Calva Road, Seaton, Workington, Cumbria. CA14 1DF

Phone: 01900 67389

E-mail: wthc@btopenworld.com

Brief description: A collection based around buses and fire engines from West Cumberland area. It is the aim to open to the public once a suitable building and funding have been arranged.

Registration	Date	Chassis make	Chassis model	Body make	Original operator	Fleet No	Status
RAO 733	1956	Bristol	Lodekka LD6G	ECW	Cumberland Motor Services	416	RP
109 DRM	1961	Bristol	Lodekka FS6G	ECW	Cumberland Motor Services	550	R
AAO 34B	1964	Bristol	MW6G	ECW	Cumberland Motor Services	231	R
DAO 295K	1972	Bristol	RELL6L	ECW	Cumberland Motor Services	295	RP
GRM 353L	1973	Leyland	National 1151/1R/0401	Leyland National	Cumberland Motor Services	353	RP
HHH 272N	1975	Bristol	VRTSL6G	ECW	Cumberland Motor Services	401	RP
VKU 78S	1978	Leyland	National 11351A/1R	Leyland National	Chesterfield Corporation	78	RP
WHH 556S	1978	Leyland	National 11351A/1R	Leyland National	Leyland Bus	REV01	R
KHH 378W	1980	Leyland	National 2 NL116L11/1R	Leyland National	Cumberland Motor Services	378	R
PHH 149W	1980	Bristol	VRT/SL3/6LXB	ECW	Cumberland Motor Services	431	R
F251 JRM	1989	Leyland	Lynx	Leyland	Cumberland Motor Services	251	R

Amongst the many privately preserved vehicles is this 1953 Bristol LS6B coach, Southern Vectis 311 (JDL 760). It is currently configured to provide useful overnight accommodation at events far away from its base. It is seen here taking part in a road run to Conwy during the 2008 Festival of Transport at Llandudno. PHILIP LAMB

The subject of a long and painstaking restoration, Derby 27 (ACH 627), a 1947 Brush-bodied Daimler CVD6, is a credit to its owner, British Bus Preservation Group Secretary, Geoff Clark. PHILIP LAMB

This section is included with the help and co-operation of the British Bus Preservation Group (BBPG). There are known to be many excellent privately preserved buses, coaches and trolleybuses in this country, and the list which follows is prepared from data provided by the group. All the vehicles are owned by BBPG members, and every effort has been made to ensure that the information given is correct at the time of going to press.

Condition of the vehicles varies; some having been fully restored (even to public operational standard in some cases) — others are undergoing restoration, often a lengthy job with limited resources, or are awaiting their turn for the day when the restoration task can be started. Those vehicles that are restored generally make visits to bus rallies the length and breadth of the country, details of such events may be found in *Bus & Coach Preservation* magazine.

If you are the owner of a preserved bus, coach or trolleybus that is not listed, you may wish to become a member of BBPG. Services to its members include a regular newsletter 'British Bus News', the chance to contact others with similar interests, and the ability to share information on vehicle restoration problems, projects and, of course, spare parts. Membership cost is £13 per annum and the BBPG may be contacted at the address below.

Contact address: BBPG, 25 Oldfield Road, Bexleyheath, Kent, DA7 4DX
E-mail: info@bbpg.co.uk
Website: www.bbpg.co.uk

British Bus Preservation Group

Registration	Date	Chassis make	Chassis model	Body make	Original operator	Fleet No	Status
PY 6170	1926	Morris Commercial	Z 15.9hp		Robinsons of Scarborough		R
FM 6397	1931	Leyland	Titan TD1	Leyland	Crosville Motor Services	45	RP
FM 6435	1931	Leyland	Lion LT2	Leyland	Crosville Motor Services	L7	RP
FM 7443	1932	Leyland	Cub KP2	Brush	Crosville Motor Services	716	RP
FM 9984	1936	Leyland	Tiger TS7	Harrington	Crosville Motor Services	K101	RP
JA 5528	1936	Bristol	JO5G	Brush	North Western Road Car Co	728	RP
BFM 144	1937	Leyland	Tiger TS7	ECW	Crosville Motor Services	KA27	R
JA 7770	1938	Bristol	L5G	Burlingham	North Western Road Car Co	346	RP
GKE 68	1939	Bristol	K5G	Weymann	Chatham & District Traction Co	874	A
JK 8418	1939	Leyland	Lion LT9	Leyland	Eastbourne Corporation	12	R
EFM 581	1940	Leyland	Tiger TS8	ECW	Crosville Motor Services	KA158	RP

Registration	Date	Chassis make	Chassis model	Body make	Original operator	Fleet No	Status
HKE 867	1945	Bristol	K6A	Weymann	Maidstone & District Motor Services	DH159	R
ACH 627	1947	Daimler	CVD6	Brush	Derby Corporation	27	A
ANH 154	1947	Daimler	CVG6	Northern Coachbuilders	Northampton Corporation	154	R
JXN 46	1948	AEC	Regent III O961 RT	Weymann	London Transport	RT 1018	R
KNN 254	1948	Leyland	Titan PD1A	Duple	Barton Transport of Chilwell	580	RP
KNN 959	1949	Daimler	CVD6	Roberts	Gash of Newark	DD6	RP
LHY 937	1949	Bristol	K6B	ECW	Bristol Tramways	3774	RP
KYY 529	1950	AEC	Regent III O961 RT	Park Royal	London Transport	RT1702	R
FFN 446	1951	Beadle-Leyland		Beadle	East Kent Road Car Co		RP
LYF 104	1951	Leyland	Titan 7RT	Park Royal	London Transport	RTL1163	R
LYR 672	1951	AEC	Regent III O961 RT	Park Royal	London Transport	RT2688	RP
MFM 39	1951	Bedford	OB	Duple	Crosville Motor Services	SL71	R
RSK 615	1951	Leyland	Royal Tiger PSU1/15	Duple	Jackson of Castle Bromwich		A
URE 281	1951	AEC	Regal III 9612A	Harrington	Lymers of Tean		R
LTX 311	1952	Leyland	Tiger PS2/5	Massey	Caerphilly Corporation	1	R
MLL 722	1952	AEC	Regal IV 9822E	Park Royal	British European Airways	1080	A
JDL 760	1953	Bristol	LS6B	ECW	Southern Vectis Omnibus Co		R
RFM 435	1954	Bristol	Lodekka LD6B	ECW	Crosville Motor Services		RP
783 EFM	1957	Bristol	SC4LK	ECW	Crosville Motor Services	SC13	R
XCV 326	1957	Bedford	SBG	Duple	Harper & Kellow of St. Agnes		A
PFW 935	1958	Bristol	SC4LK	ECW	Lincolnshire Road Car Co	2453	RP
129 DPT	1959	AEC	Reliance 2MU3RA	Plaxton	Howe of Spennymoor		R
107 GYC	1960	Bedford	SB3	Duple	Bowerman of Taunton		RP
387 HRR	1961	Leyland	Leopard L1	Willowbrook	East Midland Motor Services	R387	A
WKG 284	1961	AEC	Reliance 2MU3RA	Willowbrook	Western Welsh Omnibus Co	1284	R
811 BWR	1962	Bristol	SUL4A	ECW	West Yorkshire Road Car Co	SMA5	R
BKG 713B	1964	AEC	Renown 3B3RA	Northern Counties	Western Welsh Omnibus Co	713	R
103 GAA	1965	Bedford	SB5	Plaxton	Princess Coaches of Southampton		RP
BNH 246C	1965	Daimler	CVG6	Roe	Northampton Corporation	246	R
GJG 750D	1966	AEC	Regent V 2D3RA	Park Royal	East Kent Road Car Co		R
HHW 452D	1966	Bristol	MW5G	ECW	Bristol Omnibus Co	2636	RP
JJD 394D	1966	AEC	Routemaster R2RH/1	Park Royal	London Transport	RML2394	R
JJD 414D	1966	AEC	Routemaster R2RH/1	Park Royal	London Transport	RML2414	R
JJD 539D	1966	AEC	Routemaster R2RH/1	Park Royal	London Transport	RML2539	R
LAX 101E	1967	Bristol	RESL6L	ECW	Red & White Services	RS167	R
NDM 950E	1967	Bedford	VAM14	Duple Midland	Phillips of Holywell		A
SMK 716F	1967	AEC	Routemaster R2RH/1	Park Royal	London Transport	RML2716	R

Above: **Former Western Welsh 713 (BKG 713B) is a 1964 Northern Counties-bodied AEC Renown, privately preserved by BBPG members.** NIGEL APPLEFORD

Below: **Wilts & Dorset Motor Services received this dual-purpose Eastern Coach Works bodied Bristol RELL6G in 1971. BBPG members have returned 846 (TRU 947J) to its original Wilts & Dorset condition, complete with cream roof to highlight its superior internal specification.** NIGEL APPLEFORD

Above: **The smaller preserved BBPG affiliated vehicle is represented by RNE 692W, a 1981 Plaxton Mini Supreme-bodied Bedford CF new to Shearings Coaches of Altrincham and seating 17.**
NIGEL APPLEFORD

Below: **Returning to its former London haunts at Holloway garage is ex-London Transport BL49 (WYL 137, *OJD 49R*), a 1976 Eastern Coach Works-bodied Bristol LH6L.** NIGEL APPLEFORD

Registration	Date	Chassis make	Chassis model	Body make	Original operator	Fleet No	Status
SMK 747F	1967	AEC	Routemaster R2RH/1	Park Royal	London Transport	RML2747	A
LFS 296F	1968	Bristol	VRT/LL/6G	ECW	Scottish Omnibuses (Eastern Scottish)	AA296	R
JVV 267G	1968	Daimler	CVG6	Roe	Northampton Corporation	267	RP
YNU 351G	1968	Bristol	Lodekka FLF6G	ECW	Midland General Omnibus Co	313	R
MJA 895G	1969	Leyland	Titan PD3/14	East Lancs	Stockport Corporation	95	RP
TTA 400H	1970	Bedford	SB5	Duple	Otter Coaches of Ottery St Mary		R
CRR 537J	1970	Bristol	RELL6L	Marshall	East Midland Motor Services	0537	A
IJI 5367	1971	Bristol	RELH6L	Plaxton	Greenslades Tours of Exeter	300	RP
STL 725J	1971	Bedford	YRQ	Willowbrook	Simmonds of Great Gonnerby		RP
TRU 947J	1971	Bristol	RELL6G	ECW	Wilts & Dorset Motor Services	846	R
VOD 123K	1971	Bristol	LHS6L	Marshall	Western National Omnibus Co	1253	RP
XRD 23K	1971	Bristol	VRT/LL6G	Northern Counties	Reading Corporation	23	R
RVO 668L	1973	Leyland	Leopard PSU3B4R	Plaxton	Barton Transport of Chilwell	1246	R
PKH 600M	1974	Bedford	VAS	Plaxton	Hull City Football Club		R
GNM 235N	1975	Bristol	LHL6L	Plaxton	Richardsons G&M Coaches of London		A
WYL 137	1976	Bristol	LH6L	ECW	London Transport	BL 49	R
LWB 377P	1976	Ailsa	B55-10	Van Hool McArdle	South Yorkshire PTE	377	RP
NDP 31R	1976	Bristol	VRT/LL3/6LXB	Northern Counties	Reading Corporation	31	RP
NDP 38R	1976	Bristol	VRT/LL3/6LXB	Northern Counties	Reading Corporation	38	R
LOI 1859	1977	Bedford	YLQ	Alexander	Ulsterbus	1859	RP
UVX 7S	1977	Bristol	LH6L	ECW	Eastern National Omnibus Co	1103	RP
EWW 207T	1979	Leyland	Leopard PSU3E/4R	Plaxton	Wallace Arnold Tours of Leeds		RP
MGC 338V	1979	Leyland	Leopard PSU5C/4R	Plaxton	Richmond of Epsom		R
MWV 840	1980	Leyland	Leopard	Duple	Maidstone & District Motor Services		R
VIB 5069	1980	Leyland	Leopard PSU3E/4R	Duple	Grey Green		RP
RNE 692W	1981	Bedford	CF	Plaxton	Shearings of Altrincham		R
BFV 222Y	1983	Leyland	Atlantean AN68D/2R	East Lancs	Lancaster City Transport	222	RP
FKK 845Y	1983	MCW	Metroliner CR126/2	MCW	East Kent Road Car Co	8845	R
A658 OCX	1984	Leyland	Olympian ONLXB/1R	ECW	Yorkshire Traction	658	R
B75 URN	1984	Leyland	Atlantean AN68D/2R	Northern Counties	Fylde Blue Buses Seagull Coaches	75	R
K727 UTT	1993	Iveco	59-12	Mellor	Thames Transit		R
L932 CTT	1994	Iveco	59-12	Mellor	Devon General	1003	R

This Leyland is not, as one might think a Titan, but a Tiger, which originally carried a coach body. The Willowbrook body seen here was fitted by enterprising Nottinghamshire independent Barton Transport in 1957, when it was re-registered with its present registration.
PHILIP LAMB

Buckland Omnibus Co Ltd

Woodbridge

Address: Unit 53a, Bentwaters Business Park, Rendlesham, Woodbridge, Suffolk. IP12 2TW

Contact address: Ivy Cottage, Marlesford Road, Hacheston, Woodbridge, Suffolk. IP13 DP

Phone: 07801 639000

E-mail: bucklandcoaches@yahoo.co.uk

Website: www.bucklandbuses.co.uk

Brief description: Conventional coach operator with two historic vehicles available for hire and also used on day trips and regular services.

Events planned in 2010: Various day trips. Woodbridge circular vintage sightseeing service

Facilities: B(e) P

Registration	Date	Chassis make	Chassis model	Body make	Original operator	Fleet No	Status
TE 7870	1929	Dennis	ES	Brush	Accrington Corporation	57	R
GRP 260D	1966	Bristol	MW6G	ECW	United Counties Omnibus Co	260	R

Buckland Omnibus of Woodbridge, Suffolk maintains two heritage vehicles including this 1929 former Accrington Brush-bodied Dennis ES, now returned to near-Accrington colours.
BUCKLAND OMNIBUS

Carmel Coaches

Okehampton

Contact address: Mr A G Hazell, Northlew, Okehampton, Devon.

Phone: 01409 221237

Registration	Date	Chassis make	Chassis model	Body make	Original operator	Fleet No	Status
LOD 495	1950	Albion	Victor FT39N	Duple	Way of Crediton		R
MTT 640	1951	Leyland	Titan PD2/1	Leyland	Devon General	DL640	R

Carmel Coaches operates a heritage service between Okehampton and Moretonhampstead during the summer season. Here, regular performer, LOD 495, a 1950 Albion Victor with Duple 'A' bodywork, loads at Okehampton station. NIGEL APPLFORD

Above: **Latest recruit to the Cumbria Classic Coaches fleet is East Lancs-bodied AEC Regent III, Bamber Bridge 4 (UTC 672). The Regent is seen here in Kirkby Stephen loading for its onward journey to Kirkby Stephen West station, Easter 2009.** PHILIP LAMB

Below: **Seen out on the rugged Cumbria fells is JTB 749, Cumbria Classic Coaches 1948 Burlingham-bodied AEC Regal III.** PHILIP LAMB

Registration	Date	Chassis make	Chassis model	Body make	Original operator	Fleet No	Status
GCD 48	1939	Leyland	Titan TD5	Park Royal	Southdown Motor Services	248	R
RUF 186	1956	Leyland	Titan PD2/12	Beadle	Southdown Motor Services	786	R
410 DCD	1964	Leyland	Titan PD3/4	Northern Counties	Southdown Motor Services	410	R
422 DCD	1964	Leyland	Titan PD3/4	Northern Counties	Southdown Motor Services	422	R
HCD 347E	1967	Leyland	Titan PD3/4	Northern Counties	Southdown Motor Services	347	R
UUF 110J	1971	Bristol	VRT/SL6G	ECW	Southdown Motor Services	510	R
WTG 360T	1978	Bristol	VRT/SL3/6LXB	Alexander	City of Cardiff	360	R
GRU 163V	1980	Leyland	Fleetline FE30AGR	Alexander	Bournemouth Corporation	163	R
GRU 164V	1980	Leyland	Fleetline FE30AGR	Alexander	Bournemouth Corporation	164	R
JWV 976W	1980	Bristol	VRT/SL3/680	ECW	Southdown Motor Services	276	R
DCA 528X	1981	Bristol	VRT/SL3/6LXB	ECW	Crosville Motor Services	DVG528	R

Classic Southdown Omnibuses

Contact address: Dormy Cottage, 2 Alan Road, Wimbledon Village, London SW19 7PT

Phone: 020 8947 3002

E-mail: Eric@TheStobarts.co.uk

Brief description: One of the largest collections of vehicles owned formerly by Southdown Motor Services. They range from a 1939 Park Royal bodied Leyland Titan TD5 to the numerically last Bristol VRT delivered to Southdown in 1980. Of particular note is a 1956 Leyland Titan PD2/12 carrying one of the last Beadle double-deck bodies built.

Events planned in 2010: Attendance at various rallies including Cobham, Horsham and Brighton

Other information: Classic Southdown Omnibuses owns two former Bournemouth Leyland Fleetlines and two open-top Bristol VRTs that are available for commercial use.

Registration	Date	Chassis make	Chassis model	Body make	Original operator	Fleet No	Status
JTB 749	1948	AEC	Regal III O962	Burlingham	Florence Motors of Morcambe		R
CRN 80	1949	Leyland	Tiger PS1	East Lancs	Preston Corporation	75	R
TSK 736	1949	Commer	Commando	Scottish Aviation	David Lawson	C8	RP
CWG 286	1950	Leyland	Tiger PS1/1	Alexander	W Alexander & Sons (Northern)	PA184	R
MTJ 84	1951	Guy	Arab III	Roe	Lancashire United Transport	440	R
UTC 672	1954	AEC	Regent III 9613S	East Lancs	Bamber Bridge Motor Services	4	R
627 HFM	1959	Bristol	Lodekka LD6G	ECW	Crosville Motor Services	DLB978	R

Cumbria Classic Coaches

Kirkby Stephen

Address: Bowber Head, Ravenstonedale, Kirkby Stephen, Cumbria CA17 4NL

Phone: 01539 623254

E-mail: wh@cumbriaclassiccoaches.co.uk

Website: www.cumbriaclassiccoaches.co.uk

Brief description: We have six buses and coaches from the 1940s and 1950s that are Class 6 tested and operated as public service vehicles. They are interesting to view at our depot along with a superb 1936 Rover 14 and a 1937 Austin LL London Taxi. We also have a 1985 Bedford MJ ex-military recovery wagon.

Events planned in 2010:

Annual Easter Saturday and Sunday Classic Commercial Vehicle Rally in Kirkby Stephen and Brough

Opening days/times: Anytime by appointment

Directions by car: 5 miles South of Kirkby Stephen off the A683

Directions by public transport: Telephone from Kirkby Stephen station or centre for directions.

Charges: Free but voluntary donations towards restoration accepted

Facilities: Guide, cups of tea (sometimes), toilets, beautiful views

Other information: B E P T

London Bus Company

Rainham

Contact address: Unit 3C, Denver Industrial Estate, Ferry Road, Rainham, Essex .RM13 7MD

Phone: 01708 631001

Website: www.thelondonbuscompany.com

One of the many and varied vehicles in the London Bus Company fleet is former London Buses V3 (A103 SUU), an experimental three-door Alexander-bodied Ailsa, seen here at the North Weald rally in 2009. NIGEL APPLFORD

Registration	Date	Chassis make	Chassis model	Body make	Original operator	Fleet No	Status
JXN 371	1949	Leyland	Titan 7RT	Park Royal	London Transport	RTL48	A
KGK 709	1949	AEC	Regent III O961 RT	Weymann	London Transport	RT1240	A
KGK 959	1949	AEC	Regent III O961 RT	Weymann	London Transport	RT2150	R
KLB 569	1950	AEC	Regent III O961 RT	Saunders-Roe	London Transport	RT1320	A
KXW 22	1950	Leyland	Titan 7RT	Metro Cammell	London Transport	RTL672	A
KXW 171	1950	AEC	Regent III O961 RT	Saunders-Roe	London Transport	RT3062	R
KXW 304	1950	AEC	Regent III O961 RT	Weymann	London Transport	RT1658	A
KXW 488	1950	AEC	Regent III O961 RT	Weymann	London Transport	RT1389	A
KYY 527	1950	AEC	Regent III O961 RT	Weymann	London Transport	RT1700	R
LLU 670	1950	AEC	Regent III O961 RT	Park Royal	London Transport	RT3871	R
LLU 732	1950	AEC	Regent III O961 RT	Park Royal	London Transport	RT3933	RP
LYR 854	1950	AEC	Regent III O961 RT	Weymann	London Transport	RT3435	R
LYR 969	1952	AEC	Regent III O961 RT	Weymann	London Transport	RT2799	R
MLL 658	1952	AEC	Regent III O961 RT	Park Royal	London Transport	RT2911	R
MXX 289	1952	AEC	Regal IV 9821LT	Metro-Cammell	London Transport	RF401	RP
MXX 360	1953	Guy	Special NLLVP	ECW	London Transport	GS60	R
OLD 587	1954	AEC	Regent III O961 RT	Saunders-Roe	London Transport	RT4823	A
SLT 59	1957	AEC	Routemaster	ECW	London Transport	RMC4	R
VLT 85	1959	AEC	Routemaster	Park Royal	London Transport	RM85	R
VLT 111	1959	AEC	Routemaster	Park Royal	London Transport	RM111	RP
VLT 268	1960	AEC	Routemaster	Park Royal	London Transport	RM268	A
VLT 298	1960	AEC	Routemaster	Park Royal	London Transport	RM298	R
WLT 646	1961	AEC	Routemaster	Park Royal	London Transport	RM646	RP
WLT 893	1961	AEC	Routemaster	Park Royal	London Transport	RML893	RP
9 CLT	1962	AEC	Routemaster	Park Royal	London Transport	RM1009	RP
215 UXJ	1962	AEC	Routemaster	Park Royal	London Transport	RML899	R
OPV 47	1962	AEC	Regent V 2D2RA	East Lancs	Ipswich Corporation	47	RP
WLT 900	1962	AEC	Routemaster	Park Royal	London Transport	RML900	R
WLT 902	1962	AEC	Routemaster	Park Royal	London Transport	RML902	RP
516 CLT	1963	AEC	Routemaster	Park Royal	London Transport	RMC1516	RP
ALD 936B	1964	AEC	Routemaster	Park Royal	London Transport	RM1936	RP
ALD 979B	1964	AEC	Routemaster	Park Royal	London Transport	RM1979	RP
CUV 260C	1965	AEC	Routemaster	Park Royal	London Transport	RCL2260	R
CUV 331C	1965	AEC	Routemaster	Park Royal	London Transport	RML2331	RP
JJD 413D	1966	AEC	Routemaster	Park Royal	London Transport	RML2413	RP
KOW 902F	1967	AEC	Regent V 3D2RA	East Lancs	Southampton Corporation	394	RP
NMY 631E	1967	AEC	Routemaster	Park Royal	British European Airways	RMA48	R
AML 1H	1970	AEC	Swift 4MP2R	Marshall	London Transport	SM1	RP

AML 88H	1970	AEC	Swift 4MP2R	Park Royal	London Transport	SMD88	RP
JPF 108K	1970	AEC	Swift 3MP2R	Alexander	London Country Bus Services	SMA8	A
THM 684M	1973	Daimler	Fleetline CRL6	MCW	London Transport	DMS1684	R
GHV 52N	1975	Daimler	Fleetline CRL6	Park Royal	London Transport	DM1052	R
THX 271S	1977	Leyland	Fleetline FE30ALR Special (B20)	MCW	London Transport	DMS2271	R
WYW 28T	1978	MCW	Metrobus DR101	MCW	London Transport	M28	RP
THX 402S	1979	Leyland	Titan TNLXB2RRSp	Park Royal	London Transport	T2	R
WYV 4T	1979	Leyland	Titan TNLXB2RRSp	Park Royal	London Transport	T4	R
A103 SUU	1984	Volvo	B55-10 Mk III	Alexander	London Transport	V3	R

Registration	Date	Chassis make	Chassis model	Body make	Original operator	Fleet No	Status
JSJ 746	1959	AEC	Routemaster	Park Royal	London Transport	RM90	
JSJ 747	1959	AEC	Routemaster	Park Royal	London Transport	RM84	
JSJ 748	1959	AEC	Routemaster	Park Royal	London Transport	RM80	
JSJ 749	1959	AEC	Routemaster	Park Royal	London Transport	RM94	
VLT 143	1960	AEC	Routemaster	Park Royal	London Transport	RM143	
VLT 163	1960	AEC	Routemaster	Park Royal	London Transport	RM163	
VLT 235	1960	AEC	Routemaster	Park Royal	London Transport	RM235	
VLT 237	1960	AEC	Routemaster	Park Royal	London Transport	RM237	
VLT 242	1960	AEC	Routemaster	Park Royal	London Transport	RM242	
VLT 281	1960	AEC	Routemaster	Park Royal	London Transport	RM281	
CUV 203C	1965	AEC	Routemaster	Park Royal	London Transport	RM2203	
CUV 241C	1965	AEC	Routemaster	Park Royal	London Transport	RCL2241	
CUV 248C	1965	AEC	Routemaster	Park Royal	London Transport	RCL2248	

Mac Tours & Edinburgh Tours

Edinburgh

Contact address: Edinburgh Tours Ltd, 55 Annandale Street, Edinburgh. EH7 4AZ

Phone: 0131 554 4494

E-mail: sales@edinburghtour.com

Events planned in 2010: Continuing with frequent departures from Waverley Bridge, hop on/off tours of Edinburgh.

PLACES TO STAY

Blossom House
Edinburgh EH9 1RG, 0131 667 5353

Classic House
Edinburgh EH9 2NH, 0131 667 5847

Alpha Guest House
Edinburgh EH16 4TE, 0131 258 0810

The Mac Tours fleet now comprises only AEC Routemasters, one of which is seen here rounding Edinburgh's Charlotte Square. JOHN BURNETT

Memory Lane Vintage Omnibus Services

Maidenhead

Contact address: 78 Lillibrooke Crescent, Maidenhead, Berkshire SL6 3XQ

Phone: 01628 825050

E-mail: info@memorylane.co.uk

Website: www.memorylane.co.uk

Registration	Date	Chassis make	Chassis model	Body make	Original operator	Fleet No	Status
KGU 290	1949	AEC	Regent III O961 RT	Weymann	London Transport	RT1530	RP
KYY 628	1950	AEC	Regent III O961 RT	Park Royal	London Transport	RT1790	R
NLE 643	1953	AEC	Regal IV 9821LT	Metro-Cammell	London Transport	RF643	RP
VLT 216	1960	AEC	Routemaster	Park Royal	London Transport	RM216	R
TYD 122G	1969	AEC	Reliance 6MU3R	Willowbrook	Hutchings & Cornelius Services of South Petherton		

Midland Classic Ltd

Swadlincote

Contact address: Unit 5, 290 Stanton Road, Burton-upon-Trent. DE15 9SQ

Phone: 01283 500228

E-mail: info@midlandclassic.com

Website: www.midlandclassic.com

Brief description: Midland Classic has a range of restored vehicles available for hire and also operates bus services in the Swadlincote and Burton-upon-Trent area.

Operations planned for 2010: Routes 9 Ashby de la Zouch — Swadlincote — Burton, 21/21E Swadlincote — Linton — Burton. Routes mostly operated with modern vehicles but classic vehicles operate on special occasions (please see website for details)

Registration	Date	Chassis make	Chassis model	Body make	Original operator	Fleet No	Status
798 UXA	1962	AEC	Routemaster	Park Royal	London Transport	RM1168	R
TOJ 592S	1977	MCW	Metrobus	MCW	MCW Demonstrator		R
WDA 4T	1979	Leyland	Titan TNLXB/1RF	Park Royal	West Midlands PTE	7004	R
HXI 3009	1986	Leyland	Lynx LX5636LXBFR	Alexander (Belfast)	Belfast Corporation		R
E72 KBF	1988	Leyland	Lynx LX112L10ZR1	Leyland	Stevensons of Uttoxeter	72	R

Former West Midlands PTE and London Buses Leyland Titan WDA 4T is one of a number of interesting vehicles available for hire in the Midland Classic fleet. NIGEL APPLFORD

Registration	Date	Chassis make	Chassis model	Body make	Original operator	Fleet No	Status
JG 9938	1937	Leyland	Tiger TS8	Park Royal	East Kent Road Car Co		R
DUF 179	1937	Leyland	Tiger TS7	Harrington	Southdown Motor Services	1179	R
AJA 132	1938	Bristol	L5G	Burlingham	North Western Road Car Co	372	R
GNU 750	1939	Daimler	COG5/40	Willowbrook	Tailby & George ('Blue Bus Services') Willington	DR5	R
CCX 777	1945	Daimler	CWA6	Duple	Huddersfield Joint Omnibus Committee	217	R
EMW 893	1947	Daimler	CVD6	Park Royal	Swindon Corporation	57	A
HUO 510	1947	AEC	Regal I 0662	Weymann	Devon General	SR510	A
JUO 992	1947	Leyland	Titan PD1	ECW	Southern National Omnibus Co	2932	A
WAL 782	1947	Leyland	PS1/1	Willowbrook	Barton Transport of Chilwell	792	R
ACH 441	1948	AEC	Regal III 0682	Windover	Trent Motor Traction Co	611	R
CCK 359	1948	Leyland	Titan PD2/3	Leyland	Ribble Motor Services	2584	A
JFM 575	1948	AEC	Regal III 6821A	Strachan	Crosville Motor Services		R
JNN 384	1948	Leyland	Titan PD1	Duple	Barton Transport of Chilwell	467	RP
JTE 546	1948	AEC	Regent III 6811A	Park Royal	Morecambe & Heysham Corporation	20	R
CFK 340	1949	AEC	Regal III 6821A	Burlingham	H & E Burnham of Worcester		R
EVD 406	1949	Crossley	DD42/7	Roe	Baxter's Bus Service of Airdrie	34	R
KTF 594	1949	AEC	Regent III 9621E	Park Royal	Morecambe & Heysham Corporation	65	R
LJH 665	1949	Dennis	Lancet III	Duple	Lee of Barnet		R
CDB 206	1950	Bristol	L5G	Weymann	North Western Road Car Co	206	R
JFJ 875	1950	Daimler	CVD6	Weymann	Exeter City Transport	75	R
KEL 131	1950	Leyland	Titan PD2/3	Weymann	Bournemouth Corporation	131	RP
KFM 893	1950	Bristol	L5G	ECW	Crosville Motor Services	KG131	R
LFM 302	1950	Leyland	Tiger PS1	Weymann	Crosville Motor Services	KA226	R
LFM 329	1950	Leyland	Tiger PS1	Weymann	Crosville Motor Services		A
LFM 717	1950	Bristol	L5G	ECW	Crosville Motor Services	KG136	A
LUO 694	1950	Leyland	Tiger PS2/3	Burlingham	Pridham of Lamerton		A
DCK 219	1951	Leyland	Titan PD2/3	East Lancs	Ribble Motor Services	1248	R
EDB 549	1951	Leyland	Titan PD2/1	Leyland	Stockport Corporation	295	R
HJG 17	1954	Dennis	Lancet UF	Duple	East Kent Road Car Co		A
BAS 563	1956	Bristol	Lodekka LD6G	ECW	Southern Vectis Omnibus Co	501	R
701 AEH	1957	Leyland	Titan PD3/4	MCW	Potteries Motor Traction Co	H701	RP
VDV 752	1957	Bristol	Lodekka LDL6G	ECW	Western National Omnibus Co	1935	R
VDV 753	1957	Bristol	Lodekka LDL6G	ECW	Western National Omnibus Co	1936	R
NDB 356	1958	Leyland	Tiger Cub PSUC1/1	Crossley	Stockport Corporation	403	R
890 ADV	1959	AEC	Reliance 2MU3RV	Willowbrook	Devon General Grey Cars	TCR890	R
805 EVT	1960	AEC	Reliance 2MU3RV	Weymann	Potteries Motor Traction Co	SL805	R
851 FNN	1960	AEC	Regent V 2D3RA	Northern Counties	Barton Transport of Chilwell	851	R

Quantock Heritage

Wiveliscombe

Contact address: The Coal Yard, Broad Gauge Business Park, Station Road, Bishop's Lydeard, Taunton. TA4 3BU

Phone: 01823 251140

E-mail: sales@quantockmotorservices.co.uk

Website: www.quantockmotorservices.co.uk

Quantock Heritage offers a range of services from registered bus operations through to wedding hire. Many vehicles though are, like this Burlingham-bodied AEC Regal III, new to Burnham's of Worcester in 1948, used at present only on free bus services.
PHILIP LAMB

Curdon Mill Bed & Breakfast
Taunton TA4 4LS, 01984 656522

Inglewood
Taunton TA4 4JA, 01984 656508

Northam Mill
Taunton TA4 3TT, 01984 656916

Registration	Date	Chassis make	Chassis model	Body make	Original operator	Fleet No	Status
AAL 522A	1960	AEC	Regent V 2D3RA	Northern Counties	Barton Transport of Chilwell	854	A
7682 LJ	1962	Bristol	Lodekka FL6G	ECW	Hants & Dorset Motor Services	1482	RP
572 CNW	1962	Daimler	CVG6LX-30	Roe	Leeds City Transport	572	R
DEL 893C	1965	Bristol	Lodekka FLF6G	ECW	Hants & Dorset Motor Services	1523	R
DPV 65D	1966	AEC	Regent V 2D2RA	Neepsend	Ipswich Corporation	65	R
XTF 98D	1966	Leyland	Titan PD3/4	East Lancs	Haslingden Corporation	45	R
HJA 965E	1967	Leyland	Titan PD2/40	East Lancs Neepsend	Stockport Corporation	65	R
GNH 258F	1968	Daimler	CVG6	Roe	Northampton Corporation	258	R
CYA 181J	1971	AEC	Reliance 6MU3R	Plaxton	Hutchings & Cornelius Services of South Petherton		RP
WDK 562T	1979	AEC	Reliance 6U3ZR	Plaxton	Yelloway Motor Services of Rochdale		R

Ron Greet Nostalgic Transport
Totnes

Contact address: Ron Greet Nostalgic Transport, Bickaton, Broadhempston, Totnes, Devon. TQ9 6BY

Phone: 01803 813039

Fax: 01803 813613

E-mail: info@rongreet.co.uk

Website: www.nostalgic-transport.co.uk

Opening days/times: Not usually open but visitors are welcome, strictly by prior arrangement.

Registration	Date	Chassis make	Chassis model	Body make	Original operator	Fleet No	Status
JMN 727	1948	AEC	Regent III O961 RT	Northern Counties	Douglas Corporation	63	R
HOD 66	1949	Beadle-Bedford		Beadle	Western National Omnibus Co	2015	R
LTA 906	1949	Bedford	OB	Duple	Southern National Omnibus Co (Royal Blue)	1430	R
MHU 52	1950	Bedford	OB	Duple	Bristol Tramways	210	R
898 FUF	1954	Albion	Victor FT39AN	Reading	Watsons of St Martins Guernsey		R
181 ECV	1959	Bedford	SB1	Duple	Jennings of Bude		R
532 DWW	1963	Bedford	SB5	Plaxton	Barnsley British Co-op		A
HAD 915D	1966	Bedford	VAM 5	Plaxton	Princess Mary Coaches		R

Ron Greet of Totnes has amongst his varied fleet this 1966 Plaxton Panorama-bodied Bedford VAM5, new to Princess Mary Coaches of Staple Hill in 1966.
NIGEL APPLFORD

Index of vehicles by registration number

Reg.	No.	Reg.	No.	Reg.	No.	Reg.	No.	Reg.	No.	Reg.	No.	Reg.	No.	Reg.	No.	Reg.	No.	Reg.	No.	Reg.	No.
CGJ 188	22	CUV 331C	136	DDR 201C	112	DX 3988	27	EHL 472D	121	EXV 253	35	FKF 801D	104	G545 RDS	92	GMB 390T	100	H74 ANG	88	HOV 685	56
CHF 565	63	CUV 51C	98	DDV 446	84	DX 5610	27	EHV 65	80	EY 5218	41	FKF 835E	104	G571 BHP	71	GN 8242	22	HA 3501	56	HPF 318N	99
CHL 772	90	CVF 31T	88	DED 797	43	DX 5617	27	EIB 8234	95	EYK 396	22	FKF 933G	104	G571 PNS	92	GNB 518D	116	HA 4963	17	HPW 133	34
CHY 419C	74	CVF 874	27	DEK 3D	122	DX 5629	27	EJR 110W	108	EZH 155	21	FKK 845Y	130	GAA 580	69	GNC 276N	40	HA 8047	18	HRG 209	50
CJG 959	87	CVH 741	59	DEL 893C	140	DX 6591	27	EJR 111W	108	EZH 170	21	FKM 706L	24	GAA 616	69	GNF 10V	83	HAD 915D	140	HRN 31	113
CJH 123V	100	CVL 850D	34	DFE 383	34	DX 7657	94	EKA 220Y	105	F107 HVK	108	FKU 758	60	GAM 216	66	GNF 15V	116	HAH 537L	79	HRN 99N	96
CK 3825	36	CVP 207	56	DFM 347H	44	DX 7812	27	EKU 743	60	F115 PHM	103	FLD 447Y	92	GAN 744J	107	GNF 16V	116	HAX 399N	75	HSC 173X	53
CK 4474	113	CWG 206	36	DFV 146	95	DX 8871	106	EKU 746	60	F251 JRM	126	FM 6397	128	GAN 745J	117	GNG 125C	28	HBD 919T	122	HSD 73V	92
CKB 166X	101	CWG 273	15	DGS 536	50	DXI 3343	93	EKV 966	23	F261 YTJ	105	FM 6435	128	GAU 728L	111	GNH 258F	140	HBF 679D	57	HSD 86V	92
CKC 308L	104	CWG 283	49	DGS 625	50	DXI 3370	101	EKY 558	60	F292 NHJ	89	FM 7443	128	GAY 171	97	GNM 232N	72	HCD 347E	135	HSO 61N	15
CKG 193	59	CWG 286	135	DHC 784E	119	DY 5029	91	ELP 223	88	F301 DRJ	117	FM 9984	128	GBB 524K	82	GNM 235N	130	HCK 204G	44	HTA 844N	126
CLE 122	103	CWG 756V	54	DHD 177	66	E131 DRS	15	ELP 228	117	F305 DRJ	117	FNV 557	114	GBJ 192	25	GNU 568N	98	HD 7905	54	HTB 656	36
CMS 201	120	CWH 717	36	DHR 192	106	E186 BNS	92	EMS 362V	92	F575 RCW	96	FOI 1629	93	GBU 1V	116	GNU 569N	98	HDB 116V	116	HTF 586	36
CN 2870	56	CWN 629C	76	DHW 293K	77	E204 PWY	123	EMW 284	76	F649 FGE	62	FON 630	17	GCD 48	135	GNU 750	139	HDM 473	72	HTF 644B	44
CN 4740	106	CWU 146T	63	DJF 349	46	E48 TYG	83	EMW 893	139	F685 YOG	18	FOP 429	20	GCK 279S	122	GNY 432C	78	HDV 624E	81	HTJ 522B	95
CN 6100	106	CXX 171	22	DJG 619C	87	E640 BRS	70	EN 9965	116	F98 STB	45	FPT 6G	113	GCK 428W	100	GO 5170	21	HDV 626E	126	HTT 487	84
CNH 860	79	CYA 181J	140	DJP 754	39	E72 KBF	138	END 832D	116	FAE 60	75	FRB 211H	57	GCM 152E	63	GO 5198	102	HDV 639E	52	HUD 476S	48
CNH 862	79	CYJ 252	50	DKC 301L	44	E901 DRG	107	ENW 980D	30	FAR 724K	121	FRC 956	56	GCS 50V	47	GOU 732	114	HE 12	105	HUO 510	139
CPM 61	106	D103 DAJ	25	DKC 330L	104	E903 DRG	107	EO 9051	71	FAS 982	50	FRJ 254D	39	GDJ 435	44	GOU 845	69	HEK 705	39	HUP 236	82
CPU 979G	20	D122 PTT	48	DKY 704	77	EA 4181	17	EO 9177	71	FBG 910	63	FRJ 511	45	GDL 33	72	*GP 14 ST*	98	HEN 868N	44	HUY 655	72
CRG 325C	73	D176 NON	123	DKY 706	59	EBB 846W	83	EOD 524D	84	FBN 232C	72	FRM 499K	98	GDL 764	29	GPC 731N	99	HET 513	106	HVF 455L	106
CRG 811	90	D275 JVR	45	DKY 711	73	EBO 919	77	EOI 2857	62	FBR 53D	82	FRP 692	79	GDT 421	60	GPD 313N	122	HF 9126	49	HVM 901F	39
CRM 927T	126	D275 OOJ	31	DKY 712	73	EC 8852	72	EPD 511V	100	FBU 827	36	FRP 828	79	GE 2446	49	GRD 576D	83	HFG 923V	100	HVO 937	40
CRN 80	125	D277 JVR	117	DKY 735	18	ECD 524	14	EPD 543V	100	FCD 294D	119	FRU 224	73	GEK 14V	45	GRM 353L	126	HFM 186N	99	HVU 244N	40
CRR 537J	130	D278 FAS	40	DL 5084	29	ECU 201E	107	ERD 145	60	FCI 323	21	FSC 182	49	GFN 273	87	GRP 260D	132	HFR 501E	91	HW 6634	74
CRS 834	90	D302 JVR	117	DL 9015	83	ED 6141	88	ERD 152	60	FCK 884	113	FSL 615W	92	GFR 799W	100	GRS 10E	15	HFR 512E	95	HWO 323	78
CRU 103C	73	D320 LNB	117	DLJ 116L	73	EDB 549	139	ERN 700	113	FDL 676	29	FTB 11	36	GFU 692	60	GRS 334E	91	HFR 516E	95	HWO 334	56
CRU 180C	73	D472 OWE	61	DLU 92	88	EDB 562	36	ERV 115W	101	FDL 927D	29	FTN 708W	108	GFY 406	118	GRS 343E	52	HG 9651	66	HWV 294	79
CRU 184C	89	D479 OWE	61	DM 2583	105	EDB 575	36	ERV 938	25	FDM 724	56	FTN 710W	108	GGR 103N	82	GRU 163V	135	HGA 983D	91	HX 2756	102
CRU 197C	73	D5 CTB	83	DM 6228	111	EDL 657	49	ES 5150	90	FDO 573	34	FTO 614	59	GHA 327D	18	GRU 164V	135	HGC 130	22	HXI 3009	138
CS 3364	49	D501 LNA	117	DMS 325C	51	EDS 288A	91	ESF 647W	53	FDV 790V	81	FTR 511	118	GHA 333	56	GRY 48D	97	HGG 359	90	HYM 768	103
CSG 29C	51	D509 MJA	117	DMS 348C	91	EDS 320A	50	ESF 801C	51	FDV 803V	81	FTT 704	76	GHA 337	56	GRY 60D	57	HGM 335E	52	HYM 812	59
CSG 43C	51	D515 HUB	123	DMS 359C	51	EDS 50A	50	ESG 652	49	FDV 827V	100	FUF 181	83	GHA 415D	57	GSC 667X	53	HGM 346E	52	IB 552	16
CSG 73S	53	D536 NDA	121	DMS 820	121	EDT 703	55	ESV 811	40	FDV 829V	100	FV 5737	125	GHB 148N	78	GSO 80V	92	HHA 101L	124	ILI 98	21
CSG 792S	51	D553 NOE	58	DMS 823	50	EDV 505D	78	ET 778	55	FEA156	18	FVA 854	90	GHD 215	66	GSR 244	106	HHA 637	56	ILJ 5367	130
CST 703N	91	D63 NOF	40	DNF 204	55	EDV 555D	81	ETA 280	72	FEL 105L	73	FW 5698	31	GHN 189	71	GSU 378	49	HHH 272N	126	IY 7383	21
CTF 423	66	D676 NNE	40	DNF 708C	116	EDW 68D	78	ETJ 108	125	FES 831W	53	FW 8990	59	GHN 574	59	GTA 395	125	HHN 202	82	IY 8044	21
CTF 627B	95	D685 SEM	105	DNT 174L	121	EF 7380	106	ETO 452C	111	FET 617	115	FWA 450V	100	GHT 127	76	GTB 903	95	HHW 452D	129	J 2503	43
CTP 200	80	D705 HUA	123	DNW 840T	30	EFJ 241	125	ETS 964	50	FET 618	60	FWA 475V	45	GHT 154	76	GTP 175F	80	HJA 965E	140	J 9567	66
CTT 23C	84	D901 MWR	86	DOC 26V	58	EFJ 666	125	ETT 995	84	FFM 135C	44	FWG 846	50	GHV 2N	98	GTV 666	59	HJG 17	139	J139 YRM	83
CTT 513C	84	D902 CSH	97	DOC 37V	100	EFJ 92	124	EUD 256K	48	FFN 399	87	FWH 461Y	117	GHV 52N	137	GUE 247	56	HKE 867	129	J216 AET	83
CTT 518C	84	DAO 295K	126	DOD 474	125	EFM 581	128	EUF 184	16	FFN 446	129	FWL 371E	48	GJ 2098	21	GUF 191	118	HKF 820	63	JA 5506	83
CTT 774C	121	DAR 120T	100	DPT 848	106	EFM 631C	122	EUF 204	125	FFU 860	34	FWW 596	66	GJF 301N	97	GUF 727	34	HKR 11	59	JA 5528	128
CU 3593	59	DBA 214C	59	DPV 65D	140	EFN 178L	87	EUP 405B	82	FFW 447D	52	FWX 914	30	GJG 750D	129	GUJ 608	17	HKW 82	66	JA 7585	36
CU 4740	65	DBC 190C	97	DPV 68D	28	EFN 568	83	EVA 324	49	FFY 402	56	FXH 521	25	GJG 751D	24	GUP 907N	107	HL 7538	72	JA 7770	128
CUB 331C	30	DBE 187	34	DR 4902	106	EFN 584	83	EVC 244	114	FFY 404	43	FXT 122	122	GJG 757D	24	GUS 926	90	HLJ 44	88	JAA 708	90
CUL 260	25	DBL 154	122	DRC 224	25	EFN 592	87	EVD 406	139	FGE 423X	92	FXT 183	88	GJN 509D	20	GUW 443W	101	HLW 159	66	JAP 698	121
CUV 121C	91	DBN 978	55	DRD 130	60	EFP 521T	17	EVL 549E	34	FGS 59D	50	FYG 663J	121	GJX 331	30	GUW 444W	101	HNB 24N	116	JBN 153	36
CUV 186C	107	DBU 246	36	DRN 289	113	EFS 229S	92	EWG 22L	70	FHF 451	63	FYS 8	91	GK 3192	102	GVD 47	49	HNN 114V	111	JC 5313	93
CUV 203C	137	DBV 100W	114	DSD 936V	53	EGA 79	42	EWM 358	43	FHF 456	44	FYS 839	60	GK 5323	102	GVV 887N	99	HNP 154S	119	JCK 530	95
CUV 208C	86	DBV 43W	126	DSE 980T	62	EGN 369J	123	EWS 130D	51	FHN 833	31	FYS 988	42	GK 5486	102	GWJ 724	54	HNP 989J	118	JCK 542	113
CUV 218C	46	DBV 831W	114	DSG 169	49	EGO 426	22	EWS 168D	51	FHN 923	71	FYS 998	42	GKA 74N	104	GWM 816	129	HNT 945N	121	JCK 852W	101
CUV 219C	57	DBW 613	47	DTP 823	80	EGP 1J	35	EWS 746W	75	FHU 59D	74	FYS 999	91	GKD 434	104	GWT 630	66	HNW 131D	30	JCP 60F	106
CUV 220C	89	DCA 528X	135	DU 4838	47	EGP 33J	89	EWS 751W	101	FHW 156D	74	FZ 7897	62	GKE 68	123	GWY 690N	30	HOD 30	66	JDC 599	83
CUV 226C	89	DCK 219	139	DUF 179	139	EHA 424D	114	EWS 812D	52	FJ 8967	80	G142 HNP	18	GKP 511	59	GYC 160K	75	HOD 66	140	JDL 760	129
CUV 229C	103	DCN 83	106	DUK 278	124	EHA 767D	57	EWW 207T	130	FJF 193	97	G186 JHG	114	GKV 94	114	GYS 896D	91	HOR 413L	98	JDN 668	34
CUV 241C	137	DCS 616	49	DUK 833	18	EHA 775	17	EX 1128	25	FJF 40D	97	G254 JYG	123	GLJ 681N	98	H140 GVM	117	HOR 590E	90	JEL 257	75
CUV 248C	137	DDB 174C	39	DWB 54H	54	EHL 335	66	EX 6566	25	FJJ 764	22	G258 HUH	78	GLJ 957	125	H262 MFX	123	HOR 592E	90	JF 2378	17
CUV 260C	136	DDL 50	29	DWG 526	46	EHL 336	114	EXV 201	25	FJJ 774	25	G292 EOG	18	GLS 265S	53	H35 HBG	45	HOU 904	69	JFJ 606	125
CUV 290C	95	DDM 652	72	DWH 706W	117	EHL 344	86			FJW 616	56	GM 6384	90			H467 GVM	117			JFJ 875	139

Reg.	No.	Reg.	No.	Reg.	No.	Reg.	No.	Reg.	No.	Reg.	No.	Reg.	No.	Reg.	No.	Reg.	No.	Reg.	No.	Reg.	No.
JFM 238D	26	JP 7538	72	JXN 371	136	KID 154	21	KVO 429P	46	LHN 784	60	LYR 533	30	MSF 750P	52	NFW 36V	34	NTW 942C	20	OOX 825R	18
JFM 575	139	JPA 121K	98	JXN 46	129	KJ 2578	88	KW 1961	66	LHN 860	71	LYR 542	60	MSJ 385P	92	NG 1109	29	NTY 416F	52	OP 237	17
JFM 650J	44	JPA 190K	22	JY 124	125	KJA 299G	44	KW 2260	30	LHT 911	94	LYR 672	129	MSJ 499	84	NHA 744	56	NUD 105L	79	OPV 47	136
JFT 228N	107	JPA 82V	91	JYC 855	114	KJD 401P	103	KW 474	31	LHW 918	75	LYR 826	22	MTC 540	113	NHA 795	56	NUD 106L	98	OPV 821	119
JFT 413X	108	JPF 108K	137	K1 GRT	15	KJD 507P	99	KW 6052	59	LHY 937	129	LYR 854	136	MTE 635	30	NHN 128	66	NUW 567Y	103	ORB 277	56
JFV 527	113	JPF 113K	107	K101 KMV	108	KJD 524P	99	KW 7604	31	LHY 976	74	LYR 910	22	MTJ 771S	104	NHN 250K	107	NVK 341	82	ORC 545P	46
JG 669	94	JPL 153K	122	K232 DAC	23	KJD 530P	99	KWA 22W	100	LIL 9929	53	LYR 915	122	MTJ 84	135	NHU 2	74	NWA 257K	44	ORJ 83W	40
JG 691	94	JPT 901T	82	K361 LWS	126	KJD 535P	99	KWE 255	54	LJ 500	73	LYR 969	136	MTL 750	14	NHY 947	74	NWU 265D	30	ORS 209R	15
JG 8720	83	JPT 906T	82	K62 KEX	25	KL 7796	94	KWE 374D	54	LJF 30F	54	LYR 997	20	MTT 640	132	NJA 568W	116	NWW 89E	86	ORU 230G	73
JG 9938	139	JRN 29	19	KAG 856	91	KLB 569	136	KXW 171	136	LJH 665	139	M627 HDV	124	MTV 760P	111	NJO 703	48	NXL 847	114	ORV 989	80
JGA 189N	91	JRR 404	56	KAH 407	27	KLB 721	76	KXW 22	136	LJW 336	17	M939 XKA	40	MUA 45P	66	NJW 719E	57	NXP 775	89	OSJ 620R	15
JGF 753K	98	JRS 22F	15	KAH 408	25	KLB 881	115	KXW 234	25	LKG 678	78	MAH 744	28	MV 8996	106	NKD 536	104	NXP 997	103	OSJ 629R	52
JHA 227L	121	JRT 82K	28	KAL 579	56	KLB 908	115	KXW 304	136	LKT 991	94	MAL 310	46	MWD 908	106	NKD 540	104	O 9926	56	OT 8283	69
JHA 868E	57	JRX 823	103	KBD 712D	122	KLB 915	115	KXW 435	89	LLU 670	136	MAN 32N	99	MWV 840	106	NKJ 849P	90	OAE 954M	74	OT 8592	69
JHJ 150V	100	JS 1972	62	KBD 715D	122	KLJ 346	73	KXW 488	136	LLU 732	136	MBN 177	113	MXX 23	56	NKR 529	72	OBN 502R	116	OT 8898	69
JHL 701	106	JS 8089	62	KBO 961	77	KLJ 749	115	KY 9106	30	LLU 957	115	MBO 512F	78	MXX 261	89	NKU 214X	96	OBU 163F	44	OT 8902	69
JHL 708	86	JSA 102V	70	KCG 627L	69	KMN 501	104	KYV 781X	92	LLU 987	115	MCK 229J	86	MXX 283	22	NKU 245K	31	OC 527	56	OTA 632G	124
JHT 802	74	JSC 869E	52	KCK 869	113	KMN 519	104	KYY 527	136	LMA 284	36	MCN 30K	107	MXX 289	136	NLE 534	98	OCK 985K	25	OTA 640G	114
JIL 2157	98	JSC 900E	52	KD 5296	121	KNG 374	27	KYY 529	129	LMJ 653G	106	MDJ 555E	44	MXX 292	98	NLE 537	103	OCK 988K	88	OTO 540M	111
JJD 394D	129	JSF 928T	53	KDB 408F	39	KNG 718	88	KYY 628	138	LMS 168W	92	MDL 880R	99	MXX 332	122	NLE 636	98	OCK 995K	95	OTO 547M	96
JJD 405D	42	JSJ 746	137	KDB 696	88	KNN 254	129	KYY 961	89	LMS 374W	53	MDT 222	60	MXX 334	122	NLE 643	138	OCK 997K	95	OTT 43	114
JJD 413D	136	JSJ 747	137	KDJ 999	44	KNN 959	129	L116 YVK	83	LN 4743	26	MFM 39	129	MXX 360	136	NLE 672	22	OCN 744M	98	OTT 55	106
JJD 414D	129	JSJ 748	137	KDL 885F	29	KNV 337	79	L247 FDV	48	LN 7270	105	MFN 888	24	MXX 364	103	NLJ 268	73	OCU 769R	107	OTT 85	98
JJD 508D	90	JSJ 749	137	KDT 393	34	KNY 495D	78	L512 BOD	126	LNA 166G	116	MFN 898	87	MXX 421	122	NLJ 272	73	OCU 807R	107	OTT 98	124
JJD 524D	86	JSX 595T	53	KED 546F	94	KO 7311	94	L929 CTT	124	LNY 903	78	MFR 306P	114	MXX 434	122	NLP 389V	118	OD 5489	125	OTV 137	60
JJD 539D	129	JTB 749	135	KEL 110	73	KOD 585	84	L932 CTT	130	LOD 495	132	MGC 338V	130	MXX 481	88	NLP 645	106	OD 5868	125	OTV 161	46
JJD 555D	105	JTD 300B	44	KEL 131	139	KOM 150	23	LA 9928	83	LOG 301	17	MHA 901F	57	MXX 489	122	NMA 328D	55	OD 7497	84	OU 7951	90
JK 5605	125	JTE 546	139	KEL 133	73	KON 311P	58	LAA 231	69	LOG 302	17	MHU 193	74	MYA 590	22	NMS 358	91	OD 7500	125	OU 9286	90
JK 8418	128	JTF 920B	61	KEP 829X	101	KOU 791P	75	LAE 13	76	LOI 1859	130	MHU 49	74	N143 PTG	78	NMS 366	50	ODL 400	29	OUH 177G	78
JK 9115	115	JTH 100F	121	KET 220	54	KOW 901F	118	LAK 309G	30	LOU 48	69	MHU 52	140	NAC 416F	48	NMS 576M	91	OEM 788S	104	OV 4090	56
JKC 178	104	JTU 588T	53	KFM 766	79	KOW 902F	136	LAK 313G	36	LOW 217	118	MHY 765	54	NAE 3	74	NMY 631E	136	OFC 205	48	OV 4486	56
JKG 497F	78	JTY 403X	108	KFM 775	56	KOW 910F	40	LAX 101E	129	LRA 801P	40	MJ 4549	83	NAG 120G	52	NMY 634E	89	OFC 393	48	OVF 229	88
JLJ 403	73	JUD 597W	48	KFM 893	139	KOX 663F	17	LC 3701	102	LRG 14G	15	MJA 895G	130	NAH 135P	88	NNB 125	36	OFC 902H	79	OVL 465	34
JMN 727	140	JUE 349	56	KFN 239	87	KOX 780F	57	LCD 52	71	LRN 321J	113	MJA 897G	40	NAH 941	88	NNB 547H	116	OFM 957K	44	OVL 473	122
JMS 452E	91	JUM 505V	30	KGJ 621D	98	KPA 369P	99	LCM 159G	104	LRV 992	118	MKB 994	104	NAT 198V	100	NNB 589H	116	OFN 721F	87	OWC 182D	72
JMY 120N	98	JUO 983	80	KGK 529	115	KPT 909	106	LDJ 985	44	LRV 996	80	MLL 550	87	NBB 628	25	NNU 123M	40	OFR 970M	96	OWE 116	54
JN 5783	106	JUO 992	139	KGK 575	115	KR 1728	88	LDS 201A	50	LSX 16P	87	MLL 658	136	NBD 311F	12	NNU 124M	40	OFS 777	50	OWE 271K	58
JNA 467	36	JUS 774N	92	KGK 708	89	KR 8385	88	LDS 279A	49	LTA 629	84	MLL 722	129	NBN 436	72	NNU 234	73	OFS 798	50	OWS 620	50
JNB 416	23	JV 9901	59	KGK 709	136	KRE 279P	99	LED 71P	44	LTA 729	55	MLL 735	89	NBU 494	39	NNY 817L	78	OFV 621X	101	OWT 776M	66
JND 646	36	JVB 908	50	KGK 758	89	KRN 422	44	LED 73P	45	LTA 748	80	MLL 740	22	NCK 106J	113	NOB 413M	58	OHK 432	34	P164 TNY	77
JND 728	55	JVF 528	48	KGK 803	22	KRR 255	40	LEN 101	86	LTA 772	124	MLL 763	98	NCK 338J	113	NOC 600R	124	OHY 938	74	PAJ 829X	108
JND 791	36	JVO 230	46	KGK 959	136	KRU 55F	73	LEO 734Y	71	LTA 813	114	MN 2615	102	NCS 16P	52	NOE 544R	58	OJ 9347	17	PAX 466F	78
JNK 681C	96	JVS 293	80	KGM 664F	52	KSD 103W	92	LEV 917	94	LTA 898	114	MNC 525W	116	NDB 356	139	NOE 602R	18	OJD 172R	22	PBC 113G	97
JNN 384	129	JVU 755	36	KGU 12	22	KSO 74P	99	LF 9967	105	LTA 906	140	MNS 10Y	92	NDH 959	60	NOV 796G	57	OJD 45R	78	PBC 734	97
JO 5032	47	JVV 267G	55	KGU 290	138	KSV 102	94	LFJ 847W	81	LTA 946	80	MNW 86	30	NDK 980	36	NOV 880G	124	OJD 879R	99	PBC 98G	97
JO 5403	47	JVV 270W	101	KGU 434	125	KSX 102X	53	LFJ 859W	101	LTC 774	36	MO 9324	16	NDL 375G	91	NPD 108L	98	OJD 898R	99	PBJ 2F	88
JOJ 222	17	JVW 430	20	KGY 4D	103	KTB 672	72	LFM 302	139	LTE 491P	95	MOD 823P	81	NDL 490G	29	NPD 145L	24	OJD 903R	92	PCD 80R	99
JOJ 245	56	JWB 416	54	KHA 301	17	KTD 768	43	LFM 329	139	LTN 501	43	MOD 973	80	NDL 656R	99	NPJ 472R	99	OJF 191	97	PCG 889G	118
JOJ 526	17	JWS 594	49	KHA 352	17	KTF 594	139	LFM 404	121	LTV 702	126	MOD 978	76	NDL 769G	71	NPK 250R	99	OJI 4371	96	PCK 618	113
JOJ 533	56	JWU 307	122	KHC 367	103	KTJ 204C	89	LFM 717	139	LTX 311	129	MOF 90	17	NDM 950E	129	NPK 257R	99	OJO 727	79	PCN 762	107
JOJ 548	17	JWU 886	30	KHH 378W	126	KTJ 502	106	LFM 767	49	LUC 210	22	MOO 177	88	NDP 3J	130	NRG 154M	26	OLD 587	136	PCW 203J	107
JOJ 847	17	JWV 976W	135	KHT 122P	99	KTT 38P	126	LFR 529F	95	LUC 381	22	MOR 581	69	NDP 38R	130	NRG 26H	91	OLD 589	103	PDH 808	56
JOJ 976	56	JWW 375	60	KHU 326P	75	KTV 493	59	LFR 540G	95	LUH 105P	78	MPU 21	79	NDV 537G	84	NRN 397P	96	OLD 714	34	PDJ 269L	44
JOV 613P	78	JWW 376	60	KHU 624	125	KTV 506	60	LFS 288F	52	LUO 694	139	MPU 52	20	NDW 407X	78	NRN 586	113	OLV 551M	104	PDL 515	29
JOV 714P	18	JWW 377	60	KHW 306E	57	KUF 199F	119	LFS 294F	52	LUS 524E	52	MPX 945R	126	NEA 101F	57	NSF 757	25	ONE 744	25	PDL 519	29
JOV 738P	124	JXC 194	88	KHW 630	74	KUS 607E	72	LFS 296F	130	LVK 123	82	MRT 6P	28	NEH 453	20	NSJ 502	51	ONF 865H	116	PDU 125M	23
JOW 499E	118	JXC 288	22	KHY 383	17	KVF 658E	88	LFS 480	50	LWB 377P	130	MSD 407	91	NFJ 592M	112	NTF 466	43	ONO 49	20	PDU 135M	58
JOW 928	118	JXC 323	76			KVH 219	60	LFW 338	54	LWR 424	66	MSD 408	91	NFM 67	46	NTT 661	84	ONO 59	34	PFE 542V	34
JOX 506P	99	JXC 432	88			KVH 473E	30	LHA 870F	17	LYF 104	129	MSF 122P	92	NFN 84R	87	NTT 679	84	ONO 995	79	PFN 867	87
JP 4712	36	JXN 370	88					LHL 164F	86	LYM 729	106			NFS 176Y	53	NTU 125	114	ONV 425	126	PFR 346	95

Reg	No	Reg	No	Reg	No	Reg	No	Reg	No	Reg	No	Reg	No	Reg	No	Reg	No	Reg	No	Reg	No
PFR 554H	95	RBD 111M	122	RTV 442X	111	SMK 747F	130	TDK 322	54	TUX 906J	121	UOA 322L	40	VKB 841	104	VYJ 808	89	WUH 585K	78	XUH 368	78
PFR 747	121	RBD 319G	122	RU 2266	73	SMS 120P	52	TDL 564K	29	TV 4484	59	UOU 417H	90	VKB 900	104	VYO 767	122	WV 1209	27	XUO 721	84
PFW 935	129	RBW 87M	79	RU 8678	49	SND 455X	117	TDL 998	103	TV 9333	59	UOU 419H	90	VKE 566S	99	WAJ 112	50	WW 4688	59	XUR 290K	121
PFY 72J	104	RC 2721	31	RU 8805	80	SND 460X	117	TDV217J	124	TVP 898S	124	UP 551	43	VKU 78S	126	WAL 782	139	WWJ 754M	61	XUS 575S	99
PHA 370M	58	RC 4615	56	RUF 186	135	SND 501X	117	TE 5780	93	TVS 367	91	UPB 308S	99	VL 1263	31	WBN 955L	116	WWM 904W	105	XVU 341M	116
PHA 505G	114	RC 7927	17	RUF 37R	119	SO 3740	49	TE 7870	132	TWE 263Y	101	UPB 312S	99	VLT 108	111	WBR 246	30	WWY 115G	121	XVU 352M	40
PHH 149W	126	RC 8472	59	RV 3411	41	SOA 658S	18	TE 8318	31	TWH 689T	95	UPB 340S	99	VLT 111	136	WBR 248	107	WX 2658	72	XVU 363M	116
PHJ 954	20	RC 8575	59	RV 4649	80	SOA 674S	122	TEC 599N	72	TWH 807K	72	UPE 203M	98	VLT 143	137	WCG 104	90	WX 3567	25	XVX 19	20
PHN 831	106	RCH 629L	40	RV 6360	43	SOE 913H	57	TET 135	54	TWH 809K	72	UPT 681V	108	VLT 163	137	WDA 4T	138	WYL 137	130	XW 9892	19
PJX 232	30	RCK 938	113	RV 6367	80	SOI 3591	93	TF 6860	30	TWL 928	48	URE 281	129	VLT 216	138	WDA 700T	18	WYV 4T	137	XWS 165K	52
PJX 35	86	RCM 493	63	RV 6368	41	SOU 456	69	TFJ 808	126	TWM 220V	104	USV 324	119	VLT 235	137	WDA 835T	58	WYV 6T	100	XWV 416A	118
PKG 532H	78	RCP 237	103	RVB 977S	87	SOU 465	69	TFN 980T	87	TWW 766F	30	UTC 672	135	VLT 237	137	WDA 956T	58	WYW 28T	137	XWX 795	60
PKG 587M	78	RCS 382	50	RVO 668L	130	SPK 203M	98	TGM 214J	52	TWY 8	86	UTC 768D	44	VLT 242	137	WDF 569	57	WYW 6T	22	XX 9591	21
PKH 600M	130	RCU 588S	107	RWB 87	54	SPT 65	106	THM 601M	98	TXJ 507K	40	UTF 733H	84	VLT 25	89	WDK 562T	140	XAK 355L	30	XXA 859M	52
PND 460	36	RCU 838S	107	RWU 534R	66	SPT 963V	87	THM 684M	137	UBD 757H	122	UTG 313G	78	VLT 268	136	WEX 685M	86	XBU 17S	30	YD 9533	83
PNF 941J	116	RD 7127	77	SAS 859T	53	SPU 985	96	THX 101S	89	UBN 902	72	UTN 501Y	82	VLT 281	137	WEX 687M	98	XBU 1S	116	YDB 453L	116
PNU 114K	40	RDB 872	83	SB 8155	17	SR 1266	23	THX 217S	99	UCS 659	51	UTU 596J	57	VLT 298	136	WFM 801K	30	XC 8059	102	YDK 590	39
POR 428	69	RDH 505	56	SBC 525R	122	SRB 424	23	THX 220S	99	UCX 275	86	UTV 218S	111	VLT 44	20	WG 1620	49	XCV 326	129	YDL 315	103
POU 494	90	RDL 309X	29	SBF 233	57	SRJ 328H	40	THX 271S	137	UDT 455F	61	UU 6646	21	VLT 8	98	WG 2373	49	XCW 955R	114	YEV 308S	20
PPT 446P	107	REN 116	39	SBK 740S	99	SRS 56K	15	THX 402S	137	UEL 564J	98	UUA 212	106	VLT 85	136	WG 3260	49	XDH 516G	57	YF 714	80
PRA 109R	40	RFE 416	34	SCD 731N	119	SS 7159	83	THX 646S	89	UF 1517	16	UUA 214	20	VLW 444G	122	WG 4445	90	XDH 519G	18	YFM 280L	44
PRG 124J	15	RFM 435	129	SCH 237	18	SS 7501	50	TJ 6760	113	UF 4813	16	UUF 110J	135	VM 4439	36	WG 8107	49	XDH 56G	57	YFR 351	95
PRG 40J	15	RFM 641	43	SCN 268S	108	SSA 5X	92	TJ 836	83	UF 6473	16	UUF 116J	119	VMO 234H	122	WG 8790	49	XFM 42G	52	YFS 310W	53
PRN 145	113	RFR 424P	107	SCS 333M	52	SSF 237H	52	TJO 56K	79	UF 6805	16	UUF 335J	119	VMP 10G	91	WG 9180	49	XG 9304	49	YFY 4M	98
PRN 906	113	RFU 689	79	SCS 335M	91	SSN 248S	92	TKG 518J	78	UF 7428	16	UVK 290T	108	VMP 8G	91	WH 1553	31	XGA 15J	91	YG 7831	105
PRR 454R	99	RG 1173	15	SCS 366M	52	SSX 602V	53	TKU 467K	30	UFC 430K	48	UVL 873M	34	VNB 101L	40	WHA 237H	107	XHA 482	57	YH 1173	21
PRX 187B	118	RGS 598R	88	SDA 757S	58	STJ 847L	95	TME 134M	107	UFF 178	50	UVX 7S	130	VNB 132L	116	WHH 556S	126	XHA 496	57	YHT 802J	98
PSL 234	125	RHS 400W	53	SDK 442	39	STK 129T	107	TMS 585H	52	UFJ 292	107	UWA 296L	54	VNB 173L	116	WHL 970	86	XHO 369	69	YHY 592J	98
PSX 188Y	101	RKC 262	104	SDL 268	29	STK 131T	112	TNA 496	39	UFJ 296	84	UWH 185	72	VNB 177L	116	WHN 411G	107	XJA 534L	116	YHY 80	76
PSX 189Y	101	RLN 237W	126	SDL 638J	29	STK 133T	112	TNA 520	39	UFM 52F	63	UWW 7X	83	VNB 203L	116	WJY 758	112	XLG 477	30	YJG 807	87
PTC 114C	39	RLS 469T	53	SEO 209M	71	STL 725J	92	TNB 759K	116	UFP 175S	97	UXD 129G	122	VO 6806	106	WKG 284	129	XLV 140W	45	YL 740	47
PTD 640S	116	RMA 435V	45	SFC 610	48	STO 526H	111	TOB 377	17	UFP 233S	97	UZH 258	21	VO 8846	46	WKJ 787	114	XLV 156W	105	YLG 717F	10
PTD 655S	95	RMA 442V	100	SFV 421	113	SUG 591M	123	TOB 997H	124	UGB 138H	62	VAU 397J	111	VOD 101K	82	WKO 137S	24	XM 7399	102	YLJ 147	73
PTD 673S	99	RMS 400W	92	SG 2030	25	SUK 3	57	TOE 527N	124	UGB 196W	92	VBD 310H	121	VOD 123K	130	WLT 371	89	XMD 47A	16	YLJ 286	25
PTE 944C	39	RMS 714	50	SGD 407	20	SV 6107	111	TOF 702S	79	UHA 255	56	VDV 123S	85	VOD 542K	84	WLT 506	17	XMS 252R	53	YMA 99W	45
PTF 714L	113	RN 7588	113	SGD 448	91	SVA 438	72	TOJ 592S	138	UHA 941H	58	VDV 137S	124	VOD 545K	84	WLT 529	78	XNG 770S	28	YNA 321M	116
PTF 718L	113	RN 7824	113	SGD 500	91	SVS 281	59	TPD 109X	122	UHA 956H	57	VDV 139	139	VOD 550K	85	WLT 646	136	XNX 136H	17	YNU 351G	130
PTF 727L	113	RN 8622	113	SGD 65	91	SVS 904	46	TPE 159S	99	UHA 981H	58	VDV 753	139	VOD 88K	85	WLT 736	30	XNY 416	78	YNW 33X	21
PTT 106R	126	RNA 220J	116	SGR 935V	82	SVV 587W	101	TPJ 61S	103	UHG 141V	92	VDV 760	54	VOI 8415	93	WLT 882	136	XO 1038	21	YPL 433T	100
PTW 109	20	RNA 236J	121	SHA 431	56	SVV 588W	101	TRJ 109	44	UHG 353Y	40	VDV 798	84	VPT 598R	82	WLT 893	136	XO 7696	21	YPL 449T	100
PUF 165H	119	RNE 692W	130	SHA 645G	57	SVV 589W	101	TRJ 112	39	UHG 736R	99	VDV 817	84	VR 5742	36	WLT 900	136	XON 41J	17	YPT 796	82
PV 817	27	RNU 433X	111	SHN 80L	40	SWS 671	59	TRN 481V	114	UHY 359	75	VDV 818	84	VRC 480S	111	WLT 902	136	XPK 51T	122	YR 3844	102
PV 8270	27	ROD 765	84	SIB 6706	101	SWS 715	50	TRN 731	113	UHY 360	74	VER 262L	48	VRC 611Y	111	WNO 478	21	XRB 415L	98	YRT 898H	25
PV 9371	28	RRG 289	15	SJ 1340	49	SWV 155J	107	TRN 810W	100	UHY 362	124	VF 2788	27	VRD 186	18	WP 6114	72	XRD 23K	130	YSD 350L	52
PVH 931	60	RRM 148M	88	SJR 612Y	108	SYG 561	66	TRU 947J	130	UHY 384	74	VF 8157	27	VRD 193	60	WPG 217M	98	XRU 277K	73	YSG 101	50
PW 8605	105	RRM 386X	53	SKB 168	104	TAX 235	78	TRY 122H	97	UIB 5303	121	VG 5541	114	VRF 372	121	WRA 12	54	XSA 620	70	YT 3738	19
PWL 413	48	RRM 634X	70	SKB 224	104	TBC 163	97	TSJ 47S	92	UK 9978	18	VH 2088	93	VSB 164M	91	WRJ 179	55	XSL 945A	50	YTE 826	25
PWL 999W	79	RRN 405	95	SKB 695G	104	TBC 164	14	TSK 736	135	UKA 23V	104	VH 6217	73	VSC 86	50	WRJ 448X	117	XSN 25A	50	YTG 304	118
PWO 87Y	101	RRN 428	113	SKL 681X	87	TBC 50X	97	TSO 16X	72	UKA 562H	104	VHB 678S	92	VTU 76	30	WRL 16	126	XSS 345Y	15	YTS 916A	91
PWS 492S	94	RRS 46R	52	SKR 556R	99	TBK 190K	80	TTA 400H	130	ULS 716X	53	VHF 57V	105	VTY 543J	126	WRP 767J	122	XSS 43Y	70	YWL 134K	79
PWY 582W	100	RRU 903	123	SLT 56	103	TCD 374J	119	TTD 386H	40	ULS 717X	53	VIB 5069	130	VUD 30X	79	WS 4522	49	XTA 839	84	YYB 118	121
PY 6170	128	RRU 904	73	SLT 57	103	TCD 383J	119	TTR 167H	118	UMA 370	36	VJG 187J	87	VV 5696	79	WSD 756K	91	XTC 684	44	YYJ 914	50
Q995 CPE	126	RSC 194Y	92	SLT 58	22	TCD 481J	119	TTT 168X	112	UMO 180N	98	VJO 201X	79	VV 8934	31	WT 7101	30	XTF 98D	140	YYS 174	91
RAG 400	91	RSD 973R	92	SLT 59	136	TCD 490J	119	TTT 170X	112	UMP 227	22	VJW 882	29	VVK 149G	107	WT 7108	43	XU 7498	105	ZJ 5904	21
RAG 411	90	RSG 820V	111	SMK 686F	107	TCK 465	113	TTT 171X	112	UNB 524	98	VJY 141V	112	VVP 911	57	WT 9156	93	XUA 73X	86	ZO 6960	21
RAG 578	50	RSJ 747	122	SMK 716F	129	TCK 726	113	TUH 13	78	UNB 629	39	VK 5401	43	VVV 956W	101	WTG 360T	135	XUF 141	118	ZS 8621	21
RAO 733	126	RSK 615	129	SMK 732F	107	TCO 537	112	TUO 74J	84	UO 2331	125	VKB 711	104	VW 203	80	WTS 266T	53			ZU 5000	21
RAU 804M	111	RTC 645L	44	SMK 734F	95	TDH 912	18	TUP 859	82					VY 957	36	WTS 708A	107			ZV 1510	107
RB 4757	93	RTT 996	80			TDJ 612	44									WTS 937A	15			ZY 1715	21
RBC 345G	121																				